CONTENTS

INTRODUCTION

Of all the scientific disciplines chemistry seems to be particularly concerned about its public image. Indeed, popular associations with chemistry range from poisons, hazards, chemical warfare, and environmental pollution to alchemical pseudo-science, sorcery, and mad scientists. Despite repeated campaigns for convincing the public that chemistry would bring health, comfort, and welfare, chemists frequently meet with hostility in popular culture. As student enrollment numbers has been shrinking, chemistry departments have been closed in several countries. Also in humanist culture chemistry has a very low profile; philosophers in particular keep to their traditional neglect of anything related to chemistry. Of course, chemists have always been complaining about their low prestige, the lack of public acknowledgment of their achievements, and the misguiding popular associations with chemistry, such that we now have a long record of complaints of almost two centuries. More recently, in response to their public image, chemists have tried to launch slogans such as 'green chemistry' or even dropped the term 'chemistry' altogether and adopted more fashionable labels such as 'materials science', 'molecular science', or 'nanotechnology'.

Surprisingly or not, chemists have never translated their complaints into serious research programs to understand the public image of chemistry in its cultural and historical contexts. To be sure, chemical societies and, particularly, the chemical industry have commissioned many reports for promotional or marketing purposes. Yet, such reports usually scratch only on the surface and may well have recommended one or the other camouflage tactics. Even the recent boost of academic research in Public Understanding of Science (PUS) has virtually excluded chemistry and, instead, focused on topics such as 'Frankenfood' and genetic engineering. The failure to deal with chemistry in PUS studies is more serious than the traditional neglect in the humanities, because stereotypes of chemistry have dominated the popular image of science in general. Even the most feared image, the 'mad scientist', was originally a nineteenth-century literary portrait of chemists, such as Mary Shelley's original Victor Frankenstein was, of course, a chemist. Thus, the present volume on the public image of chemistry also helps understand the public image of science overall and fills an important gap in understanding the relationship between science and society.

Today's public image of chemistry is certainly linked to recent explosions, to hazards and pollution. However it is deeply rooted in our culture, as it is the result of historical interactions between chemistry and society. Thus, the chapters of this volume investigate how the public image of chemistry has been shaped both by chemists in popularizing chemistry and by nonchemists in responding to contemporary chemistry in various phases. The result of this investigation is surprisingly more complex than we expected. Strictly speaking there is not a single image of chemistry in the public sphere but at any time a variety of images in continuous interaction. On the one hand, there are public self-images produced by chemists to promote their discipline. On the other, the popular images of chemistry in various mass media draw on different cultural sources and express both public expectations and fears of chemistry. As the production of popular images partially responds to the production of self-images and vice versa, both depend on each other. Thus the production of public images is negotiated between chemists and nonchemists in public institutions, and new images emerge in between. There is consequently a wide spectrum of public images, ranging from public self-images to popular images with mediated images in-between, all interacting with one another. With the additional historical dimension and the impact of particular events, from Nobel Prizes to toxicity scandals, the full complexity of the dynamics of the public images emerges.

While this volume cannot of course cover the full complexity of the issue, it does however provide for the first time an in-depth understanding of the historical origin and development of the public images of chemistry. Keeping in mind the gradual differences and interactions, the volume is divided into three parts devoted to popular images, self-images, and mediated images of chemistry in the nineteenth and twentieth centuries.

The first part on popular images focuses on representations of chemistry in fiction literature and movies – not surprisingly the mad scientists figures prominently here. ROSLYNN HAYNES, one of the very rare English literature scholars with a background in chemistry, argues that since the early nineteenth century the popular figures of scientists in fiction have been shaped on the model of sinister, dangerous, and mad alchemists (Chapter 1). She points out that this figure embodies suppressed desires and fears of recurrent fascination. With a closer look at the history of science, JOACHIM SCHUMMER explains the origin of the mad scientist in nineteenth-century literature as a part of a literary response to the emergence of modern science in general and of experimental chemistry in particular (Chapter 2). In his quantitative analysis of scientists in twentieth-century movies, sociologist PETER WEINGART illustrates that chemistry has become the iconic discipline of the mad scientist (Chapter 3). Apart from these clichés, however, a more complex picture of chemistry in society has recently emerged, as PHILIP BALL shows in his analysis of contemporary American literature (Chapter 4).

How did chemists respond to the public challenge of being related to mad scientists? The second part provides five case studies of chemists developing a popular image of their discipline. In the early nineteenth century, chemists were still busy with establishing chemistry as an independent discipline, which they did by strongly engaging with the public. For instance, Humphry Davy in England, as DAVID KNIGHT shows in Chapter 5, popularized chemistry through public lectures with spectacular experiments. And Justus von Liebig in Germany, as MARIKA BLON-DEL-MÉGRELIS argues in Chapter 6, published popular books and articles on chemistry in which he argued that chemistry is both the most useful and the most fundamental of all sciences. Later in the nineteenth century, when chemistry grew mature both academically and industrially, popular chemistry books tried to make chemistry appear more attractive in order to cope with the increasing workforce demand, as ERNST HOMBURG points out in Chapter 7. These books eventually created the public chemistry image of some wondrous, magic technology. When, after World War I, chemistry's reputation was particular damaged, because of research and deployment of chemical weapons, U.S. chemists responded with an influential popularization project. By analyzing its images and text, ANDREW EDE illustrates in Chapter 8 how the wondrous chemist-magician moved to the level of a benevolent god in a white lab coat who nourishes and takes care of his people. Strangely enough, the more chemists felt the need to popularize their discipline, the more did they employ elements of magic and literary clichés, including those of the mad scientist, which they disliked on the other hand. Moreover, in current visual images that chemists use to portray themselves, their discipline, and the chemical industry, they frequently and unknowingly employ visual stereotypes fraught with negative connotations, as JOACHIM SCHUMMER and TAMI SPECTOR argue in Chapter 9. For instance, the favorite pose of a chemist, *i.e.* a person hold up a flask and gazing at it, was for centuries a symbol of quackery and fraud before chemists assumed it as their visual icon.

In the twentieth century, professional science journalists and mediators made all possible efforts to go beyond the conflict between the popular images produced by nonchemists to caricature or mock chemistry and the self-images chemists use to promote their discipline to the public. The first two chapters of part three discuss the creation of such images in institutions that were built to mediate between science and society. MARCEL LAFOLLETTE's study of the emergence of science journalism in the 1930s (Chapter 10) illustrates the difficult negotiations and compromises between professional supply of information and public interest and demand that eventually result in chemical 'news' worth broadcasting. PETER MORRIS provides a similar account of the institution of science museums throughout the twentieth century with an additional emphasis on the competition between the disciplines to be displayed. Compared to the sometimes aggressive campaigns launched by chemical communities, science museums seem rather shy in their displays of chemistry. In many cases chemistry is given a modest place in exhibitions. Our volume concludes with PIERRE LASZLO's reflection in Chapter 12 on how the self-image of chemists has changed since the mid-twentieth century as a result of internal scientific and organizational developments as well as external environmental and societal challenges.

For today's chemists interested in improving their public image, it might be surprising to learn that such efforts have been undertaken for more than two centuries. However, neither the issues that chemists are concerned with nor the approaches to popularize chemistry are totally new. The lack of success of these strategies suggests that, rather than repeating the same old mistakes over and again, it would be wiser to pause for a moment, take lessons from history, and reflect more carefully on the complex relationship between science and society.

Among the many lessons one could draw from the history, one is particularly obvious. Rather than shaping an adequate image of chemistry, chemists have frequently preferred to react to what they considered as public prejudices against chemistry and to adopt a defensive attitude. Instead of making efforts to present the dual face of chemistry – a natural science and a set of technologies – they enrolled publicists to market their new synthetic products. For instance Du Pont's famous slogan, "Better things for better living... through chemistry", initially aimed at erasing the image of chemistry as an agent of death resulting from the company's participation in chemical warfare during World War I. However, it helped create an image of chemistry as a new style of life, where consumption is the indicator of technological progress and civilization. And when public questions grew more critical, they frequently responded with exaggerated promises of technological, if not magical, progress, even if nobody would listen. Most often their responses only confirmed and even reinforced public prejudices against chemistry.

As this volume makes unmistakably clear, the public image is a very complex social and cultural phenomenon at the interface between various publics, scientists, and mediating institutions. Working on public images thus requires sensitivity and detailed cultural knowledge, which chemists, eager to improve their image, might not always be aware of.

This volume makes a start in developing the cultural knowledge and sensitivity required to understand the meanings of public images of chemistry. It does so by drawing on scholarship rather than on complaints and the wisdom of public relation. Its twelve chapters are written by experts from philosophy, history of science, literature studies, sociology, and chemistry from eight countries. They invite chemists to reflect on their public image and the role they have played therein as well as humanists and social scientists to work on a crucial and much neglected issue of the science-society relationship.

Many of the chapters are based on contributions to two conferences: *The Public Images of Chemistry in the 20th Century* by the Commission for the History of Modern Chemistry (CHMC) in Paris, France, 17-18

September 2004; and a session on 'Contexts of Popularization' at the *5th International Conference on the History of Chemistry* in Lisbon, Portugal, 6-9 September 2005. Additional papers have been invited to complement the scope. Most of the chapters have been published before in 2006 and 2007 in serious of special issues of the journal *HYLE: International Journal for Philosophy of Chemistry* (www.hyle.org). Putting them all together now, we can firmly say that this is the first comprehensive volume on the public image of chemistry.

Joachim Schummer   June 2007
Bernadette Bensaude-Vincent
Brigitte Van Tiggelen

CHAPTER 1

THE ALCHEMIST IN FICTION: THE MASTER NARRATIVE

Roslynn Haynes

School of English, University of New South Wales, Sydney 2052, NSW Australia;
R.Haynes@unsw.edu.au

In Western culture, as expressed in fiction and film, the master narrative concerning science and the pursuit of knowledge perpetuates the archetype of the alchemist/scientist as sinister, dangerous, and possibly mad. Like all myths this story may appear simplistic but its recurrence suggests that it embodies complex ideas and suppressed desires and fears that each generation must work through. This chapter explores some of the most influential examples of such characterization, links them to contemporary correlatives of the basic promises of alchemy and suggests reasons for the continuing power of such images.

1. Introduction

The most widely known creation myth of modern times is not that of *Genesis* or Darwin but *Frankenstein*. Why does Mary Shelley's novel, first published in 1818, still provide the most universally invoked imagery for science in the twenty-first century? Western culture relies on and reveres science far beyond any known precedent; yet, paradoxically, the master narrative of scientific knowledge in both literature and film focuses on an evil and dangerous maniac, obsessive, secretive, ruthless, and arrogant, drawing on many of the qualities popularly associated with medieval alchemy. This chapter explores the reasons for this disjunction between the regard and monetary reward heaped on science and technology in the 'real world' and the judgment these disciplines receive in the world of film and fiction.

Fundamentally this master narrative concerning science and scientists is about fear – fear of specialized knowledge and the power that knowledge confers on the few, leaving the majority of the population ignorant and therefore impotent. In a typical scenario the mad scientist achieves a knowledge break-through that threatens the social order (sometimes the whole planet), either through evil designs or by accident ('collateral damage' in today's media-speak). Even though the disaster may be (and usually is) averted, the memory of disempowerment remains, augmenting the repository of previous fears, to be recalled the next time there is a new knowledge breakthrough and hence the perception of a new threat.

The origins and trappings of this potent story lie in the precursor of chemistry, alchemy. Although dismissed by scientists as outmoded and irrelevant to their practice, alchemy has continued to provide a potent source of myth-making for the critique of modern science. Its chequered reputation has been revived and reinforced as perennially pertinent by writers, by artists and film-makers and, perversely, by scientists themselves in response to both their own psychological proclivities and the constraints placed on them by contemporary scientific culture with its emphasis on the priority of publication and by military or industrial requirements of secrecy.

2. The Popular Appeal of Alchemy

The craft of alchemy both intrigued and frightened those who hovered on its fringes. Its allure lay in the immensity and immediacy of its promises and its professions of power surpassing that of kings or priests. In their most crude form these promises might now seem to appeal only to the excessively naïve or the inordinately greedy, yet in their generic form they continue to be highly attractive. To understand the ongoing fascination with the figure of the alchemist, we need to review some of the perceived foci of alchemy and the way in which they achieved a paradigmatic status, as well as the origins of the evil reputation that coalesced about such practices.

The history of alchemy has been well documented (Burckhardt 1967, Caron et al. 1961, Cummings 1966, Debus et al. 1966, Edwardes 1977, Gettings 1986, Hollister 1990, Lindsay 1970, Read 1947) and will be familiar to readers of this journal, so here I shall select for mention only those particular preoccupations that seized the imagination of the medieval public and have continued to provide material for fiction, being constantly re-invented and reapplied to claim relevance to contemporary issues or to add a degree of universality to fictional representations of the scientist.

Among the foundational concepts of alchemy the following have retained an allure that is both theoretically satisfying and appealing to self-interest.

(a) The notion that all things are interchangeable and exist in a state of flux. One source for this premise was the Taoist belief, originating in China in the fifth century BCE, that transformation and change are essential and innate in all things. In Europe, parallel ideas were put forward by the philosopher Empedocles and further developed by Aristotle in his thesis regarding the unity of matter and the interchangeable qualities of the four elements. The aspect of Aristotle's theory immediately seized upon was his premise that everything in nature strives towards perfection. Since gold was considered the most perfect and noble state of matter, it followed that all baser metals must necessarily 'aspire' to become gold. This changed a general, theoretical principle into a specific, material one, with the added implication of inevitability. The alchemist's task was simply to assist nature in realizing its goal. In practical terms, this role had been regularly performed by Egyptian metalworkers who, using the secret recipes of the goddess Isis, were adept at 'extending' a given quantity of gold by producing alloys with silver, copper, tin, and zinc. Thus, from the beginning, alchemy was associated both with the apparent 'production' of gold and, simultaneously, with the suspicion that this was a deception, a confidence trick practiced on the greedy and the gullible.

In the eighth century these secrets of metallurgy passed to the Arabs who, through trade with the Chinese, added the idea of a transforming catalyst, the origin of the Philosopher's Stone, that would enable, or at least assist, base metals to be transformed into gold. Inevitably such a catalyst conferred power and subsequently wealth on the alchemist who claimed to possess it and to have the knowledge necessary to activate it.

(b) The 'elixir of youth', a universal panacea that would cure illness and prevent ageing, thereby conferring longevity, perhaps even immortality. Like the Philosopher's Stone for transformation of metals, the elixir of youth was a catalytic substance, usually a powder or liquid. As pharmacy developed from herbalism this alleged elixir achieved greater credibility.

These two aspects of alchemy were studied and written about at length by the Arabs for whom they were associated with the Islamic faith, part of a holy search for perfection. In medieval Christian Europe it was a very different story. These two projects were cause enough for suspicion but the third major preoccupation of alchemy finally placed it beyond the tolerance of the Church.

(c) Creation of homunculi. Compared with the previous two, this project might seem less desirable, even bizarre, but it constituted an even greater threat to the social fabric and to the doctrines of the medieval Church. Although the other claims of alchemy involved a degree of arrogance in the profession of 'unnatural' powers, the attempt to produce a tiny human being (always a masculine person) was an example of extreme hubris, since it claimed to by-pass both the Creator and the divinely ordained method for reproduction. It challenged the Church's teaching that the soul was created at the moment of conception and mimicked both the Greek legend of Prometheus moulding humans from clay and breathing life into them, and the creation story of Adam in *Genesis*. The sub-title of *Frankenstein* is '*or, the Modern Prometheus*' and in her epigraph from Milton Shelley makes specific reference to the parallel between Frankenstein's creation of his Monster (an outsize parody of the homunculus) and the genesis of Adam:

> Did I request thee, Maker, from my clay
> To mould me man? Did I solicit thee
> From darkness to promote me? [Shelley 1996, p. 3]

The Monster, too, compares his own creation to that of Adam. "Remember, that I am thy creature: I ought to be thy Adam: but I am rather the fallen angel, whom thou drivest from joy for no misdeed."(Shelley 1996, p. 66)

We can understand the appeal of the homunculus-peddlers better if we realize that robots are of the same conceptual family. They, too, represent 'beings' we have created at will through our intellect, without recourse to female biology, and which we hope to enslave. In contemporary biological terms, cloned organisms, genetic engineering, *in vitro* fertilization, and embryo transfers involve a comparable desire to take control of the genesis of organisms, especially in relation to humans.

3. The Public Image of Alchemists

Because alchemy re-entered Europe through translations of Arabic writings, it became a casualty of transferred racism and religious prejudice. Its practical and socially acceptable origins in metallurgy and medicine were soon obscured and instead it was associated by name and origin with a race regarded as infidels. Linked with the black arts, with heresy, astrology, and magic, it was decried and finally outlawed by the Church. A series of Acts were passed forbidding the practice of alchemy, culminating in Pope John XXII's formal edict *Spondent*, denouncing the alchemists as tricksters and counterfeiters (Duncan 1968, pp. 636f.). It was widely believed that alchemists were in league with the devil and that those who patronized their services were in danger of eternal damnation. Concealment, isolation, and the arcane symbolic language of the Hermetic tradition were evolved not only as a mechanism to guard secret knowledge, but also as a strategy for survival in the face of persecution. At first the astrological signs of the planets were used as alchemical symbols; later alchemists invented their own secret symbols. The 'Table of Chemical Symbols' in the *Encyclopédie* of Denis Diderot and Jean d'Alembert in the late eighteenth century still resembles the medieval alchemists' symbols. These characteristics, accidents of history, have been perpetuated in fiction, not only in relation to alchemists but as essential features in the characterization of modern scientists, especially chemists, as cloistered, secretive, engaged in practices that violate the norms and moral values of society, speaking a language and writing in symbols designed to exclude the uninitiated.

Despite this reputation of illicit practices and even condemnation by the Church, alchemists exerted a continuing fascination because of their alluring promises. In various forms these all represented power to transcend the normal limitations of the human condition – the power of wealth, power over ageing and death, and power over the creation of life.

For this reason alchemists were wooed by princes[1] and paupers alike, even though their clients may have suspected that they were being deluded. In modern dress these promises remain universally attractive and lucrative propositions, appearing closer to realization than ever before.

4. Prototypes of the Alchemist in Literature

The simple medieval stereotypes of the alchemist, memorably represented in Chaucer's *The Canon's Yeoman's Prologue and Tale* (Chaucer 1957, pp. 473-98), were the deluded 'puffer' who wasted his life and money in the pursuit of alchemy and the unscrupulous trickster who defrauded others. Although these were later tempered by more benign successors – the natural philosopher and the scientist – the recurrent fictional image of the knowledge-seeker retains many of the characteristics of the alchemist obsessed with the pursuit of dangerous or socially unlawful knowledge. These characters, invariably male, still shroud their research in secrecy and isolation. Likewise, the master narrative in which they feature perpetuates the same concerns and repeats the same moral strictures as were leveled against their predecessors.

The alchemist stereotype as we know it today results largely from an amalgam of two fictional characters, so universally recognized and enduring that they have become prototypes in their own right. Dr Faustus and Victor Frankenstein have continued to provide the imagery, even the iconography, for representations of both the alchemist and modern scientists. The former figure provides the link between medieval superstition and Renaissance aspirations to understand Nature, while the latter situ-

---

[1] In 1583 the Holy Roman Emperor Rudolph II moved his court from Vienna to Prague, where it became a center for the discussion of the occult and its relation to medicine, cosmology, and the production of gold. The search for the philosopher's stone consumed Rudolph and much of Prague's nobility. The famed English astrologer/ wizard John Dee and his partner Edward Kelly spent five years together in Prague (much of it financed by Rudolph) performing magic tricks alleged to foretell the future. Kelly stayed on when Dee returned to England, claiming to have discovered the coveted secret methods for turning lead into gold. Kelly gained a knighthood, but was eventually imprisoned on charges of sorcery and heresy. Queen Elizabeth I of England also encouraged alchemy in the hope of replenishing the royal coffers (French 1972).

ates archetypal desires and knowledge hubris within the context of a recognizably modern world.

4.1 Faust

Probably derived originally from the real-life Georg Faust of Knittlingen,[2] Faust in all his literary manifestations was depicted as displaying intellectual arrogance and an obsession with transcending the boundaries of human knowledge. Circulated orally, the Faust legends became increasingly exaggerated, involving magic and familiars. The first written account, the anonymous Spieß edition of *Historia von D. Johann Fausten* of 1587 had an unmistakable religious moral, focusing on the pact with the devil and Faust's gruesome end, accompanied by suitable passages from Scripture. However, *The Tragical History of Doctor Faustus* (1604), written only seventeen years later by English playwright Christopher Marlowe, presented the story in a quite different light. Although the incidents of Marlowe's play were based on those in the English translation of the Spieß text, the assessment of the protagonist is totally divergent.

Marlowe's Faust is a man of his time. His Renaissance-humanist longing to transcend the limitations of the human intellect is still tempered by the medieval awareness that such an aspiration, like Lucifer's revolt against God, is doomed to destroy him. Yet Marlowe contrives to imply that his ultimate destruction is the tragic waste of a gifted man. The kind of Faust figure that predominates at any point in history is an index of the status accorded by a society (or an author) to the individual and to the intellect, as opposed to the value placed on obedience to the prevailing hegemony, whether Church or State. At one end of the evaluation spectrum, Faust is condemned for his *hubris* and arrogant denial of God-given limits, and thoroughly deserves his terrible end. At the other extreme, Faust represents a noble Prometheus figure, asserting the right to freedom of knowledge and the full development of the individual's

---

[2] Georg Faust was born around 1480 and appears to have had the reputation of a traveling conjuror, hypnotist, and quack doctor on the one hand and of an alchemist and serious student of natural science on the other (Smeed 1975, p. 13).

powers against a repressive regime, whether of Zeus, the Church, or public opinion. This is the Faust of German Romanticism, of Klinger, Goethe, and Lessing. Scientists are still regularly characterized across a similar range, depending on prevailing social and moral support for the intrinsic value of knowledge or for the contrary view that it should be subsidiary to the public interest and, if necessary, suppressed.

4.2 Frankenstein

Mary Shelley's character Frankenstein has become an archetype in its own right, universally referred to and providing the dominant image of the scientist in twentieth-century fiction and film. Frankenstein is the prototype of the mad scientist who hides himself in his laboratory, secretly creating not an elixir of immortality but a new human life, only to find he has created a Monster. Not only has his name become virtually synonymous with any experiment out of control, but also his relation with his creation has become, in popular misconception, complete identification: Frankenstein *is* the Monster. The power of the Frankenstein story can be attributed to the fact that, in its essentials, it was a product of the subconscious rather than the conscious mind of its author and thus, in Jungian terms, draws upon the collective unconscious of the race.

The circumstances of the composition of *Frankenstein*, as described by the author in her Introduction to the 1831 edition, are almost as well known as the story itself and have themselves inspired other fictional accounts including a film and an opera[3]. Yet it is worth stressing that, according to Mary Shelley, the story was produced by the concurrence of two specific factors: the need to produce a horror story and the account of an alleged scientific experiment. Mary and Percy Shelley, their baby son William and Mary's step-sister Claire Clairmont were spending the summer of 1816 near Geneva, as neighbors of the poet Lord Byron and his personal physician Polidori. Kept indoors by a stretch of bad weather, Byron, Percy, Polidori, and Mary each agreed to write a ghost story as entertainment. Mary records that she found great difficulty in thinking of

---

[3]   Ken Russell's film *Gothic* (1986) and the opera *Mer de Glace* (1991), libretto by David Malouf.

a suitable plot until the evening when the others were discussing the latest experiments allegedly conducted by Erasmus Darwin whereby he was said to have "preserved a piece of vermicelli in a glass case till by some extraordinary means it began to move with voluntary motion. Not thus, after all, would life be given. Perhaps a corpse would be reanimated; galvanism had given token of such things: perhaps the component parts of a creature might be manufactured, brought together, and endued with vital warmth" (Shelley 1996, pp. 171f.). That night Mary allegedly dreamed the central scene of her novel. Doctor Darwin has been transformed into "the pale student of unhallowed arts, kneeling beside the thing he had put together" (Shelley 1996, p. 172). This suggests that the very attempt to create life was already associated, at least in Mary's subconscious mind as accessed by her dream, with alchemy, the "unhallowed arts", with the demonic and the horrific. The problem of finding a subject for her story was instantly solved: "What terrified me will terrify others; and I need only describe the specter which had haunted my midnight pillow. [...] making a transcript of the grim terrors of my waking dream." (Shelley 1996, p. 172)[4]

---

[4] In her Introduction to a recent edition of *Frankenstein*, Marilyn Butler has pointed out that the original (1818) edition of the novel carried no such moral implications. The scientific references were to the celebrated public debate of 1814–1819 carried on between John Abernethy and William Lawrence, two professors at London's Royal College of Surgeons, on the origins and nature of life. Abernethy rejected materialist explanations and opted for an added force, "some subtile, mobile, invisible substance" analogous equally to the soul and to electricity. Lawrence, who was Percy Shelley's physician, put forward the materialist position as being the only intellectually respectable one. His views had considerable influence on both Mary and Percy Shelley and his aggressive materialism was strongly represented in the first edition of Frankenstein. It seems certain that the discussion between Percy Shelley and Byron later described by Mary in her Introduction of 1831 was concerned with the vitalist debate and Butler further suggests that the Frankenstein of the first edition, the blundering scientist attempting to infuse life by means of an electric spark, is a contemptuous portrait of Abernethy while the unhealthy relationships of the aristocratic Frankenstein family recall Lawrence's research on heredity and sexual selection. When Lawrence's *Lectures on Physiology, Zoology and the Natural History of Man* elicited a virulent review in the influential *Quarterly Review* of November 1819 and Lawrence himself was suspended from the Royal College of Surgeons until he agreed to withdraw his book, Mary Shelley feared the same fate would befall *Frankenstein*. She therefore revised it extensively in 1831, removing all controversial references, adding suitably remorseful statements by Frankenstein and, of course, the Introduction with its indication that we should read the novel as a frightful "human endeavour

It is not difficult to supply reasons why the account of Darwin's alleged experiments should have had such a profoundly unsettling effect on Mary Shelley, aged eighteen, the youngest and least assured person present, and clearly intellectually overawed by the discussion (she tells us that she was "a devout but nearly silent listener"). Only the preceding year, Mary had lost her first child born prematurely and had recently undergone a second, difficult confinement. Inevitably she would have felt emotionally disturbed, even violated, by a discussion which not only abolished the role of the female in the creation of life, but trivialized the process by reducing it to "a piece of vermicelli in a glass case". Unable to argue at a rational level with the intellectual giants Byron and Shelley, she doubtless suppressed her disquiet, which emerged violently in her subsequent dream. What is more interesting for the purpose of this exploration of images is her immediate identification of the highly visual nightmare image of the attempt to create life with her earlier aim "to think of a story [...] which would speak to the mysterious fears of our nature and awaken thrilling horror" (Shelley 1996, p. 171).

Frankenstein is not only the Romantic over-reacher determined to transcend human limitations; he is also the heir of Baconian optimism and Enlightenment confidence that everything can ultimately be known and that such knowledge will inevitably be for the good. "I doubted not that I should ultimately succeed [...]. A new species would bless me as its creator and source; many happy and excellent natures would owe their being to me." (Shelley 1996, pp. 31f.).

Frankenstein also accepts uncritically the reductionist premise of the eighteenth-century mechanists, that an organism is no more than the sum of its parts. As heir to a such a view, he has no sense of the extraordinary irony involved when he sets out to create a "being like myself" from dead and inanimate components, ignoring the possible need for any living or spiritual elements. Even in retrospect he seems to see no anomaly in this, for he tells Walton, not without pride: "In my education my father had taken the greatest precautions that my mind should be impressed

---

to mock the stupendous mechanism of the Creator of the world" (Shelley 1996, p. 172). This is the edition most commonly reproduced and it is consequently the one that has colored successive interpretations of the novel (Butler 1993, pp. 302-13).

with no supernatural horrors. I do not ever remember to have trembled at a tale of superstition, or to have feared the apparition of a spirit." (Shelley 1996, p. 30)

But the being he creates is not merely a mechanism, the sum of its inanimate parts; it is indeed a being like himself, with free will not subject to Frankenstein's control. As such, it enacts Frankenstein's own unconscious desires, both good and evil, which have been sublimated by the discipline of his research program and by cultural censorship. The Monster responds to the beauties of nature, to the joys of domesticity and the ideas of great books, occupations that Frankenstein had put aside for his research. But it also kills Frankenstein's younger brother William, his fiancée Elizabeth, and his friend Henry Clerval, the very people whom Frankenstein is duty-bound to love but whom he has subconsciously wished to be rid of because they attempt to distract him from his obsession. The Monster is thus both an *alter ego* and a substitute for the natural child he has denied existence by deferring his marriage with Elizabeth. This *Doppelgänger* relationship symbolizes the belief in the essential duality of man, the complex of rational and emotional selves, mutually alienated but finally inseparable (Bloom 1965, pp. 611-18; Levine *et al.* 1979, p. 15; Miyoshi 1969, pp. 79-89). This image was to be expanded in Stevenson's *The Strange Case of Dr Jekyll and Mr Hyde* (1886). In the image of the larger-than-human Monster, Shelley reaffirms the Romantic position that the unconscious is an intrinsic and more powerful part of the human experience than the rational mind and, if suppressed, will ultimately emerge to destroy the latter.

It is not surprising that playwrights and film makers have returned with such frequency to the story, modifying it to suit the prevailing tastes, values, and scientific debates of their time, but it is interesting that no screen version has retained Shelley's pessimistic ending.

The first physical presentation of Frankenstein was H.M. Milner's play of 1826, *Frankenstein; or, the Man and the Monster* and the story became the subject of one of the earliest films, the Edison Company's *Frankenstein* (1910). This film concentrated on the psychological aspects of the story, emphasizing the fact that the creation of the Monster was possible only because Frankenstein allowed his normal healthy mind to be overcome by evil and unnatural thoughts. Edison's ending was far

more positive and romantic than Shelley's, echoing contemporary optimism about science: the Monster finally fades away, leaving only his reflection in a mirror. And even this is subsequently dissolved into Frankenstein's own image by the power of Elizabeth's love. Frankenstein has
been restored to mental health and hence the Monster can no longer
exist.

Carlos Clerens, the historian of horror films, rates the 1931 Universal
film classic, *Frankenstein*, which introduced Boris Karloff as the Monster, as "the most famous horror movie of all time" (Clerens 1967, p. 64).
Yet by comparison with the novel the film is hardly horrific at all. The
heavily underlined moral, stated at the beginning, that "it is the story of
Frankenstein, a man of science who sought to create a man after his own
image without reckoning upon God", restores an element of supernatural
order and justice to Shelley's entirely secular and unredeemed situation.
In this version, Henry Frankenstein (who, following Peggy Webling's
1930 play on which the film is based, has exchanged given names with
Clerval) is presented as the innocent victim of a mistake whereby his
careless assistant has brought him the brain of a murderer instead of a
noble person, for inserting into his creature. The evil character of the
Monster is therefore merely an experimental error, rather than the inevitable result of Frankenstein's *hubris*, and the implication is that the creation of the Monster *per se* posed no abiding procedural problem; with
due precautions a better result could be obtained next time. Such an attitude, including the otherwise anomalous introductory moral, was consistent with the adulation of scientists, and particularly of inventors, in the
United States during the 1930s (Haynes 1994, pp. 163-5). Although the
film ended with the Monster being burnt to death and the celebration of
Frankenstein's wedding to the (spared) Elizabeth, the box-office success
indicated a sequel. The final scenes of the 1931 film were cut from all
prints in circulation and *Bride of Frankenstein* (1935) opened with a
scene in which Mary Shelley relates to Shelley and Byron the sequel to
her novel. In this film Frankenstein becomes the pawn of another scientist, the mad, evil Dr Pretorius who, having constructed various homunculi, now wishes to produce something larger. He forces Frankenstein to
create the mate for which the Monster of the novel had begged. The female Monster (in an extension of the *Doppelgänger* effect in the novel

she is played by the same actress, Elsa Lanchester, as Mary Shelley) is striking but not hideous and she immediately rejects the Monster who in despair electrocutes her, Dr Pretorius, and himself. In this film Frankenstein has become entirely absolved of guilt, and the role of the evil scientist bent on creating life, has passed to the alchemist-like Pretorius.

Bride of Frankenstein was followed by a long succession of Frankenstein derivatives whose titles are sufficiently indicative of their content and of the way in which Frankenstein has been integrated into Western culture as an ever-contemporary by-word, almost as a real person, engaging in dialogue with other characters both real and imaginary.[5] At different periods the emphasis falls variously on horror, space travel, sexuality, or comedy associated with the figure of the scientist. One of the most interesting films in terms of the application of the Frankenstein story to a contemporary scientific debate is *Frankenstein 1970* (1958) in which Boris Karloff returns to the screen as the disfigured Victor Frankenstein, victim of Nazi torture. By means of an atomic reactor he raises to life the Monster from his ancestor's 1757 experiment, but they both die a horrible death from radioactivity when the reactor blows up. Only then is the Monster's face revealed. It is the face of a youthful Victor Frankenstein, symbolizing in startling visual imagery the identification of creator and creature, in this case the atomic scientist and his dangerous and faulty creation, atomic power.

5.   The Endurance of the Alchemist Stereotype

It may seem anomalous that, after the rise of the great scientific societies in the seventeenth century and the European Enlightenment of the eighteenth century with its emphasis on rationality, this archetype has en-

---

5   *Son of Frankenstein* (1938), *The Ghost of Frankenstein* (1942), *Frankenstein Meets the Wolf Man* (1943), *House of Frankenstein* (1944), *Abbott and Costello Meet Frankenstein* (1948), *I was a Teenage Frankenstein* (1957), *The Curse of Frankenstein* (1957), *The Revenge of Frankenstein* (1958), *Frankenstein's Daughter* (1958), *Frankenstein 1970* (1958), *El Testamento del Frankenstein* (1964), *The Evil of Frankenstein* (1964), *Jesse James Meets Frankenstein's Daughter* (1965), *Frankenstein Conquers the World* (1965), *Frankenstein Meets the Space Monster* (1965), *Frankenstein Created Woman* (1967), *Frankenstein Must be Destroyed* (1969), *Gothic* (1986), *Frankenstein, the Real Story* (1993).

dured, not only in fiction but also in the more recent medium of film. From his extensive analysis of horror films in English between 1931 and 1960, Andrew Tudor estimated that 30% of the villains were scientists; 40% of the threats were spin-offs from science; and a mere 10% of the heroes were scientists (Tudor 1989b, pp. 589-92). It should be noted that, whether noble or evil, the scientist figure remained overwhelmingly male even when this no longer reflected the actual degree of involvement of women in science.

The most obvious reason for the perpetuation of the evil alchemist figure is that the personality traits to which alchemy appealed – greed, vanity, desire for power, immortality, and manipulation of other human beings – remain prevalent and those who profess to satisfy them in some form continue to be regarded with mingled fascination and fear.

However, I want to suggest ten more specific reasons for the persistence of the alchemist-derived character and for the imaginative power it continues to exert.

(i) One of the most common forms of the stereotype, the seeker after forbidden knowledge, has its roots in much older mythology, suggesting that it is deeply ingrained in human consciousness, perhaps within the subconscious: the narratives of Eden, of Prometheus, of Daedalus and Icarus, and of Pandora's Box all feature protagonists who sought transcendent knowledge and were punished by some higher authority or by the inevitability of events. Coming from this implicit lineage, their modern descendants carry a transferred kudos and more powerful resonances than any 'new' story could generate. The scientist who discovers some power (whether it be a weapon or nuclear power or the ability to create, clone, or modify life) that cannot be contained or controlled is Pandora trying vainly to push the escaping Troubles back into the box. Like these archetypal myths, nearly all alchemist narratives focus on a reversal of expectation and consequent nemesis: the glorious promises turn to ashes and destruction – sometimes because they are not achieved, as in Balzac's *La Recherche de l'Absolu* (1834), but more often because they *are* achieved in the short term but bring unforeseen disaster in their train. The preeminent literary example here is Frankenstein, whose tragedy begins at the precise moment of his experimental success.

I saw the dull yellow eye of the creature open; it breathed hard and a convulsive motion agitated its limbs.

How can I describe my emotions at this catastrophe? [...] I had desired it with an ardour that far exceeded moderation; but now that I had finished, the beauty of the dream vanished, and a breathless horror and disgust filled my heart. Unable to endure the aspect of the being I had created, I rushed out of the room. [Shelley 1996, p. 34]

(ii) Science, like alchemy, claims access to a kind of power that cannot be gained by force of arms or other traditional forms of supremacy. The medieval Church was therefore justified in regarding alchemy as a rival *power*. Francis Bacon's aphorism 'knowledge is power' is nowhere so obvious as in the allure of science. To those trained in a scientific discipline, knowledge is not threatening; it is more likely to be regarded as one of the highest achievements of the human intellect. To understand how it appears to the uninitiated, who feel disempowered through lack of understanding or inability to control its consequences, we might consider an analogy with other contemporary forms of power and their concomitant sources of fear: the seductive power of an idea for which its supporters willingly die, international terrorism, the power of cataclysmic natural events, such as earthquakes, volcanic eruptions, cyclones, tsunamis, and, less immediate but no less real, potential long-term environmental disaster for our planet.

(iii) The most publicized goals of modern science bear a striking similarity to those of alchemy. It seems that our wish list has changed little since our medieval ancestors visited their local alchemist under cloak of darkness, fearful of being observed but greedy for results.

(a) Perpetual motion represents limitless power at close to zero cost. In the nineteenth century electricity filled this role; in the twentieth it was nuclear power. Both have been regarded with similar ambivalence as both benefactor and destroyer. Albert Robida's illustration "The Energy Explosion" in *La Vie électrique* (1887) personifies Electricity as a provocative woman who both liberates and enslaves the world. In the case of nuclear power, writers have been only cautiously optimistic. The scientific utopia, pioneered by Sir Francis Bacon's *The New Atlantis* (1626), has had few successors. H.G. Wells' scientific utopias were balanced by his dark studies of scientific monomania. Simon Newcombe's patriotic American novel *His Wisdom the Defender* (1900) posits a 'thermic engine', forerunner of a nuclear power plant, which can precipitate a new industrial revolution. The scientist-hero Campbell uses this power to enforce world peace and cooperation. Such benign use of physical power was later characteristic of the pulp science fiction magazines *Amazing Stories, Astounding Stories,* and *Marvel* of the 1920s and '30s.

(b) The transmutation of metals to gold was superseded by the promise of producing artificial diamonds and then by the discovery of radioactive elements and industrial processes with immense profits out of all proportion to outlay. Our contemporary equivalent is the use of biological processes to create complex end-products more efficiently and cheaply than from *in vitro* chemical reactions, but with considerable scope for potential accidents and unforeseen problems.

(c) In place of elixirs for eternal youth we have been offered herbal remedies from tea fungus and garlic to Manchurian mushrooms and gingko, magnetism, positive ions and, more recently, anti-oxidants, botox, testosterone, and hormone replacement therapy.

(d) Our strategies to cheat death include ever-new miracle drugs, organ transplants, stem cell grafts, and injections of blood stem cells.

(e) Superseding the preoccupation with homunculi, twenty-first century cloning techniques, artificial insemination, genetic engineering, embryo transplants, surrogate parenting, and reproductive material produced from the DNA of somatic tissue are highly sought after by those prepared to outlay the immense cost.

All have been greeted with a combination of exultation at the possibility of overcoming human limitations and fear of unscheduled consequences and socio-moral dilemmas.

(iv) The most radical and widespread literary criticism of science emerged in the nineteenth century as part of the Romantic reaction against the European Enlightenment. It was characterized by an uncompromising rejection of rationalism, mechanism, reductionism, and scientific materialism as necessary and sufficient explanations of the world and, in particular, of human experience. In contrast to the Cartesian dream that reason, epitomized in mathematics, would simplify and ultimately resolve all problems, the Romantics argued for something much more than mechanism – for a metaphysical or spiritual dimension beyond the parameters of measurement and for the validity of non-rational forms of knowing: imagination, intuition, dreams, the emotions, and the subconscious. The villains of Romanticism were neo-alchemists, reducing the world to symbols and isolating themselves from the healing power of Nature, which might have restored them to sanity and wholeness. These images have been powerfully presented in fiction, vindicating the Modernist premise that twentieth-century society had no humanity touch or emotional well-being.

This vilification of science began prior to the Romantics, with the eighteenth-century English satirists who presented the virtuosi[6] of their day as divorced from reality, unable to relate to human concerns, and so obsessed with their narrow focus of interest that they fell into grave errors of fact as well as moral disrepute. Thomas Shadwell's popular play *The Virtuoso* (1676) and its many imitators, notably Samuel Butler's *The Elephant in the Moon* (1676), Jonathan Swift's *Gulliver's Travels* (1726), especially Book III ridiculing the astronomers of Laputa and the Projectors of Balnibarbi, and Alexander Pope's *Essay on Man* (1733) all satirized the arrogance of contemporary natural philosophers.[7]

These criticisms were amplified in the wholesale rejection of science by the English Romantic poets, Blake, Wordsworth, and Keats, and to a

---

[6]   The term 'virtuoso' was used for wealthy patrons of natural philosophy who enthusiastically undertook miscellaneous projects, without rigor or training. Indiscriminate hoarders and collectors of anything and everything, the virtuosi amassed private museums or 'cabinets' (Haynes 1994, pp. 35-49).

[7]   Butler's poem satirized almost the whole membership of the Royal Society of his day, including Hooke, Boyle, and Leeuwenhoek (Haynes 1994, pp. 43f.). It was widely (and wrongly) assumed that through his 'Virtuoso', Sir Nicholas Gimcrack, Shadwell was lampooning the Royal Society since many of the experiments described were only slightly altered from those reported in contemporary *Transactions of the Royal Society* (Haynes 1994, pp. 45f.). Swift's term 'Projectors' had particular significance since 'real life' Projectors were speculators whose extravagant projects threatened innocent investors with financial ruin. The most notorious of such financial speculations was the 'South Sea Bubble'. The Flying Island of Laputa carries references to Newton's calculations and to William Gilbert's experiments in magnetism. Through his Laputans and Projectors Swift parodied John Locke's theory of knowledge and specific experiments of the Royal Society (Haynes 1994, pp. 68-72). Pope, although he produced the most famous epigraph on Newton – "Nature and Nature's laws lay hid in night; God said, 'Let Newton be!' and all was light."– was nevertheless critical of the arrogance of natural philosophers who confused mere observation of phenomena with understanding (Haynes 1994, pp. 67f.).

lesser extent by the views of their German counterparts who proposed a *Naturphilosophie* affirming a continuity between the spirit of Man and a spiritual dimension in Nature.[8] Of these Blake was the most condemnatory. His 'infernal trinity' comprised Francis Bacon, the exponent of experimentalism, Newton the arch-mechanist and John Locke, representing the philosophy of the five senses (Blake 1966, pp. 636, 685). In Blake's view these three men were dangerous heretics who, blinded by materialism, failed to see the complexity of truth. Wordsworth and Keats viewed the practitioners of a science more in pity than in anger – pity for their limitations of perception and experience and their rejection of imaginative truth.

The Romantic view has remained particularly influential among prose writers as well as poets. Thomas Carlyle lamented, "Men are grown mechanical in head and in heart as well as in hand" (Carlyle 1915, p. 228), and Charles Dickens satirized the British Association for the Advancement of Science, which met for the first time in 1831, as "The Mudfog Association for the Advancement of Everything" (Dickens 1837, pp. 397-413). Its members are depicted as having lost all humanitarian sympathies and values, as socially irresponsible and emotionally and morally deficient.

Balthazar Claës of Balzac's novel *La Recherche de l'Absolu* (1834) is far more complex. Although Balzac's major interest is the psychological, almost clinical, study of a genius and the effect of his obsession on his family, the underlying moral is the Romantic belief that preoccupation with science atrophies the normal emotions that sustain personal relations and social responsibilities. Claës's wife, Josephine, pleads the case for the emotions when she tells him, "Science has eaten away your heart" (Balzac, n.d., p. 84), and contrasts her own selfless devotion with his uncaring obsession with his chemistry. His response, a piece of unwitting self-condemnation, is to redefine feelings in the current chemical term,

---

[8]   Friedrich Schelling proposed that nature was an immense living organism and hence the goal of science was to discover the *Weltseele* of this organism. On the other hand, many of the German Romantic poets had received a scientific education. Novalis had studied mineralogy, physics, chemistry, and mathematics; Schlegel had studied physics; Goethe had studied botany, as well as being well read in chemistry and optics; Ritter was a pharmacist, chemist, physicist, and physiologist (Haynes 1994, pp. 76-8).

'affinities': "Unluckily, such affinities as these are too rare, and the indications are too slight to be submitted to analysis and observation" (Balzac, n.d., p. 85).[9]

The notion of the homunculus was resurrected to provide a useful symbol of such mechanistic philosophy, no longer as a tiny figure but expanded to a full-scale person – or even bigger – dangerous in his power. In a macabre parody of Julien Offray de La Mettrie's *L'Homme machine* (1747), Shelley's Frankenstein assembles his eight-feet-tall 'child' from the components of corpses and brings it to life with an electrical discharge, a method that would have been regarded by her contemporaries as at least feasible, since it mimicked Benjamin Franklin's well-known experiment with a kite in an electrical storm and popular demonstrations of the time practiced publicly on the corpses of executed criminals to show the effect of galvanic action.[10]

In E.T.A. Hoffmann's novel *Der Sandmann* (1817) the title character Dr Coppelius, overtly a lawyer, is also a closet alchemist. As a child, the protagonist Nathanael had watched in horror as Coppola and his father attempted to produce an automaton in a setting that is heavily suggestive of an alchemist's laboratory. Returning years later in the guise of a dealer in scientific glasses, Coppelius persuades Nathanael to look through his telescope and see the beautiful girl Olimpia, technically flawless but lacking emotions and spontaneity. In the descriptions of Olimpia, Hoffmann vividly expresses the Romantic abhorrence of mechanism. The infatuated youth Nathanael is perturbed to discover how stiffly she holds herself and how mechanically she dances. She plays and sings like a clockwork model, with the emotionless tone of a singing machine, and when Nathanael bends to kiss her, her lips are ice-cold.[11] Her mechanical

---

[9]   This is almost certainly a reference to Goethe's novel *Die Wahlverwandtschaften* (*Elective Affinities*) (1809).

[10] Percy Shelley had long been interested in electricity and galvanism. He had constructed a large-scale battery and repeated Franklin's experiment (Holmes 1976, pp. 44f.).

[11] Hoffmann is believed to have been inspired to write his stories of mechanical inventions after seeing an exhibition of automata in Dresden in 1813 (Warrick 1980, p. 34). He may also have been inspired by Jean-Paul Richter's novel *The Death of an Angel*. Hoffmann's *Der Sandmann* in turn inspired Adolphe Adam's *La Poupée de Nuremberg* and the ballet *Coppelia: or the girl with the enamel eyes* (1810).

nature is finally demonstrated when he hurls her to the floor causing her dismemberment. But Nathanael, too, is destroyed by his dalliance with mechanism and the deluding instruments of Coppelius. Under the spell of the distorting telescope he flings himself to his death from the top of a tower. Simultaneous fascination with, and fear of, mechanism is also apparent in Ambrose Bierce's story, 'Moxon's Master' (1894). Bierce's story is important because it explicitly discusses, through a dialogue between the narrator and the scientist-inventor Moxon, who has constructed a chess-playing automaton, the question of what, if anything, distinguishes living systems from machines. Instead of the mechanist view that all organisms are merely complex machines, Moxon takes the contrary view, namely that "all matter is sentient, that every atom is a living, feeling, conscious being" (Bierce 1946). He claims to have shown that plants think and he now believes that even the constituent atoms of minerals think, as they arrange themselves into mathematically perfect patterns. Moxon has made a machine to entertain himself and to demonstrate his theories; but he has not worked through the consequences, for it is the validity of those very theories that is his undoing. In accordance with Moxon's own postulates, the machine is alive and therefore not content to accept a subservient, machine-like role. In frustration at losing the game and anger against its opponent, it reaches forward and strangles its creator with its iron hands. This ending looks back to *Frankenstein* and forward to the twentieth-century stereotype of the scientist unable to control his created beings.

Conceived eighty years after *Frankenstein*, Wells' *The Island of Dr Moreau* (1896), although its protagonist is a biologist, draws heavily on the same tradition of the alchemist and his attempts to produce life by mechanical means. Forced to flee England because of his illegal research in vivisection, Moreau works in isolation in his island laboratory creating his Beast People by vivisecting and transplanting parts from various living creatures to produce new hybrids, the biological counterparts of interchangeable, modular constructions. Like Frankenstein and Moxon, Moreau dies when his creatures revolt against him.

In twentieth-century mainstream fiction the successors to chess-playing automata were robots. These have been used largely to encapsulate the amoral mentality that the authors associated with scientists, engineers and, in some cases, the general ethos of a technological society. For writers with a humanities background the authorial voice is invariably critical, usually satirical, as in the prototypical work on robots, Karel Čapek's *R.U.R.* (1921). On the other hand, the robot stories by writers who have come to fiction from a career in science are usually markedly different in tone. Isaac Asimov's robots, for example, are the heroes of the stories in which they appear, being 'morally' as well as intellectually superior to the flawed human characters whom they so devotedly serve.[12]

Specters of mechanism continued to haunt twentieth-century horror films. Apart from the many versions of *Frankenstein*, *The Cabinet of Doctor Caligari* (1919), *Dr Cyclops* (1940) and the three film versions of Wells' *The Island of Doctor Moreau*[13], the Romantic condemnation of rationalism and mechanism finds expression in numerous details. For example, we should *know* from film conventions that Dr Strangelove (1963) is suspect because his withered hand and his motorized wheelchair mark him as being cut off from Nature, just as, in medieval times, physical ugliness was believed to indicate the moral imperfection of alleged witches.

(v) The alchemist figure is often also an idealist, intense, highly motivated, and focused totally on his quest to transcend the human condition. Frankenstein is the heir of Baconian optimism and Enlightenment confidence that everything can ultimately be known and that such knowledge will inevitably have a beneficial outcome. Deterred by M. Krempe's emphasis on the daily grind of chemistry, he responds ecstatically to M. Waldman who, in language reverberating with biblical echoes, claims for modern chemistry supremacy over other branches of knowledge because

---

[12] Asimov's robots have spawned a lucrative progeny of 'cute', harmless robot characters, popularized in films, such as the R_2-D_2 and C-3PO models of *Star Wars* (1977). Like E.T., these robots are essentially novel pets with just enough initiative to make the games interesting but always, in the long run, deferential to their humans. In some ways, the complacency they generate could be regarded as the most sinister response of all.

[13] *The Island of Lost Souls* (1933) directed by Erle Kenton and starring Charles Laughton as Doctor Moreau; *The Island of Doctor Moreau* (1977) directed by Don Taylor and starring Burt Lancaster as Doctor Moreau; *The Island of Doctor Moreau* (1996) directed by John Frankenheimer and starring Marlon Brando.

of the transcendent power it offers. Speaking of the "modern masters" of his subject, he asserts:

> [T]hese philosophers [chemists] have indeed performed miracles. They penetrate into the recesses of nature and show how she works in her hiding places. They ascend into the heavens; they have discovered how the blood circulates and the nature of the air we breathe. They have acquired new and almost unlimited powers; they can command the thunders of heaven, mimic the earthquake, and even mock the invisible world with its own shadows. [Shelley 1996, p. 28]

What captivates Frankenstein is less the lure of knowledge for its own sake than the promise of the power it confers. "Life and death appeared to me ideal bounds which I should first break through, and pour a torrent of light into our dark world. A new species would bless me as its creator and source; many happy and excellent natures would owe their being to me." (Shelley 1996, p. 32) That is, he sees himself as re-enacting the role of the Creator and, in accordance with the Romantic quest, wrenching opposites into unity at his will.

The word 'Absolute' in Balzac's *La Recherche de l'Absolu* also suggests a transcendent reality beyond the analytical procedures and chemical terms of a particular experiment. Thus although Claës is presented as deficient in feelings toward his family, there is an aura of grandeur attaching to him, not only in his acknowledged genius, but in his devotion to an ideal, his self-sacrifice and the insults which he endures from 'ordinary people'. Balzac's characterization, in fact, reflects the same complexity of response as Blake's rendering of Newton, a visionary even while attempting to confine the universe within a reductive, analytical system. Like Robert Browning's character, Paracelsus, Claës discovers the secret of the Absolute only at the moment of death, for it is a metaphysical, rather than a physical truth. Echoing Marlowe's Faustus, Claës is presented as a tragic figure whose essential nobility and human potential are wasted. Similarly, Aylmer, the protagonist of Hawthorne's short story 'The Birthmark' (1845), is unmistakably introduced as an alchemist: "a man of science, an eminent proficient in every branch of natural philosophy, ... He had left his laboratory to the care of an assistant, cleared his fine countenance from the furnace-smoke, washed the stain of acids from his fingers, and persuaded a beautiful woman to become his wife" (Hawthorne 1987, p. 175). Like Frankenstein he has studied the works of Albertus Magnus, Cornelius Agrippa and Paracelsus. Aylmer, too, is an idealist. Living in a time when "kindred mysteries of Nature seemed to open paths into the region of miracle" (Hawthorne 1987, p. 175), he becomes obsessed with perfection and determines to remove his wife's one tiny blemish, a birthmark, symbol of the inescapable imperfection of the human condition. The elixir vitae he persuades her to drink in order to remove the mark kills her.

(vi) Alchemists and scientists are typically presented in literature as having different allegiances from other people. Like religious and political extremists, they are ruthless in their idealism, prepared to sacrifice people or animals in the cause of their experiments. Wells' Invisible Man kills and robs without remorse to finance his research, while Doctor Moreau is deaf to the screams of pain of his experimental animals. More recently the scientist character frequently enacts the view that the pursuit of scientific knowledge justifies any means, for example, suppressing knowledge of likely side effects, environmental pollution, the possibility of 'jumping genes' or contamination from genetically engineered organisms, lest research projects be curtailed.

(vii) A major factor in the continuing appeal of the alchemist narrative is its ability to evoke perennially convincing patterns of horror, mystery, and evil. Horror continues to fascinate us. Even though most of the examples from past centuries with their focus on graveyards and charnel houses, corpses, ghosts, and monsters have ceased to frighten us, many elements of the Frankenstein narrative remain perpetually relevant as symbols of changing technology, if not of that technology itself. Films have intensified this relevance with special effects, reaching out to a far wider audience than the written word. Horror fiction and horror movies allow us to indulge our worst impulses and fears, to be, at least vicariously, complicit in what violates culturally sanctioned norms. They transgress the boundaries of 'decency' and blur the categories that make up social structures. The writer Stephen King asserts that the effect of horror fiction is to shore up the *status quo*, because we see that the alternative is too terrible and hasten back to the 'real world' with a sense of relief.

> Monstrosity fascinates us because it appeals to the conservative Republi-
> can in a three-piece suit who resides within all of us. We love and need
> the concept of monstrosity because it is a reaffirmation of the order we
> all crave as human beings [...] it is not the physical or mental aberration
> in itself which horrifies us, but rather the lack of order which these aber-
> rations seem to imply. [...] After all, when we discuss monstrosity, we
> are expressing our faith and belief in the norm and watching for the mu-
> tant. The writer of horror fiction is neither more nor less than an agent of
> the *status quo*. [King 1983, p. 30]

While this comment applies to any example of horror from the supernatural to the psychological, from drug-induced states to the rampage of
a serial killer, in the case of the evil alchemist and particularly of his
fictional scientist descendant there are additional intensifiers. First, an
audience is prepared to suspend disbelief about the 'chamber of horrors'
that science might unleash in the foreseeable future; from extra-terrestrial
events through *Silkwood* (1983) and *Jurassic Park* (1993) to *Erin
Brockovich* (2000*)* it seems that scientists can be plausibly implicated in
almost any disaster. Turney (1998) has explored this latent suspicion of
science, particularly in the biological sciences. Second, there is the
attraction of seeing the powerful one dragged down (and in fiction and
film he almost invariably is: the threat is averted, natural order is restored). Third, there is the lingering suggestion that such fictional events
could recur in the real world, causing similar havoc and disaster.

(viii) Scientists themselves have continued to provide writers and
film-makers with ongoing instances of the alchemist stereotype in the
following ways.

(a) Mystery and obfuscation. The symbols, formulae, and theories of
chemistry and physics are as opaque to non-initiates as those of alchemy
were in their time.

(b) Ruthless determination to achieve their goal. A 2001 BBC program *Celluloid Scientists* opened with the words: "the scientists were so
preoccupied with whether they *could* that they didn't stop to think if they
should". Enrico Fermi is quoted as having said in relation to his work on
the bomb, "Don't bother me with your conscientious scruples. After all,
the thing is beautiful physics." (Buck, 1959, p. 206) and there have been
copious literary examples of this attitude derived from twentieth-century

science. In C.P. Snow's novel *The New Men* (1954) it is widely believed amongst the nuclear physicists "that the plutonium bomb was dropped [on Nagasaki] as an experiment to measure its 'effectiveness' against the other. 'It had to be dropped in a hurry', said someone, 'because the war will be over and there won't be another chance'." (Snow 1954, p. 201)

(c) Failure to show concern about the social and moral impact of their research. This has been most pronounced in the case of nuclear physicists. J. Robert Oppenheimer regarded the 'success' of the atomic bomb as "technologically sweet". Edward Teller was the alleged prototype of Dr Strangelove and of Richard Tzessar in Heinrich Schirmbeck's *Ägert dich dein rechtes Auge* (translated into English as *The Blinding Light* [1957]). Tzesssar refuses to acknowledge a moral dimension to his research. "We serve the God of free research, the God who says *'Fiat scientia pereat mundus* – let there be knowledge though the world perish! ... We have no power to prevent it." (Schirmbeck 1957, p. 341) Irving Langmuir of the General Electric Company inspired the amoral Felix Hoenikker in Vonnegut's *Cat's Cradle* (1963) who discovers and plays with the lethal substance, Ice 9. Turney (1998) has catalogued numerous instances of such lack of concern for consequences in the area of genetics.

(ix) Also contributing to the ongoing use of the alchemist stereotype is the appeal of a simplistic, universally understood image. The name 'Frankenstein' has become instantly recognized shorthand for any field of experimentation popularly perceived as dangerous or likely to backfire. From developing viruses for germ warfare, to delivering genetically modified vegetables ('Frankie foods'), cloning sheep, or growing new organs from embryonic stem cells, media reports almost invariably invoke Victor Frankenstein.

(x) On the other hand, the psychological *complexity* of Mary Shelley's protagonist makes him endlessly relevant as a figure of modern science. Unlike the film-makers who have adapted her novel for the screen, Shelley was not greatly interested in the scientific effects beyond the claim that they were "not of impossible occurrence" (Shelley 1996, p. 5). Frankenstein's laboratory is disposed of in one sentence, "In a solitary chamber, or rather cell, at the top of the house, and separated from all the other apartments by a gallery and a staircase, I kept my workshop of filthy creation" (Shelley 1996, p. 32), because the main theatre of action is located within the man himself.

Many of his characteristics are perceived as fitting very well with the popular image of a scientist's life.

(a) Delusion that his research is solely for the benefit of humanity rather than for his own career-path, self-aggrandizement, or satisfaction. Scientists are prone to present research applications in similar terms.

(b) Secrecy about what he is doing and the psychological effects on his personality of this chosen isolation from other human beings. The knowledge that his research is illegal (involving grave-robbing and dissection of corpses) causes Frankenstein to become even more secretive. Similarly, scientists' fear of having their research curtailed by ethics committees, animal liberationists, or environmentalists now engenders a parallel kind of secrecy. Additionally, many employers, in both the government and the private sector, demand such secrecy for processes tied up in patents or involved with national security. In many cases scientists working in industry or for the military are not permitted to publish their work in professional journals.

(c) Obsessive dedication to his research, to the exclusion of relations with family and friends and the suppression of human affections. This obsession includes a fanatical desire to complete a project no matter what the cost, and especially to complete it *first*, a perennial concern of scientists enforced by the requirement of publication and funding.

(d) Exclusion of those who might have given him the ethical advice he did not wish to hear. Rejecting the overtures of his father, his fiancée, and his friend Clerval, Frankenstein leaves their letters unanswered. He has also isolated himself from Nature until, working day and night in his laboratory without regard to natural rhythms, he has lost the ability to appreciate natural beauty and diversity.

(e) Rejection of responsibility for the results of his research. His inability to retain or reclaim control over the outcomes actually disempowers Frankenstein. He cannot (or chooses not to) restrain his Monster. Until recently scientists felt it an unfair imposition to be expected to deal with the consequences of their research, the possible development of their experiments, and their ethical and social implications. Now, in most cases, they have no such option. Under pressure Frankenstein agrees to create a female as a mate for the Monster, then reneges on this agreement. Similarly, dependent on funding from granting committees or corporations, today's scientists are required to work in specific 'fashionable' areas.

Shelley also explores the relation between Frankenstein's pursuit of scientific success, his failure as a human being, and his social guilt. The inevitable neglect of human ties involved in the scientist's total dedication to his research results not only in his own isolation and loneliness but also in a moral and emotional loss to society. Whereas many other Romantic treatments of the scientist's isolation assumed that this was a voluntary state that could, at will, be reversed, Shelley suggests that there is an inevitable loneliness and guilt contingent on scientific research. Frankenstein begins by frequenting remote and lonely places. At first this isolation is dictated by the requirements of his research since he collects his materials from graveyards and charnel houses; but subsequently his separation from society becomes a necessity imposed by the result of his experiment – the existence of the Monster. In relating his tale to Walton, another scientist pursuing an obsession in contravention of the natural ties of affection, Frankenstein digresses to moralize explicitly: "If the study to which you apply yourself has a tendency to weaken your affections, and to destroy your taste for those simple pleasures in which no alloy can possibly mix, then that study is certainly unlawful, that is to say, not befitting the human mind." (Shelley 1996, p33)

6. Terror and Desire

Ultimately the perennial fascination of the master narrative of alchemy is that it tells a story of what we both desire and fear to know– the story of power beyond our dreams but also beyond our control. Paradoxically, no century has had more control over the material universe than ours, and yet we are still confronted with an unpredictable world where we are stalked by terrorism, by AIDS and other pandemics, and by a latent and recurrent nuclear threat. Caught between terror and desire, we are a captive audience for stories that make sense of our uncertain existence by embedding it in the archetypal legend of the powerful mage, the sinister alchemist, the perplexed chemist.

Our society still desires to do a range of secret deals with its scientists, even while professing to treat them with suspicion: nuclear power plants and nuclear waste dumps, in vitro fertilization, cloning, genetically engineered organisms and production processes, surrogate parenting, the trade in organs and genes, anti-diversity treaties with seed companies marketing the total package of genetically modified, fungus-resistant crops as their exclusive intellectual property and hence a monopoly.

7. Conclusion

By bringing together in Frankenstein the apparently opposite qualities of the scientist and the Romantic visionary, Mary Shelley not only enriched immeasurably her depiction of the scientist over earlier representations, but extended the basic Romantic protest against materialism and rationalism. She showed that Frankenstein, although apparently so rational, so desirous of secularizing the world and denouncing its mysteries, is actually, at crucial points, highly irrational, suppressing those considerations which might conflict with his obsession. Levine points out that Frankenstein "as a modern metaphor implies the conception of the divided self, the creator and his world at odds. The civilized man or woman contains within the self a monstrous, destructive, and self-destructive energy" (Levine *et al.* 1979, p. 15). The novel thus becomes a scientific formulation of the archetypal myth of *psychomachia* or the conflict within the soul, epitomized in Stevenson's *Dr Jekyll and Mr Hyde*. In these wholly secular versions, science and technology are a concretization of inner desires, masquerading as rational but, like the Monster, equally capable of springing from the dark, unacknowledged depths of their creator's subconscious. This perception suggests an important qualification of the Enlightenment belief that the pursuit of knowledge is, by definition, rational and good and should not be restricted by any socio-moral considerations.

The pervasive and enduring narratives featuring alchemist-like figures and in particular the two prototypical protagonists Faust and Frankenstein, suggest the prevalence and universality of this particular knowledge myth and raise the question of what alternative knowledge myths there might be. There have been other narratives – the utopian, science-based society of Sir Francis Bacon's *New Atlantis*, H.G. Wells' scientific utopias, the happy robot lands of Isaac Asimov – but they have failed to survive catastrophes, the innate pessimism or resentment of writers, and perhaps of our skeptical selves. We may ask whether science, and specifically chemistry, can ever align itself on the other side in the archetypal saga of good versus evil, for example by offering solutions to the environmental disasters that we are only just beginning to acknowledge, or by working to equalize the distribution of material wealth in the world, the inequality of which is a major cause of racial, political, and religious terrorism.

References

Balzac, H. de: n.d., *The Quest of the Absolute*, trans. E. Marriage, Newnes, London.

B.B.C.: 2001, 'Celluloid Scientists', Radio 4, producer L. Moyes, presenter M. Kermode.

Bierce, A.: 1946, ''Moxon's Master', in C. Fadiman (ed.), *Collected Writings of Ambrose Bierce*, Citadel Press, New York, pp. 429-37.

Blake, W.: 1966, 'Jerusalem', in: G. Keynes (ed.), *Blake. The Poetical Works*, Oxford University Press, London, pp. 636-85.

Bloom, H.: 1965, 'Frankenstein, or the New Prometheus', *Partisan Review*, **32**, 611-18.

Buck, P.: 1959, *Command The Morning*, John Day, New York.

Burckhardt, T.: 1967, *Alchemy: Science of the Cosmos, Science of the Soul*, trans. W. Stoddart, Penguin, Baltimore.

Butler, M.: 1996, '*Frankenstein* and Radical Science', in: J.P. Hunter (ed.), *Frankenstein*, Norton, New York and London, pp. 302-13.

Caron, M. & Hutin, S.: 1961, *The Alchemists*, trans. H.R. Lane, Evergreen Books, London.

Chaucer, G.: 1957, 'The Canon's Yeoman's Prologue and Tale', in: N. Coghill (ed.), *Chaucer: The Canterbury Tales*, Penguin, Harmondsworth.

Clerens, C.: 1967, *An Illustrated History of the Horror Film*, New York, Capricorn.

Cummings, R.: 1966, *The Alchemists*, McKay, New York.

Debus, A.G. & Multhauf, R.P.: 1966, *Alchemy and Chemistry in the Seventeenth Century*. William Andrews Clark Memorial Library, University of California Los Angeles.

[Dickens, C.] "Boz": 1837, 'Full Report of the Mudfog Association for the Advancement of Everything', *Bentley's Miscellany*, **2**, 394-413.

Duncan, E.H.: 1968, 'The Literature of Alchemy and Chaucer's *Canon's Yeoman's Tale*: Framework, Theme and Characters', *Speculum*, **43**, 636-7.

Edwardes, M.: 1977, *The Dark Side of History*, Stein and Day, New York.

French, P.: 1972, *John Dee: The World of an Elizabethan Magus*, Routledge and Kegan Paul, London.

Gettings, F.: 1986, *Encyclopedia of the Occult*, Rider, London.

Gifford, D.: 1974, *Movie Monsters*, Studio Vista, London.

Goethe, J.W. von: 1971, *Faust* Part I, trans. T. Martin, Dent, London.

Hawthorne, N.: 1987, 'The Birthmark', in: *Young Goodman Brown and Other Tales*, Oxford UP, Oxford, pp. 175-92.

Haynes R.D.: 1994, *From Faust to Strangelove: Representations of the Scientist in Western Literature*, Johns Hopkins UP, Baltimore & London.

Hoffmann, E.T.A.: 1983, *The Sandman*, trans. J.T. Bealby, in: *Isaac Asimov Presents the Best Science Fiction of the Nineteenth Century*, ed. I. Asimov, C.G. Waugh & M. Greenberg, Gollancz, London.

Hollister, C.W.: 1990, *Medieval Europe: A Short History*, 6th ed., McGraw-Hill College, Blacklick, Ohio.

Holmes, R.: 1976, *Shelley: The Pursuit*, Quartet Books, London.

King, S.: 1983, *Danse Macabre*, 3rd ed., Berkeley Books, New York.

Levine G. & Knoepflmacher U.C. (eds): 1979, *The Endurance of Frankenstein*, University of California Press, Berkeley.

Levine, G.: 1996, 'Frankenstein and the Tradition of Realism', in: J.P. Hunter (ed.), *Frankenstein*, Norton, New York & London, pp. 208-14.

Lindsay, J.: 1970, *The Origins of Alchemy in Graeco-Roman Egypt*, Muller, London.

Miyoshi, M.: 1969, *The Divided Self: A Perspective on the Literature of the Victorians*, New York UP, New York, New York UP, pp. 79-89.

Read, J.: 1947, *The Alchemist in Life, Literature and Art*, Nelson, London.

Schirmbeck, H.: 1960, *The Blinding Light*, trans. N. Denny, Collins, London.

Shelley, M.: 1996, *Frankenstein, or The Modern Prometheus,* ed. J.P. Hunter, Norton, New York.

Smeed, J.W.: 1975, *Faust in Literature*, Oxford University Press, New York.

Snow, C.P.: 1954, *The New Men*, Macmillan, London.

Tudor, A.: 1989a, *Monsters and Mad Scientists: A Cultural History of the Horror Movie*, Blackwell, Cambridge.

Tudor, A.: 1989b, 'Seeing the Worst Side of Science', *Nature*, **340**, 589-592.

Turney, J.: 1998, *Frankenstein's Footsteps: Science, Genetics and Popular Culture*, Yale University Press, New Haven and London.

Warrick, P.S.: 1980, *The Cybernetic Imagination in Science Fiction*, MIT Press, Cambridge Mass.

Wells, H.G.: 1967, *The Island of Doctor Moreau*, Penguin, Harmondsworth.

CHAPTER 2

HISTORICAL ROOTS OF THE 'MAD SCIENTIST': CHEMISTS IN NINETEENTH-CENTURY LITERATURE

Joachim Schummer

*Department of Philosophy, University of Darmstadt,
Schloss, 64283 Darmstadt, Germany; js@hyle.org*

This chapter traces the historical roots of the 'mad scientist', a concept that has powerfully shaped the public image of science up to today, by investigating the representations of chemists in nineteenth-century Western literature. I argue that the creation of this literary figure was the strongest of four critical literary responses to the emergence of modern science in general and of chemistry in particular. The role of chemistry in this story is crucial because early nineteenth-century chemistry both exemplified modern experimental laboratory research and induced, due to its rapid growth, a ramification, and fragmentation of knowledge that undermined former ideals of the unity of knowledge under the umbrella of metaphysics and religion. Because most writers considered contemporary chemistry an offspring of 'wrong alchemy', all four responses drew on the medieval literary figure of the 'mad alchemist' to portray chemists. Whereas early writers considered the quest for scientific knowledge to be altogether in vain, later writers pointed out the narrow-minded goals and views specifically of chemistry. A third response moved that criticism to a metaphysical and religious level, by relating chemistry to materialism, nihilism, atheism, and hubris. The fourth response, the 'mad scientist', elaborated on the hubris theme by attaching moral perversion to the 'mad alchemist'.

1. Introduction

In a speech to the American Association for the Advancement of Science in 1999, the famous Hollywood play writer and film director Michael

Crichton (1999) replied to complaints by scientists that the media, particularly films, have shaped the bad public image of science by presenting scientists in a very distorted and negative manner. Crichton, who is currently working on another 'mad scientist' film,[1] turned the tables and argued that, instead of the media misunderstanding science, scientists actually misunderstand the media. Filmmakers do not reflect society but present interesting and entertaining stories with extreme figures, such that "All professions look bad in the movies".

It is the task of the humanities, rather than of filmmakers, to reflect on society, in which filmmakers are but influential actors. Obviously, there is more to say about the literary clichés of scientists, about the historical roots and literary sources that make filmmakers routinely employ such figures as the 'mad scientist' (Tudor 1989, Skal 1998). As Brian Stableford, in his entry on "Scientists" in the *Encyclopedia of Science Fiction*, laconically says: "the scientist had inherited the mantle (and the public image) of the medieval alchemists, astrologers and sorcerers. This image proved to be extraordinary persistent. It was still very prominent at the end of the nineteenth century, and its vestiges remain even today" (Stableford 1979, p. 533). Also, Rosalynn D. Haynes, in her study on representations of scientists in the literature, finds among other figures the "alchemist, who reappears at critical times as the obsessed or maniacal scientist" (Haynes 1994, p. 3; see also the previous chapter in this volume).

In this chapter, I explore the link in literature between today's public image of science and medieval alchemy in more detail and with reference to the history of science, and I will do so by focusing on the literary representation of chemists in the nineteenth century. Since twentieth-century films and popular literature featuring 'mad scientists' frequently draw on, exploit, and simplify classics from the nineteenth century (Toumey 1992), it is this period that deserves particular attention. We will see that such figures as the 'mad scientist' were created not for entertainment reasons, as Crichton believes, but in a nineteenth-century

---

[1]   The film in the making is based on Crichton's science fiction horror novel *Prey* (New York: Harper Collins, 2002), which is largely composed of ingredients to be dealt with in Sections 3 & 6 of this chapter.

literary response to the emergence of modern chemistry. Whereas science in general, including its various subject fields, heroes, and methodologies, was treated in the literature in all kinds of ways, this is not the case with the representation of chemists. Chemistry is crucial in this story for two reasons. On the one hand, chemistry was the prototype of the experimental laboratory sciences that exploded in the nineteenth century and induced an ongoing fragmentation and specialization of knowledge, which posed a serious threat to any ideas of the unity of knowledge. On the other hand, literary representations of chemists could easily draw on the well-developed literary figure of the medieval 'alchemists', which was already loaded with moral, social, metaphysical, and religious criticism. Thus, in their critique of the emergence of modern science, writers focused on chemists, whom they depicted in the fashion of the medieval alchemist but equipped with some new attributes.

After some brief notes about the origin and characteristics of the medieval alchemist in the early literature (Section 2), I discuss the literary discourse about the emergence of modern science and chemistry in four steps, which are layers of severity of criticism rather than historical steps.[2] The third section deals with Christian Romanticism, which renewed the older discourse about the 'true alchemy' by arguing for religion and moral knowledge as opposed to natural philosophy or modern science. In the fourth section, we meet approaches that reintroduced the medieval alchemists in order to warn of the narrow-minded goals and misleading promises, particularly of experimental chemistry. The conflict then turns into a battle fought out with metaphysical and theological weapons in literary form. Taking chemistry as the embodiment of the

---

[2] The texts that are mentioned in the following are taken from a sample of hundreds of texts collected over the past five years with the additional aid of searching many voluminous online collections of classical texts for occurrences of 'chemist' or equivalents in other languages. With only few exceptions, all the texts from the nineteenth century featuring a chemist fall into one or more of the four classes described below. Because it is common practice in literary studies to read the (nonironic) employment of mad scientists by authors as a form of criticism of science by these authors, I follow that practice also in analyzing the historical roots of the mad scientists. Although that may occasionally sound naive, I find the other option even more naive with regard to pre-twentieth-century literature, according to which 'the work', and not the author, speaks to the reader, particularly if hundreds of 'works' speak a similar language.

Enlightenment ideas of science, writers related chemistry to atheism, materialism, nihilism, and hubris (Section 5), and eventually reinforced the negative view by transforming the 'mad alchemist' into the 'mad scientist' (Section 6). My overall thesis is that nineteenth-century writers created the 'mad scientist' as one of four literary responses to the emergence of modern science in general and of chemistry in particular. Since these responses appeared in all Western countries, by their most prominent writers in different languages and in different literary styles and forms,[3] it had far-reaching consequences, including the ongoing split between the so-called 'two cultures' and the peculiar public image of chemists.

Unfortunately, the topic has not attracted much attention from scholars of literature studies,[4] whereas the impact of alchemical theory, allegories, and hermeticism on nineteenth- and twentieth-century authors has recently become a 'hot topic' in the field.[5] The only monograph on the representations of scientists in (mostly English) literature is the already mentioned excellent study by Rosalynn D. Haynes. There is an older book on the 'pharmacist' in the literature, written by Georg Urdang (1921, enlarged and modified as Urdang 1926). However, unlike what is suggested by the English term, the chemist, in the sense of the pharmacist, plays quite a different role in the literature that I omit in the follow-

---

[3] Although there is, of course, some variation, depending on the literary form and the specific cultural traditions of authors, such differences are, from the comparative point of view of this study, less important in face of the overwhelming similarities. Future studies might explore whether cultural differences in the current public image of science are related to nuances in their corresponding literature traditions.

[4] However, there are numerous literature studies that deal with the much wider Faustian and Promethean tradition, which may include almost any profession from philosophers to writers, engineers, and politicians, and several studies on the legacy of Mary Shelley's *Frankenstein*, on which I occasionally draw. In addition, there are several studies on the literary image of medical doctors, including Browner 2005 and Rothfield 1992.

[5] The best comprehensive book on various nineteenth- and twentieth-century authors is Meakin 1995; on French authors, although somewhat disappointing, there is Marteau 1995; a study on some English and American authors is Clack 2000. There are numerous monographs about the 20 or so most famous writers, first of all about Goethe, and their relations to alchemy and hermeticism, references to which may be found in the books above. I mention only two studies not cited there: Stiasny 1997 and Deghaye 2000. A recent anthology is Lembert & Schenkel 2002. From a history of science point of view, it is not always clear to what kind of alchemy these studies are referring.

ing.[6] In addition, Otto Krätz has collected some material on the role of chemists in nineteenth- and twentieth-century literature, on which I occasionally draw (Krätz 1990, 1991, 2004).

2. Preliminary Notes about the Medieval Alchemist in the Literature

The literary figure of the alchemist had already been created in the fourteenth century by writers such as Dante Alighieri, Francesco Petrarch, and Geoffrey Chaucer, and then became one of the favorite figures in social satires from the fifteenth to the seventeenth centuries, *e.g.* by Sebastian Brant, Desiderius Erasmus, Agrippa of Nettesheim, Reginald Scot, Johannes Claius, Thomas Lodge, Ben Jonson, and many more.[7] Its roots go back to alchemical texts, to a debate on the true alchemy that accompanied alchemy throughout its existence. In fact, alchemical fiction and nonfiction were never as clearly separated as we are inclined to see them from our present point of view.[8] A classic topic in alchemical treatises was the defamation of those who did not follow what the author himself considered the true alchemy. Opponents were usually called stupid and greedy, 'puffers' without reason who blindly strive for gold instead of insight and spiritual improvement, and who in their greed ruin themselves and cheat others. Writers such as Petrarch and Chaucer elaborated on this motif in great detail, and they did so by dividing the

---

[6]   The dominant theme of the pharmacist in the literature is, according to Urdang, the intermediate social position, between being a scientist or a physician and a seller, which has led to some pseudoscientific characters, for instance 'Homais' in Gustave Flaubert's *Madame Bovery* (1857).

[7]   Dante Alighieri, *Divine Comedy* (1310-21), Inferno, Cantato XXIX, l.118-39; Francesco Petrarch, "De Alchimia", *De remediis utriusque fortunae* (1353-66), chap. 111; Geoffrey Chaucer, "The Canon's Yeoman's Prologue" and "The Canon's Yeoman's Tale", in *Canterbury Tales* (ca. 1390); Sebastian Brant, "Von Fälscherei und Beschiss", in *Das Narrenschyff* (1494), chap. 102; Desiderius Erasmus, "Beggar Talks" and "Alchemy/Alcumistica", in *Colloquia* (1524); Heinrich Cornelius Agrippa von Nettesheim, "Alchimia", in *De incertidudine et vanitate scientiarum atque artium* (1530), chap. XC; Reginald Scot, *The Discoverie of Witchcraft* (1584), fourteenth book; Johannes Claius, *Altkumistica* (1586); Thomas Lodge, "The Anatomie of Alchymie", in *A Fig for Momus* (1595), Epistle 7; Ben Jonson, *The Alchemist* (1610/ 12). The best survey of the English literature is Linden 1996; see also Read 1947.

[8]   For a selection of alchemical poetry, see Schuler 1995.

alchemist into two figures, or two phases, of 'wrong alchemy'. The first one is the 'mad alchemist', the miserable seeker who is obsessed with the idea of gold-making and who spends all his money for nothing, ruins his health and his family, loses his social reputation, and ends up in the gutter. The second figure (or phase) is the tempting or 'cheating alchemist'. Like a junkie turned into a drug dealer, he tries to finance his obsession by inducing the same obsession for gold-making in others. Once his victims are infected and become 'mad alchemists', the 'cheating alchemist' uses some simple alchemical tricks to drain them dry.

Late medieval and early modern satires featuring the 'mad alchemist' and the 'cheating alchemist' had a much more general moral than being simply a critique of alchemical gold-making efforts. They were criticizing the striving for material goods, such as money, or physical health and immortality, as in corresponding alchemist stories about 'elixirs of life'. They were arguing for a spiritual life guided by moral and religious values. And by making kings, aristocrats, clerics, and representatives of other social classes the blind victims of 'cheating alchemists', they were denouncing the corruptness of their society. These alchemical figures slowly faded during the seventeenth century, as writers employed new figures, such as the 'miser' and the 'gamester', for propagating similar moral messages.[9] In addition, alchemy became extremely popular among educated people, as indicated by the number of published books in the seventeenth and eighteenth centuries. And since most of the popular philosophies of nature (from Aristotle to Bacon, Descartes, Boyle, Newton, and Leibniz) supported, or at least did not exclude, the transmutation of metals, the stories lost some of their plausibility for mediating the general message. It was not until the late eighteenth century that writers re-

---

[9]   The 'miser', which goes back to Plautus's *Aulularia* (ca. 200 BC), was revived by Lorenzino de Medici in his *Aridosia* (1536) and then became a popular theme, particularly in French comedies, *e.g.* de Larivey (*Les Esprits*, 1579), de Boisrobert (*La Belle Plaideuse*, 1655), Chappuzeau (*L'Avare Dupé*, 1636), and, of course, Molière (*L'Avare*, 1668). In England, the usurer Shylock in Shakespeare's *The Merchant of Venice* was certainly influential. The 'obsessed gamester', who replaced the 'mad alchemist', was made popular, for instance, by Espinel (*Vida del Escudero Marcos de Obregón*, 1618), Shirley (*The Gamester*, 1633), de la Forge (*La Joueuse Dupée*, 1663), Dancourt (*La Désolation des Joueuses*, 1688), and Dufresney (*Le Chevalier Joueur*, 1697).

vived the alchemical figures with new industry when modern chemistry emerged.[10]

Just as the alchemist and to a lesser extent the astrologer had been the main (pre)scientific figures in medieval literature, the 'al-chemist' and some related figures, such as the 'physician' engaged in chemistry or pharmacy, became the main scientific figures in the nineteenth-century literature. I prefer using the term 'al-chemist' because either the figures are really called alchemists or it is simply the medieval alchemist who appears in the disguise of a chemist or physician, if, for instance, gold-making is replaced with diamond-making or some drug fills the place of the elixir of life. Nonetheless, writers, while borrowing their literary equipment from medieval colleagues, were actually writing about contemporary science, as we soon see.

3. Renewing the Discourse about the True Alchemy in Christian Romanticism

Throughout the history of Latin alchemy there was debate on the true alchemy. Apart from differences concerning the right experimental approach and the correct theory of metals and transmutation, the dispute was about whether alchemy goes beyond material improvement to include spiritual (*i.e.* intellectual, moral, and religious) improvement of the adept and on how both aspects are to be combined. During the late eighteenth century, when experimental and theoretical chemistry became an increasing part of scientific research, that medieval debate was renewed in a particularly romantic fashion and with quite extreme positions. An early example is the German Romanticist Johann Heinrich Jung (1740-

---

[10] As Barbara Benedict (2004) observes, the virtuoso and the medical doctor were subject to many satires in the seventeenth and eighteenth centuries. I disagree, however, with her thesis that this period created the 'mad scientists', because satires on virtuosi and, even more so, on medical doctors are much older. Instead, I argue in this chapter that the 'mad scientist' was created in the early nineteenth century by transforming the mad alchemist of the fourteenth century. In addition, in contrast to a widespread view, alchemy seems to be rather unimportant in early British gothic novels. Among the 208 gothic novels analyzed by Ann B. Tracy (1981), there are only three that include some alchemy, including only one (William Godwin's *St. Leon*, 1799, see below) with an alchemist featuring as a main character, which some do not consider a gothic novel.

1817) who called himself "Stilling" and about whom there was a rumor that he had been an alchemist because he dealt with alchemy in his quasi-autobiographical novel *Henrich Stillings Jünglings-Jahre* (1778).[11] Stilling, then a teacher, describes a cheating alchemist, his colleague Graser, who tries hard to lead Stilling into temptation to become his companion. Stilling finally resists, but not without confessing that his own inclination to alchemy is actually his "inexhaustible hunger for knowledge about the prime forces of nature" that cannot be satisfied by philosophies of nature – he names Newton and Leibniz. We also learn that Stilling eventually drops alchemy altogether in favor of a more promising way, because alchemy is not in accordance with his primary sources of truth, among which he names the Bible. Stilling, who later became a leading figure of a Protestant movement, also had a priest-alchemist, his grandfather Pastor Moriz, in the first part of his quasi-autobiographical novel, *Henrich Stillings Jugend* (1777), which was, incidentally, published by Goethe without Stilling's knowledge. The old priest-alchemist, to be sure not of the gold-making kind, remorsefully confesses that all his life has been spent in vain, leading to unhappiness. The miserable seeker, not of gold but of pure knowledge, explains that such a quest is led by egoistic motives leading to unhappiness as opposed to altruism, which, thanks to God's blessing, leads to happiness.

Stilling's autobiographical account is interesting not only because of the early rediscovery of the medieval alchemical figures but also because of a new emphasis. The cheating alchemist is reduced to a mere criminal and clearly distinguished from the 'seeking alchemist', who appears to be, rather, a philosopher of nature. Attractive as the latter appears at first glance, there are religious and moral reservations that push the seeker in another direction. Alchemy, or natural philosophy, is rejected because mere knowledge of nature lacks morality; it is amoral. If there is a true alchemy, a true 'philosophers' stone', then it must focus on morality and religion.

---

[11] The two autobiographical novels mentioned here were first published by G. J. Decker: Berlin-Leipzig (1777/1778), and were reprinted along with further autobiographical novels in J. H. Jung-Stilling, *Lebensgeschichte*, ed. G. A. Benrath, 3rd ed. (Darmstadt: WTB, 1992). On Stilling's religiously motivated publications, see Hahn 1988 and Hirzel 1998.

There are many famous fairy tales of the time that carry a similar message, although in a clumsier manner. If we assume that the Grimm brothers in the period 1812-15 only wrote down older tales, their *Wasser des Lebens* (Water of Life) is probably the oldest one. The elixir of life, according to their moral, is to be found only if the seeker is morally perfect. The German writer and philosopher Christoph Martin Wieland (1733-1813) narrated a fairy tale called *Der Stein der Weisen* (The Philosophers' Stone, 1786-89)[12] in which he employed the full-fledged medieval figure of the cheating alchemist. His victim is a king of Cornwall who is as credulous and stupid as he is greedy and heartless. After his deception, he goes through a series of fanciful transformations, controlled by fairy-like figures, through which the king's former credulity and greed give way to the reason and morality of a simple and happy man. At the happy end, we learn that the true philosophers' stone, *i.e.* a remedy for happiness, is to be searched for in reason and morality. There is another fairy tale called *The Philosophers' Stone* written by the Danish writer Hans Christian Andersen (1805-75) around 1835. Here, it is a wise old Indian who is reaching for the 'stone', a remedy against death, that is said to be composed of the true, the good, and the beautiful, *i.e.* the medieval *verum, bonum et pulchrum*. After a series of unsuccessful attempts by his four sons, who are each characterized by extraordinary capacities of one of the senses, his blind daughter is finally able to collect the ingredients. This reveals to her father, as the tale finishes, that the secret stone is Faith, leading via Hope and Love (*i.e.* the three Christian virtues) to immortality.

All these literary examples revive the discourse about the true alchemy. Writers involved in that discourse argued in favor of a spiritual alchemy based on morality or religion, or they even reformulated alchemy in pure terms of the Christian doctrine, as Anderson did. In this context, as in the internal medieval debates, the cheating alchemist only

---

[12] This is part of a collection of fairy tales first published anonymously as *Dschinnistan oder Auserlesene Feen- und Geistermärchen* (Winterthur: Steiner, 1786-89; repr. Zürich-Stuttgart: Manesse, 1992). Wieland's tales bear some similarities to the *Tales of the Thousand and One Nights*. His 'Stein der Weisen' is probably inspired by the 'Story of Hasan of El-Basrah' (see below). For a structuralist interpretation of Wieland's 'moralistic tale', see Nobis 1976, chap. IV.

helps point out the distinction between true and wrong alchemy. However, the new opposition has different elements now. Whereas the true alchemy is the Christian belief system or the search for God, the wrong alchemy is modern science or the search for scientific knowledge. The writers of what might be called Christian Romanticism rejected modern science altogether, because it no longer had any basis in Christian religion. Echoing Augustine, they considered curiosity-driven search for knowledge as idle, useless, and misleading.[13] They strongly opposed the contemporary efforts to separate knowledge of nature from moral knowledge. In sum, they revived the discourse about the true alchemy in order to express their strong opposition, not to alchemy or chemistry in particular, but to the general Enlightenment idea of science, which at that time flourished.

4. Reinventing the Medieval Alchemists in a Discourse about Chemistry

Unlike the aforementioned writers, who rejected science altogether, there are more specific romantic positions with particular attitudes towards chemistry. In his autobiographical *Dichtung und Wahrheit* (1814), Johann Wolfgang von Goethe (1749-1832) described his early interest in and fascination with experimental chemistry. Furthermore, his detailed analogies between chemical relations and social relations in his *Wahlverwandtschaften* (1809) revealed profound knowledge of contemporary chemical theories. How, then, did this 'chemistry-friendly' Romanticist, who helped establish a chair of chemistry in the philosophical faculty at the University of Jena in 1789,[14] consider the development of modern chemistry in his literary work?

His two-part tragedy *Faust* (1806, 1832) provides surprisingly detailed insight. In fact, the tragedy includes a certain genealogy – Faust's father, Faust himself, and Faust's famulus Wagner – that reflects his view on the historical development of chemistry. In Part I (vv. 1034-55),

---

[13] A similar criticism of science can be found in the works of the early eighteenth-century British moralists Alexander Pope, Samuel Johnson, and William Cowper.

[14] See Döbling 1928. On Goethe's general relationship to chemistry, see also Kuhn 1972 and Schwedt 1998.

Faust provides a brief account of his father, who is introduced as an adept of the iatrochemical tradition and who worked hard in the laboratory to produce various medicines according to cryptic prescriptions. However, these medicines killed more people than the pestilence, says Faust. Despite that, people praised iatrochemists like his father, who were in fact nothing else than "cheeky murderers". Unlike Faust, Wagner, who according to standard interpretations represents Goethe's contemporary academia, including chemistry, strongly approves of the practice of Faust's father. What he did, says Wagner, was to apply the knowledge of his time in a conscientious and meticulous manner. Moreover, Wagner suggests that one should honor Faust's father and take his state of the art as an important step in the progress of science. For Faust, the intermediate figure in the genealogy, belief in that progress of science is a grave error, because such science provides only useless and fragmentary knowledge. The tragic Faust, the poet-philosopher with 'two souls in his breast', represents the splitting state of romantic natural philosophy reaching out for a new orientation. The new chemistry, represented by the famulus with only limited knowledge, is no alternative, since it is allied with blind and unscrupulous applications of former days. Goethe did not provide optimistic prospects in his tragedy, as he did not argue for a true alchemy. Instead, his play is full of specific attacks on chemistry, among which I pick out but one.

In Part II (1832), Faust leaves the university and his former famulus Wagner, who in the meantime has become a famous doctor of science (vv. 6643ff.). This scholarly chemist, whom Goethe provided with many characteristics of the medieval 'puffer' (vv. 6678-82), has been busy for months with his "great work". Eventually, the right mixture and processing of "hundreds of substances" yield the intended result, a chemically created homunculus. Rather than being a Frankensteinian monster, to which we come back in Section 6, the homunculus is a witty and curious little man who is soon taking the initiative during the subsequent travels of Faust and Mephistopheles. The baffled chemist, seeking advice from his creation about what his job should now be, is told by the homunculus to stay at home, upon which Mephistopheles sardonically comments that eventually we all depend on our own creations. The obvious moral is that chemists, if they successfully apply their skills, lose control over their own creations. As compared to their extremely powerful skills, chemists' capacities to understand, foresee, and evaluate the effects of their own doings are very poor because they lack the deeper understanding of a more comprehensive philosophy of nature. Since the relationship between the famulus/chemist Wagner and the master/alchemist Faust is exactly mirrored in Goethe's earlier ballad *Der Zauberlehrling* (1797, *The Sorcerer's Apprentice*), we have good reasons to interpret that ballad along the same line. Here again, the apprentice/chemist, while the master/alchemist is temporarily out of town, tries to employ the master's skills for his own purposes, although without real understanding. After initial success, the apprentice loses control over his work. This time, the apprentice is less lucky than Wagner because his work quickly grows dangerous. The catastrophe is prevented only by his master's return at the very last moment.

If these famous passages reflect the relationship between romantic alchemy or a holistic natural philosophy, on the one hand, and modern experimental chemistry, on the other, as I suggest, then we have little reason to read Goethe in the ahistorical or even prophetic way that is widespread nowadays. At the beginning of the nineteenth century, there was not yet the kind of powerful industrial technology, let alone genetic engineering, that we have today. Instead, there was a debate about the scope of natural philosophy and its fragmentation into the modern scientific disciplines. In this drama, chemistry was the main character, because it emerged as the first experimental discipline, leaving natural philosophy and the metaphysical tradition behind. Unlike later writers, Goethe saw nothing wrong with chemistry as such, since it owed everything, including its powerful skills, to its ancestors, as the master-apprentice or master-famulus relation suggests. Problems arose only if this newborn child pretended to be independent, if it applied its mother's skills for its own purposes without her wisdom.

Goethe is but one example, and not even the earliest, among many authors who, by literary means, expressed their critical view on chemistry's growing independence from natural philosophy. A widely used scheme was first to convert the miserable seeker of the Middle Ages into a successful seeker and then to point out that the alleged success is actually a failure or at least worthless. By so doing, writers criticized the narrow-minded scope of aims and the reduced circumspection of chemists, while at the same time acknowledging the power of chemical experimentation. However, as they anachronistically employed the medieval alchemists for their purpose, with the aims of making gold, elixirs of life, or homunculi, their criticism did not represent what contemporary chemists were actually doing. It seems that writers were too much occupied by the motifs of their literature tradition.

An early example is Wieland's already mentioned fairy tale *Der Stein der Weisen* (1786-89), where the author discusses at length how the economy would break down if alchemical gold-making were successful. Exactly the same thread of economic inflation, although expressed in a completely different literary style and with several references to contemporary chemists (Humphry Davy), is expounded in Edgar Allen Poe's hoax short story "Von Kempelen and His Discovery" (1849).[15] In his tragedy *Der Adept* (1838),[16] the Austrian writer Friedrich Halm (1806-71) let his "Magister of chemistry", through the successful making of gold, become morally corrupted and guided only by avarice, excessiveness, and unrestrained ambitions. As a kind of curse, the poor chemists meets the same vices in all other people, before he returns to his old virtues of altruistic and idealistic scientific research at the happy end. Compared to Halm's simple moralistic play, William Godwin's second and much earlier novel, *St. Leon* (1799),[17] is rather subtle and was both more original and influential. Godwin revived the medieval topic of the alchemist's obsession with the philosophers' stone and the elixir of life, but, as his sixteenth-century hero is indeed successful, the obsession is extended towards using these gifts for the benefit of humanity. Thus, the miserable seeker turns into a miserable benefactor. Wherever he tries to apply his gifts, the results are disastrous. What the tragic alchemist underestimates and ignores is that society is driven by different forces, po-

---

[15] First published in *The Flag of Our Union*, 4 (14 April 1849). Burton R. Pollin (1970, chap. 10) considers the story as the "culmination of Poe's efforts in the field of the literary hoax" (p. 166). Resuming "the entire orientation of Poe to experimental and theoretical science", he concludes that "Poe humorously maintained that modern inventions are inferior copies or postludes to the glories of Egypt and makes a poor joke about the present lack of advance" (p. 184).

[16] First published Wien: Gerold, 1838; repr. in *Werke* (Gerold: Wien, 1856), vol. 2.

[17] First published London: Robinson, 1799.

litical and religious ideas. Inasmuch as Godwin's hero owes a lot to Paracelsus, and the legends spun around this historical figure, we find a similar plot a few decades later in Robert Browning's huge pseudo-biographical poem *Paracelsus* (1835).[18] Let us now consider two other nineteenth-century elixir of life stories. In Honoré de Balzac's *L'Elixir de longue vie* (1830),[19] Don Juan's father successfully gained an elixir that needed to be applied only after death, but his son refused to do so because of selfishness and avarice. The successful but dying alchemist in Richard Garnett's short story *The Elixir of Life* (1881) does not even try to use his invention, and nor is he willing to give the elixir to anybody else, except a monkey, because he "forbore to perpetuate human affliction, and bestowed a fatal boon where alone it could be innoxious".[20]

Of course, the making of gold, elixirs and such things has always been a metaphor for striving for material goods, against which writers have been using their skills at any time and with various literary means, including the alchemical figures. However, the medieval alchemist underwent an extraordinary literary revival at the beginning of the nineteenth century, after nearly two centuries of virtual absence. It seems that, in the view of many writers, the emerging chemistry was the scientifically professionalized form of striving for material goods, and thus became their new target. The old alchemical motifs, originally giving a general message against avarice and stupidity, were now directly related to chemistry. Clichés as they were, they worked well to transport the literary ideas without bothering much about details of contemporary chemistry. Those who did bother carefully searched for further links between the new chemistry and the old alchemical ambitions – or invented them, as did Poe with his reference to gold-making in a "Diary of Sir Humphrey Davy". Some writers even familiarized themselves with details of the new chemistry, in order to elaborate a modern, state-of-the-art variant of the medieval alchemist – the chemist as diamond-maker.

---

[18] First published London: Effingham, 1935.
[19] First published in *Revue de Paris*, vol. 19 (24 October 1830): 181-210.
[20] First published in *Our Times* (July 1881): no. 1; repr. in R. Garnett, *The Twilight of the Gods and Other Tales* (New York: A. A. Knopf, 1888; 2nd ed. 1926). Garnett was a distinguished scholar of literature history before he became a writer.

Once established, numerous diamond-makers would follow in the literature. The earliest example I found, and perhaps the most original one, is the last and fragmentary novel by Jean Paul (1763-1825), *Der Komet oder Nikolaus Marggraf* (1820-22).[21] Like all of his satirical novels, the story is full of fantastic fictions and parodies. Nikolaus Marggraf, the diamond-maker, is not really a chemist but a chemically skilled apothecary with strong social ambitions or, to be more correct, egomaniac delusions. Owing to the riches eventually resulting from his successful diamond-making – for which Jean Paul, as always, gives scientific details – the would-be nobleman is able to buy himself a court with all its pomp and glamour, including a court society. Yet soon a rival appears who calls himself the devil and disputes Marggraf's right to the court, and the fragmentary novel abruptly ends during the quarrel. Instead of drawing a simple moral, Jean Paul used the story of social advancement to furnish it with many satires on political events of the time as well as on contemporary literary movements such as German Romanticism. Perhaps the latest classic example is one of the earliest short stories of H. G. Wells (1866-1946), entitled *The Diamond Maker* (1894).[22] Here, it is an amateur chemist who obsessively performs chemical experiments in his small apartment during fifteen years of increasing poverty, during which he nearly starves to death, and who in great detail resembles the medieval 'mad alchemist'. When he eventually succeeds in making diamonds (or some similar stuff), he gets into trouble with the police, to the effect that he is unable to sell and thus benefit from his creation.

All the stories mentioned thus far reintroduce the medieval alchemist as the miserable seeker but modify the plot, in that they concede some experimental success in the making of gold, elixir, or diamonds. In so

---

[21] First published Berlin: Reimer, 1820-22, 3 vols. (repr. Zürich: Manesse, 2002). On this 'comedy' see Gierlich 1972.

[22] First published in *Pall Mall Budget* (16 August 1894); repr. in *The Stolen Bacillus and Other Incidents* (1895). Wells's oeuvre is, of course, a rich source of 'alchemists', including, from the nineteenth century alone, Nebogipfel in 'The Chronic Argonauts' (1888), Moreau in *The Island of Doctor Moreau* (1896), and Griffin in *The Invisible Man* (1897). As J.R. Hammond (1979, p. 63) observes, these "are variants on a similar theme. Each, in their different ways, testifies to his deep conviction that science has unlimited possibilities for both good and evil and that knowledge without moral responsibility corrupts and ultimately destroys its possessor".

doing, writers acknowledged to some extent the experimental power of chemistry but criticized the experimenters' narrow-minded scope of aims. As the British writer Wilkie Collins (1824-89) put it in his *The Woman in White* (1860) "the illimitable power of Chemistry remains the slave of the most superficial and the most insignificant ends".[23] Thus, the medieval plot needed to be modified in order to point out that experimental success is by no means success overall, that the human condition is much more complex, and that reducing one's effort to chemistry is but blind obsession. Writers thereby reflected the growing impact of chemistry on society and warned of uncritical hopes and promises.

There are also other nineteenth-century stories that reintroduced the medieval alchemist with only little modification but elaborated on the theme in more psychological, dramatic, or criminological detail. The most well-known, although perhaps overestimated, example is Honoré de Balzac's novel *La Recherche de L'Absolu* (1834),[24] which in English translations is known as *The Alkahest, The Quest of the Absolute*, or *The Philosophers' Stone*. Balthazar Claes, a Flemish diamond-maker, is explicitly said to have been a former a pupil of Lavoisier in Paris before he returned home to marry and run the business of his wealthy family. Nonetheless, the story retells the fate of the miserable seeker, the 'mad alchemist', which Balzac composed with every detail he could find in the medieval literature. After fourteen years of harmony and wealth, Claes suddenly becomes infected with a "moral malady", *i.e.* the addiction to diamond-making, transmitted by a Pole who figures as the medieval tempter. As it happens, Claes ruins his family both financially and morally – his wife dies from sorrow – and destroys his mental and physical health, social status, and so on. By referring to the chemical debates of the early nineteenth century, *e.g.* electrochemistry, and Prout's conception of a *materia prima*, Balzac tried hard to make the link to contemporary chemistry plausible, because his hero should, as he later confessed, "represent all the efforts of modern chemistry".[25] At the same time, it

---

[23] First published London: Sampson Low, 1860, 3 vols.
[24] First published Paris: Vve Béchet, 1834.
[25] In a letter to Hippolyte Castille, Balzac explains, "Le héros de *La Recherche de L'Absolu* représente tous les efforts de la chimie moderne" (quoted from Ambrière 1999, p. 401).

helped him to introduce the dramatically necessary ups and downs of the plot. Yet the story remains within its medieval models, as the miserable seeker keeps on with his unsuccessful work until his death at the very end.

With his preference for crime thrillers and his own admirable way of interlocking stories with each other, 'al-chemists' figure prominently in many novels of Wilkie Collins. In *Jezebel's Daughter* (1880; chap. XV),[26] the plot remains basically within the medieval scope, like that of Balzac's *La Recherche*. Placed in early nineteenth-century Germany at the University of Würzburg, the physician and professor of chemistry Dr. Fontaine is successfully tempted by a Hungarian chemist, who pretends to be able to make gold, diamonds, and the philosophers' stone. The usual process of addiction and obsession follows, such that Fontaine ruins his family financially and morally, which Collins relates in heart-rending letters written by Fontaine's wife, Jezebel. However, in *The Haunted Hotel* (1879),[27] Collins went one step further than Balzac and medieval writers. The final three chapters present, as one partial solution of that intricate crime thriller, a different 'al-chemist' story set in the 1860s. Here the 'al-chemist' is a Baron "with a single-minded devotion to the science of experimental chemistry" who has already spent all his money on his costly experiments. In need of further money for his 'final' experiment, he first marries his sister (or lover and companion) to a rich English nobleman. When this financial resource runs dry, the two of them decide to kill the Englishman in order to get his life insurance premiums. To that end, they first replace him with his butler, who is incidentally dying of bronchitis and, being in a foreign country, let a local doctor write a death certificate. Afterwards, they murder the Englishman, and the 'al-chemist' uses his chemical skills for anaesthetizing (chloroform), killing (poison), and dissolving the remains (acids). Collins went beyond the familiar medieval plot in furnishing his 'al-chemist' with much more criminal energy and with many criminal means borrowed from contemporary chemistry.

---

[26] First published London: Chatto & Windus, 1880, 3 vols. Despite the abundance of alchemists in Collins's works, reference to this is rare in the secondary literature; for an exception, see Baldick 1987, pp. 184-5.

[27] First published London: Chatto & Windus, 1879, 2 vols.

As a remarkable rule with only few exceptions, 'al-chemists' reappearing in nineteenth-century literature are said to be from different countries than the authors themselves and their primary readerships. This striking fact calls for interpretation. The most obvious reason is that authors regarded chemistry as being extremely alien to themselves. Unlike Chaucer, who let the miserable seeker, the yeoman, narrate his own story, nineteenth-century writers preferred a third-person narrative to describe the foolish and wrong deeds of their 'al-chemists' from a critical and distant viewpoint. Inasmuch as they considered chemistry a threat from the (intellectual) outside, their 'al-chemists' bear a foreign nationality, frequently reflecting a nationalistic bias of their time. Furthermore, if the plot contains a tempter (as, for instance, in Wieland's *Der Stein der Weisen,* Balzac's *La Recherche de L'Absolu,* and Collins' *Jezebel's Daughter*), that character is usually a stranger from very far away, mostly from the east, who is equipped with various xenophobic ingredients, including the attribute 'fiendish'.

Strangely enough, the literary model appears to be one of the medieval Arabic *Tales of the Thousand and One Nights,* which were very popular in eighteenth- and nineteenth-century Europe after Antoine Galland had first compiled and translated most of the tales into French (1704-17). The "Story of Hasan of El-Basrah",[28] although its origin is still uncertain, is perhaps the oldest literary source of a cheating and tempting alchemist. Hasan, impoverished by luxurious life, is tempted by a foreign alchemist from Persia who promises to teach him the art of gold-making. In spite of his mother's warning of cheating alchemists, Hasan is credulous and greedy enough to be fooled and then kidnapped by the Persian. As it turns out, the alchemist is not only a foreigner but also a follower of a pagan religion "who hated Moslems with exceeding hatred and destroyed all who fell into his power". He is "a lewd and filthy villain, a hankerer after alchemy" who is "wont, every year, to take a Moslem and cut his throat for his own purposes", which, in this case,

---

[28]   This is the title of the story in Edward Lane's edition (1838-41), vol. 3, chap. 25. In John Payne's edition (9 vols., 1882-4), one finds the story in vol. 7 as "Hassan of Bassora and the King's Daughter of the Jinn". In Richard Burton's edition (10 vols., 1885) it appears as "Hassan of Bassorah" in vol. 8. I am indebted to J.C. Byers for this information.

means sacrificing Hasan as part of some magical practice.[29] Ironically, European writers borrowed their xenophobic motifs from Arabic sources, just as Latin alchemists had taken their knowledge from Arabic alchemists many centuries before.

Unlike the authors who had general Christian reservations about science overall discussed earlier, the authors discussed in this section expressed specific objections to chemistry, including pharmacy and chemical physiology, and they did so by picking up the medieval alchemist. Because they acknowledged to some extent the success of experimental chemistry, the medieval plots needed to be revised and modified. On the one hand, they furnished their figures with some modern ingredients, such as diamond-making, and references to contemporary chemistry and chemists. On the other hand, they tried to show that, even if experimental efforts are successful, all the goals pursued by such efforts are narrow-minded and blind and lead to failure rather than success overall. For many writers, who saw themselves in the humanistic tradition of moral education, the increasing impact of experimental science on society, on societal promises and hopes, was a threat, something alien to themselves and their moral ideas. Thus, during an atmosphere of growing nationalism in Europe, they transformed the fiendish temptation of medieval alchemy plots into a threat from those countries most different from and hostile to their own.

Some of the writers discussed in this section went much further than that, however. They started what would nowadays be called a 'Science War', by bringing up a battery of metaphysical and religious weapons to which we now turn.

5. Chemists against God, I: Materialism and Nihilism

God created everything out of nothing.
But you alchemists,
False children of light,
God's antagonists!
You make nothing out of everything.

---

[29] Quoted from Burton's edition, vol. 8, 781st Night.

(*God and the Alchemists*)[30]

At first glance, the above epigraph appears to express a strong position in the medieval debates about alchemy. However, the phrase "false children of light" reveals that it was really a conservative response to the Enlightenment, which was linked to contemporary chemistry. Alchemists continued to be a pejorative term for contemporary chemists in nineteenth-century poetry. In fact, it was the German poet Friedrich Haug (1761-1829), a friend of Schiller, who composed the poem in 1805. Since the poem summarizes the attitude of many famous later writers, Haug's lack of poetical fame is probably undeserved.

The story 'Chemists against God' has many chapters, if it is not the framing theme of nearly all occurrences of 'al-chemists' in nineteenth-century literature. At its core, however, there are two interrelated issues, materialism and hubris. Materialism, in the view of writers, included first of all atheism, and then positivism, nihilism, and the denial of all sorts of spiritual and mental realms, including morality, free will, and immortal soul, *i.e.* everything that the popular meaning of 'metaphysics' has since come to include. Moreover, since materialism/atheism also means denying that material nature is God's Creation, any chemical change of matter is suspected to be against God's will. Hubris, on the other hand, is more complex. If hubris means comparing or measuring one's own capacities with God's capacities, then somebody accused of hubris cannot at the same time, without self-contradiction, be accused of materialism/atheism, *i.e.* the denial of God. Thus, hubris is only one step towards atheism, in that God's authority, both as creator and moral legislator, is not acknowledged in the appropriate or desired manner. Moreover, while materialism is a metaphysical position, in the strict sense, hubris is a property of somebody's character, which usually makes it easier to employ in literary plots. Although nineteenth-century writers frequently combined both themes, despite the risk of self-contradiction, I will deal with them

---

[30] Johann Christoph Friedrich Haug (also: F. Hophthalmos, Frauenlob d. J.), *Epigramme und vermischte Gedichte* (Berlin: J. F. Unger, 1805), no. 77 "Gott und die Alchymisten" [repr. in J. C. F. Haug, *Gesellige Gedichte*, ed. H. Schlaffer (Stuttgart: Cotta, 1996), 38]: "Gott schuf Alles aus Nichts. / Aber ihr Alchymisten, / Falsche Kinder des Lichts, / Gottes Antagonisten! / Schaffet aus Allem Nichts."

separately. I begin with materialism and its cousin nihilism in this section, before dealing with hubris and the emergence of the 'mad scientists' in the next section.

Since materialism was first popular in France, I take the first example from Honoré de Balzac (1799-1850). His *Comédie humaine*, particularly the *Éditudes philosophiques*, are full of 'chemists'. Some of them are actually historical figures provided with detailed characters and a human face, for instance Vauquelin in *César Birotteau*. In *La Peau de Chagrin* (1831, *The Magic Skin*), however, Balzac presented a rather general view of his contemporary scientists.[31] There is a wondrous piece of leather in the possession of Raphael that fulfils all his lustful wishes. However, for each wish, as the fiendish pact goes, Raphael loses a period of his remaining lifetime, represented by the stepwise shrinkage of the skin. When the piece has already shrunk to an alarmingly small size in chapter 3 ("The Agony"), Raphael is seeking advice from scientists to learn more about the skin and how to expand it in order to prolong his lifetime. The first scientist to be asked (for this metaphorical elixir of life) is a *naturaliste*, *i.e.* a historian of nature. This "high priest of zoology" gives a great many details about animal species, but finally confesses that he has nothing to say about the issue. The second is the mathematician Planchette, a professor of the mechanical philosophy of nature, who at first delivers a long pseudo-philosophical speech about the principles of movement, nature, and God, and then suggests that the skin should be subjected to his ingenious invention, a gigantic hydraulic press. As it happens, the skin resists the press, which instead flies in all directions. Finally comes the chemist Baron Japhet. Without much talking, he suggests a battery of methods for chemical analysis (*e.g.* fluoric acid, melted potash, nitrogen chloride, electric shock, galvanic battery), which all turn out to be like playthings to the skin. Science, so Balzac's general moral goes, is powerless concerning existential matters.

Besides his generally low opinion of the sciences, Balzac provides a series of particular attacks on chemistry during a conversation in the chemical laboratory. One reinforces the powerlessness of chemists:

---

[31] First published as *La Peau de Chagrin: Roman Philosophique* (Paris: Gosselin et Canel, 1831), 2 vols.; see Schaffner 1996, pp. 72ff.

"Since you cannot invent substances, you are obliged to fall back on inventing names." Another one is directed against their positivism: chemists are as "stupid as a fact". For our purposes, the most interesting attack is unraveled in a brief dialogue between Japhet, the chemist, and Planchette, the mechanical philosopher:

> "I believe in the devil," said the Baron Japhet, after a moment's silence.
> "And I in God," replied Planchette.
> Each spoke in character. The universe for a mechanician is a machine that requires an operator; for chemistry – that fiendish employment of decomposing all things – the world is a gas endowed with the power of movement.

We are now at the heart of the problem. The mechanical philosophy of nature, that seventeenth-century child of natural theology, might be powerless in its deeds, but at least it includes – according to Boyle and Newton, it even strongly emphasized – the necessary existence of God. Chemistry, on the other hand, has no need for God. According to Balzac, the chemical worldview is materialism proper, because for chemists there exists nothing else than matter with its own principle of motion, or self-organizing matter, to use a term more fashionable nowadays.[32] Moreover, not only do chemists explain the world without an operator God, but according to Balzac, even worse, they also destroy His Creation by "decomposing all things". Thus, their atheistic worldview is complemented by their fiendish practice – chemists are "God's antagonists", as Haug had already said before.

The nineteenth-century literature of various genres and countries is full of both materialistic-atheistic and fiendishly destructive chemistry. From the materialism-atheism genre, I will give but one prominent example from Russia and then a general response from a U.S. chemist.

In Fyodor Mikhailovich Dostoyevsky's (1821-81) *Brothers Karamazov* (1879), Mitya Karamazov is charged with the murder of his father and imprisoned. Although he regards himself to be innocent, he feels

---

[32] It is not clear what contemporary chemist Balzac actually had in mind concerning this position of Stoic, Neo-Platonic, or Hermetic heritage, which has incidentally led many Christians, such as Giordano Bruno, to the heresy of pantheism. Perhaps he was referring to the physician Pierre Jean Georges Cabanis (1757-1808), as he actually did in his *La Messe de l'Athée* (1836).

prepared to endure the fate of the threatening punishment (20 years in Siberia) with a martyr-like attitude, inspired by the idea that God will help him, as he later confesses to his brother Alyosha (pt. 4, bk. 11, chap. 4). But then the atheist Rakitin visits him in prison and tells him about the latest news regarding the chemical physiology of nerves – Dostoyevsky mentioned Claude Bernard. When Alyosha arrives shortly after Rakitin's departure, he finds his brother crying in confusion and despair: "I am sorry to lose God [... and the belief that] I've got a soul, and that I am some sort of image and likeness [...]. It's chemistry, brother, chemistry! There's no help for it, your reverence, you must make way for chemistry."

Now that chemistry was regarded as the protagonist of atheism, in the literature as well as in public discourses, how did contemporary chemists respond to that accusation? In a remarkable book entitled *Chemistry and Religion* (1864),[33] Harvard professor of chemistry Josiah Parsons Cooke (1827-94), a very pious Christian with profound knowledge of theology, tried not only to reconcile chemistry with religion but also to prove that modern chemistry reinforced belief in God. His theological arguments were not original, but he combined the old approach of natural theology with the new chemical and physical knowledge of the time. First, he developed the chemical complexity of the atmosphere as global circles of great harmony in order to provide "numberless indications of adaptation in the materials of our atmosphere" (p. 8). Since there are two possible explanations for such adaptation, divine design and material self-organization, Cooke tried to exclude the latter in order to argue for the former. By referring to contemporary approaches of kinetic theory (his main source was John Tyndall's *Heat Considered as a Mode of Motion*, 1863), Cooke argued for a strict mechanistic-atomistic reduction of all chemical phenomena. This accepted, the divine designer is required as creator of the atoms and the mechanical laws and as the prime cause of motion in the mechanistic universe – here, Cooke could easily follow traditional lines of deism or Leibnizian natural theology. Thus, chemistry provides "evidences of design, and therefore evidences of the existence of a personal God, infinite in wisdom, absolute in power" (ibid.) only if it be-

---

[33] New York: Scribner, 1864; 2nd ed. 1880.

comes part of the mechanical philosophy of nature. In other words, rec-
onciliation of chemistry and religion depended heavily on mechanistic
reductions. However, for the majority of writers who, like Balzac, did
not believe in mechanistic reduction, chemistry was opposed to religion.
That is the nineteenth-century religious background of the reductionism
issue, which is again in vogue nowadays.

What about Balzac's second line of attack, chemistry as the fiendish
destruction of divine creation? It echoes the medieval complaint that
chemical manipulation changes nature at the basic level and thus destroys the Creation (Schummer 2003). If applied to material (and personal) destruction, this line was frequently elaborated on together with
the hubris theme, to be dealt with in Section 6. However, once the notion
of destructive chemistry had been established, it also became part of an
interesting analogy between chemistry and critical thinking: just as
chemical analysis destroys material bodies, so does critical analysis destroy ideas and beliefs. In his *Fathers and Sons* (1862),[34] Ivan Turgenev
(1818-83) mentions "young chemistry students [at the University of
Heidelberg], who cannot distinguish oxygen from nitrogen, but are
brimming over with destructive criticism and conceit". Thus, the main
character of the novel, the arch-nihilist Bazarov, is characterized by his
fascination with and practice of experimental chemistry. And when Pavel
Petrovich complains that Germans have from romantic poets "turned into
chemists and materialists", the nihilist cries: "A decent chemist is twenty
times more useful than any poet" (chap. 6).

Turgenev was not the inventor of nihilism, and nor did he invent its
association with chemistry. The earliest association is probably in the
novel *Die Ritter vom Geiste* (1850/51; bk. VII, chap. 12)[35] by the German writer Karl Ferdinand Gutzkow (1811-78):

> Oleander was reading a book of the new philosophical school, the critical
> or chemical school as he called it. "Chemical" because these philoso-
> phers of the absolute Nothing are the Liebigs of the invisible world, as he
> told Siegbert. Such as the chemical retort invents element after element,

---

[34] First published in *The Russian Herald* magazine in March 1862; on the nihilist character, see also Seeley 1991, chap. 10.
[35] First published Leipzig: Brockhaus, 1850-51, 9 vols. (repr. Frankfurt: Zweitausend-
eins, 2000).

each being decomposed over and again, such does the philosophical, heartless intellect of the school resolve Everything into the perfect Nothing by criticism [...] even believing that the immortality of the soul would have been disproved.[36]

Without going over Liebig's elemental analysis, there was of course also a direct way to link chemistry with nihilism, because what writers usually meant by nihilism was nothing else than materialism (including atheism) or some sort of sensualism, as in Turgenev's novel. To end this section with another French example, Alexandre Dumas père (1802-70) showed us how 'chemical nihilism' consequently, but not without tragedy, leads to self-destruction and death. The story is told in the "Epilogue" to his play *Le Comte Hermann* (1849),[37] which in English is also known separately under the title *Dr. Sturler's Experiment*. This Dr. Sturler is a German chemist-physician, once more at the University of Heidelberg in 1840, who is weary of his life because his scientific endeavors have turned out to be unsuccessful. His last experiment, "for the betterment of science", is actually carried out on two different levels. On the profane level, he takes a well-known deadly poison and then carefully records every change of his body, while he has his latest chemical invention, the antidote, up his sleeve for the second phase of the experiment. On the spiritual level, the experiment is designed to test the depth of his nihilism by the strength of his wish to die, since Dr. Sturler believes neither in moral improvement nor in any religious idea. Instead, "I believe in nothing [...] To nothingness from which I came – to nothingness, I am going to return." If he takes the antidote in time, the profane experiment will be completed for the benefit of humanity, whereas the spiritual experiment would yield the weakness of his nihilism, to the detriment of scientific materialism. Constructed as the plot is, Dumas did not hesitate to employ contradictions by letting Dr. Sturler argue for atheism (deny-

---

[36]   "Oleander las in einer Schrift der neuen philosophischen Schule, der kritischen oder chemischen, wie er sie nannte. 'Chemisch' deshalb, sagte er zu Siegbert, weil diese Philosophen des absoluten Nichts die Liebigs der unsichtbaren Welt sind. Wie die chemische Retorte Urstoff auf Urstoff entdeckt und diesen immer wieder aufs Neue zerlegt, so hat der philosophische, gemüthlose Verstand der neuesten Schule Alles durch die Kritik bis zum vollkommensten Nichts aufgelöst und [...] nun auch glaubt, die Unsterblichkeit der Seele selbst widerlegt zu haben."

[37]   First published Paris: Marchant, 1949.

ing the existence of God) via hubris (comparing oneself with God): "Am
I not God like God – more God than God since I can retake and give
back life, cause death to be born, and destroy death?" This idea makes
him disdain to take the antidote, because "If I believed in something
beyond this world, I should have drunk [the antidote] and I would be
saved – I believe in nothing and that convinced me to die!" With his
dying breath, when it is much too late to take the antidote, the spiritual
experiment takes a sharp turn. For the spiritual betterment of science,
Dumas let the dying chemist shout: "My God! Lord – pardon me!"

The historical parallel of the 'Chemical Revolution' and the 'French
Revolution' at the heyday of the Enlightenment let many conservative
writers, particularly of the French Restoration, lump both together.
Emerging as the first and for some time dominating experimental discipline from the received natural philosophy, chemistry became, for many
writers, the embodiment of the Enlightenment idea of science and thus
the target of severe metaphysical and religious criticism. They considered chemistry's focus on the analysis and synthesis of materials and the
investigation of material change, which was a necessary confinement in
the course of discipline formation, a metaphysical commitment to materialism. It is probably due to the legacy of eighteenth-century French materialism that nineteenth-century writers associated with nineteenth-
century chemistry a series of metaphysical positions, such as atheism and
the denial of all sorts of spiritual, mental and moral realms, including
morality, free will, and an immortal soul, which all came to be known as
nihilism. The antimetaphysical attitude of the new chemistry, through its
basis in operationally defined elements, the lack of any reference to natural theology, unlike mechanics, and the establishment of (organic) chemical analysis as the basis of experimental research, all contributed to the
metaphysical bias and the religious indignation by Christian authors. In
sum, chemistry was not only alien to these writers, but became the embodiment of everything they opposed.

6.   Chemists against God, II: Hubris and the 'Mad Scientist'

Hubris or presumption, in the sense of comparing one's own capacities
with those of the divine creator, is an issue deeply rooted in the pecu-

liarities of Christian theology. If the divine creator creates humans in his own image, as *Genesis* 1:27 says, then human imitation of the creator's creation, including the comparison of divine and human capacities, is the natural consequence (Noble 1997). In addition, medieval theologians strictly confined alchemy in particular and technology in general to the imitation of nature, to the effect that alchemists tried to investigate and apply the secrets of the divine creation in their laboratory (Schummer 2003). Thus, accusations of hubris are always dubious, because what is forbidden is at the same time demanded, such that the concept lacks a consistent ethical and theological basis. As we will see in this section, this lack of ethical arguments proper called for additional literary efforts, the offspring of which is the 'mad scientist'.

Before dealing with the hubris theme in nineteenth-century literature, I would like to start with an early example in which the related imitation-of-nature theme is developed with regard to chemistry. Despite his utmost perversion, Donatien Alphonse François de Sade (1740-1814) had a philosophical feeling for the weakness of woolly traditional notions, which made him, in the view of many modern historians, a prominent child of the Enlightenment. In the third part of *La nouvelle Justine ou Les malheurs de la vertu* (1797), we find de Sade in Sicily experiencing raptures about the destructive power of the fire-spewing volcano Aetna and wishing to copy its disastrous effects for his own 'sadistic' inclination.[38] Suddenly, a chemist appears who confesses that he shares the same enthusiasm. This chemist, called Almani, explains at length how his scientific studies have revealed to him the evil and destructive character of nature, including the secrets of her devastating power. During the past twenty years, he has used this knowledge to imitate nature's destructive effects to the detriment of humans, and now offers de Sade his chemical assistance in the imitation of the volcano. Thus, the two of them start building their artificial volcanoes, bombs with which they eventually kill 25,000 Sicilians, as de Sade proudly states.

Whatever one might think about de Sade, he was one of the first authors who employed a chemist, instead of the medieval alchemist, in his novel – a 'sadistic' chemist who cynically drives the old imitation-of-

---

[38] See also Krätz 1990, pp. 74f. for this scene.

nature theme into absurdity. De Sade remarkably arranged the matter in such a way that applying the most destructive forces of chemistry for the most evil purposes, *i.e.* what we would consider morally deeply corrupted science, eludes the accusation of hubris. One should keep this contrast in mind when regarding the following examples, which all try hard to make hubris a moral failure.

In explicit terms, the hubris theme with reference to the 'al-chemist' is most prominent in French literature, particularly in the works of Balzac and Dumas père. In *La Recherche de L'Absolu* (1834), at a time when synthetic organic chemistry was still in its infancy, Balzac presented the hubris theme in a most ambitious manner in a dialogue between Claes, the 'al-chemist', and his religious wife (chap. VI):

> "I shall make metals," he cried; "I shall make diamonds, I shall be a co-worker with Nature!"
>
> "Will you be the happier?" she asked in despair. "Accursed science! Accursed demon! You forget, Claes, that you commit the sin of pride, the sin of which Satan was guilty; you assume the attributes of God."
>
> "Oh! Oh! God!"
>
> "He denies Him!" she cried, wringing her hands. "Claes, God wields a power that you can never gain."
>
> At this argument, which seemed to discredit his beloved Science, he looked at his wife and trembled.
>
> "What power?" he asked.
>
> "Primal force – motion," she replied. "This is what I learn from the books your mania has constrained me to read. Analyse fruits, flowers, Malaga wine; you will discover, undoubtedly, that their substances come, like those of your water-cress, from a medium that seems foreign to them. You can, if need be, find them in nature; but when you have them, can you combine them? Can you make the flowers, the fruits, the Malaga wine? Will you have grasped the inscrutable effects of the sun, of the atmosphere of Spain? Ah! Decomposing is not creating."
>
> "If I discover the magisterial force, I shall be able to create."

In nineteenth-century literature, such chemical ambition to equal the total capacity of divine creation is difficult to find. Instead, the elixir of life and its counterpart, poison, figure prominently in the literature as God-like means to control life and death. As we have already seen, that is why Alexandre Dumas père let his Dr. Sturler say "Am I not God like God – more God than God since I can retake and give back life, cause death to be born, and destroy death?" Dumas had already employed the same idea in *Joseph Balsamo: Mémoires d'un médicin* (1846-48),[39] his version of the life of the famous eighteenth-century Sicilian 'alchemist' and impostor Cagliostro (1743-95), pseudonymous 'autobiographies' of whom were very popular at the beginning of the nineteenth century. Here it is Cagliostro's alchemical master Althotas who, in chapter 60 entitled "The Elixir of Life", in a dialogue with Cagliostro about contemporary materialist philosophers, says: "Some jokers are debating about the existence or non-existence of god instead of trying, like me, to become God himself." His way of trying is, of course, the mixing of an elixir of life. Because the final ingredient is still missing, the aged alchemist orders his pupil to bring him this crucial material into his hidden laboratory. According to Dumas's bizarre fantasy, the successful elixir requires the last three drops of a child's arterial blood, for which, of course, the child must be killed. Since Dumas considered the hubris theme alone not convincing, he felt obliged to add some moral perversion to his main characters. This essential lack of moral argument for the hubris theme is, I suggest, the common origin of the 'mad scientist', of which Dumas was by no means the inventor, in the literature.

Balzac had already applied the same combination of hubris, moral perversion, and bizarreness in his already quoted *L'Elixir de longue vie* (1830). Here, Don Juan, greedy to inherit the wealth of his dying father, hypocritically says to him "we must submit to the will of God", whereupon the father, in possession of the elixir, responds, "I am God!" When it is Don Juan's turn to die or to 'play God', through an accident the elixir revives only his head. Balzac finished his grotesque story with a bizarre scene inside a church: the head of Don Juan, while shouting blasphemies, removes itself from the dead body, gets a firm hold with its teeth on the head of a priest, and kills the priest, crying "Idiot, tell us now if there is a God!" Compared to his usual narrative style, with his meticulously detailed descriptions of characters and environments, this is perhaps the weirdest scene of Balzac's complete oeuvre.

The need to add further plausibility to the hubris theme inspired the imagination of writers more than anything else. We should recall that the

---

[39]   First published Paris: Cadot, 1846-48.

actual contemporary target, represented by the elixir motif, was nothing else than rudimentary medicinal chemistry, against which neither commonsense morality nor philosophical ethics could and did raise any objections. However, writers had strong concerns about the use and possible abuse of chemistry's power, which they thereby conceded to exist. "There is nothing that human imagination can figure brilliant and enviable, that human genius and skill do not aspire to realise," wrote William Godwin at the very beginning of his 'al-chemist' novel *St. Leon* (1799). In retrospect, this sounds like a programmatic division of labor, where the writers should take the part of the imagination for the purpose of warning, and then decide how scientists might realize it.

Although there is still debate about how much she was influenced by her father, twenty-year-old Mary Shelley (1797-1851) seems to have taken these words of her father to heart in writing her famous novel *Frankenstein, or the Modern Prometheus* (1818), the most famous of all stories that combine hubris with the 'mad scientist'.[40] The plot is much too well known to require a detailed description. The ambitious Swiss scientist Frankenstein creates an artificial human being that eventually turns out to behave like a monster, killing his brother, his friend, and his wife, and finally committing suicide, after Frankenstein himself dies during his remorseful but unsuccessful hunting of the monster. The interesting point here is how Shelley tried to relate all this to contemporary chemistry, because Frankenstein is, of course, a chemist of the late eighteenth century.[41]

Chapters 2-4 of the novel, while at the surface level describing steps in the adolescence of Victor Frankenstein, provide an interestingly detailed version of the history of science, which has largely been over-

---

[40] All quotes below are from the 1831 edition (London: Colburn & Bentley).

[41] Strangely, the reference to chemistry has received little attention in the hundreds of existing *Frankenstein* interpretations. Baldick (1987, pp. 6ff.) distinguishes between ahistorical psychological interpretations and what he calls the "technological reductions", which, again, ahistorically project all kinds of mechanical, electrical, and genetic engineering onto the novel. Whereas Baldwick himself seeks a historically informed multidimensional interpretation to explain *Frankenstein* as the birth of a "modern myth", my point is that the "Frankenstein myth" is not a modern invention but, beyond being a Faustian variant, is another transforming step from the fourteenth-century mad alchemist.

looked in literature studies.[42] Indeed, Victor's ambitions at various ages reflect periods of the history of science of the corresponding centuries, if one multiplies his age by a hundred. Describing "the birth of that passion which afterwards ruled my destiny" (p. 25), thirteen-year-old Victor became an ardent enthusiast of the thirteenth- through sixteenth-century alchemical writings of "Cornelius Agrippa, Albertus Magnus, and Paracelsus, the lords of my imagination" (p. 28). Unlike his intimate's occupation with the "moral relations of things", Victor's inclination is towards the "physical secrets of the world" (p. 24), which suggests the split of philosophy into moral and natural philosophy. He is fascinated with the philosophers' stone and, particularly, the elixir of life that "could banish disease from the human frame and render man invulnerable to any but a violent death!" (p. 27). After a couple of years of that occupation, Victor is affected by (late sixteenth-century, early seventeenth-century) skepticism: "It seemed to me as if nothing would or could ever be known" (p. 28). This period is followed by temporary enthusiasm with mathematics and the mathematical philosophy of nature, which obviously represent seventeenth- and eighteenth-century Cartesianism and Newtonianism. Interestingly, Shelley emphatically stressed the difference between alchemy/chemistry and mathematical physics by describing the latter, in Victor's retrospective narration, as "the immediate suggestion of the guardian angel of my life – the last effort made by the spirit of preservation to avert the storm [...] but it was ineffectual" (p. 28). When Victor, at the age of seventeen, enrolls at the University of Ingoldstadt[43] to study

---

[42] Martin Tropp (1976, pp. 59f.) seems to recognize the parallel, but since for him, as for many others, the "history of science [goes] from alchemy to technology" (p. 59) or from Descartes to mechanical engineering (p. 53), he overlooks most of it. This case suggests the urgent need for greater collaboration between historians of science and historians of literature.

[43] Note that the University of Ingoldstadt had moved to Landshut in 1800. In 1776, the professor of natural and canon law Adam Weishaupt founded the pseudo-freemason order of the Illuminati in Ingoldstadt, about which there was the reactionary but dubious rumor spread all over Europe in the 1790s that the Illuminati would have substantially influenced the French Revolution in 1789. Mary Shelley definitely knew this rumor, as a friend of her husband, Jefferson Hoog, had already literarily expanded on the rumor in his *Memoirs of Prince Alexy Haimatoff* (1813). There is little doubt that she chose Ingoldstadt for the education of her Frankenstein precisely because of the alleged Illuminati-Revolution connection, as also Alexandre Dumas père let his

"natural philosophy", the subject matter is completely dominated by modern (late eighteenth-century) chemistry (chap. 3). Victor, ready to revive his former alchemical passion, is at first surprised and disappointed, because he only meets professors who are followers of the new (Lavoisean) chemistry. The first professor, Kempe, is no less surprised at Victor's ambition: "Have you [...] really spent your time in studying such nonsense? [...] I little expected, in this enlightened and scientific age, to find a disciple of Albertus Magnus and Paracelsus. My dear sir, you must begin your studies entirely anew" (p. 32). What Victor dislikes in this professor, who represents the temporary state of the 'chemical revolution', is that the "ambition of the inquirer seemed to limit itself to the annihilation of those visions on which my interest in science was chiefly founded" (p. 33). A couple of days later in the lecture hall, Frankenstein is listening to a much more ambitious chemistry professor (Waldheim), who gives a "panegyric upon modern chemistry"; this is Victor's initiation as a follower of the new chemistry:

> "The ancient teachers of this science," said he, "promised impossibilities and performed nothing. The modern masters promise very little; they know that metals cannot be transmuted and that the elixir of life is a chimera but these philosophers [...] have indeed performed miracles. They penetrate into the recesses of nature and show how she works in her hidingplaces [...] They have acquired new and almost unlimited powers."
>
> Such were the professor's words – rather let me say such the words of the fate, enounced to destroy me. As he went on I felt as if my soul were grappling with a palpable enemy; one by one the various keys were touched which formed the mechanism of my being; chord after chord was sounded, and soon my mind was filled with one thought, one conception, one purpose. So much has been done, exclaimed the soul of Frankenstein – more, far more, will I achieve; treading in the steps already marked, I will pioneer a new way, explore unknown powers, and unfold to the world the deepest mysteries of creation.
>
> From this day natural philosophy, and particularly chemistry, in the most comprehensive sense of the term, became nearly my sole occupation. (pp. 34-36)

---

swindler 'alchemist' *Balsamo* (1844-46) be a member of the Illuminati and work for the French Revolution.

Shelley narrated the life of her tragic hero in parallel with a quasi-historical account of science.[44] The parallelism allowed her to transfer the biographical determinism of Frankenstein's life ("Destiny was too potent, and her immutable laws had decreed my utter and terrible destruction" [p. 28]) to the historical determinism of scientific development. In the final step, however, she encountered serious difficulties when chemistry needed to turn into the artificial creation of human beings (chap. 4). In fact, the step is obscured by letting Victor say that these dangerous secrets must not be disclosed. All we learn is that Victor makes "some discoveries in the improvement of some chemical instruments" (p. 37) and turns towards "those branches of natural philosophy which relate to physiology" in order to "examine the causes of life" (p. 37), which might reflect the actual interest of contemporary chemists and physicians in galvanism and mesmerism. In order to continue her deterministic account, Shelley presented the crucial discovery as the natural offspring of the state of the art, since it is "so simple, that [...] I was surprised that among so many men of genius who had directed their inquiries towards the same science, that I alone should be reserved to discover so astonishing a secret" (p. 38). On the other hand, she employed all the well-known details from the medieval 'mad alchemist' when she described Frankenstein's obsession and thoughtlessness in pursuing his 'great work'.

Unlike the authors of most of the later 'mad scientist' and earlier 'mad alchemist' stories, Shelley let her hero remorsefully recant his 'fiendish ambition' in the face of the disaster he caused. This enabled her to put a Stoic message into the mouth of dying Frankenstein (chap. 24, p. 196): "Seek happiness in tranquility and avoid ambition, even if it be only the apparently innocent one of distinguishing yourself in science and discoveries." The message once more emphasises the determinism, now on the psychological level. Once you allow yourself to have an am-

---

[44] Since the first appearance of the novel, there has been much debate as to whether Shelley's Frankenstein is a representative of old alchemy and occult science or of modern science; see Botting 1991, chap. 10, which also provides an interesting reflection on the relationship between technology and the humanities. Samuel H. Vasbinder (1984) rightly points out that Frankenstein is a representative of modern science, but does not appreciate the complete account of Shelley's history of science and wrongly identifies Frankenstein's science with "Newtonianism".

bition for science, you are lost. Once you get involved in the chemical investigation of nature, *i.e.* the secrets of the divine creation, you are necessary driven to commit the sin of hubris with disastrous effects. However, as with all nineteenth-century 'mad scientist' stories, and despite Shelley's efforts to point out the determinism, the disastrous effects are attached in order to make the moral plausible. *Frankenstein* not only stands out as the first modern anti-modern 'mad chemist' novel, but it is also the most radical one, because it transferred the fate of the obsessed 'mad alchemist' to the fate of science. Although we are today inclined to read the novel as a warning of *possible* scientific misconduct, it actually suggests both psychological and historical determinism, according to which the 'seeds of evil' necessarily develop in the course of the scientific endeavor.

Perhaps the second most famous early author of 'mad scientist' stories is the American writer Nathaniel Hawthorne (1804-64). His short stories are particularly interesting because they allow us to analyze in more detail the transformation from the medieval 'mad alchemist' to the modern 'mad scientist'. In one of his early tales, *The Great Carbuncle* (1837),[45] Hawthorne introduced a medieval 'mad alchemist' whose madness largely remains within the scope of self-destruction: "He was from beyond the sea, a Dr. Cacaphodel, who had wilted and dried himself into a mummy, by continually stooping over charcoal furnaces and inhaling unwholesome fumes, during his researches in chemistry and alchemy [...] he had drained his body of all its richest blood, and wasted it, with other inestimable ingredients, in an unsuccessful experiment – and had never been a well man since." Later in the story, a new, modern aspect of

---

[45] From *Twice-Told Tales* (Boston 1837), 213-34 (probably written in 1834). The alchemist/chemist is only one among seven miserable seekers of the Great Carbuncle, who each confess their different motives for the pursuit. In some sense, the whole story may be read as a metaphorical classification of various kinds of alchemists/scientists or Faustian seekers. William Bysshe Stein (1953), places Hawthorne's mad scientists in the Faust tradition, as received in Puritan New England, and points out Hawthorne's interest in ancient myths as "marvellously independent of all temporary modes and circumstances" (p. 25). By uncritically making Hawthorne's view his own, however, Stein decontextualizes Hawthorne's mad scientist stories and reads them as prophecies of "inevitable doom, a fate which the atomic and hydrogen bombs seem to confirm" (p. 148). Historian of science William R. Newman (2004, pp. 2-5) has recently argued against such ahistorical reading.

his 'madness' appears. Being one of several miserable seekers of the Great Carbuncle, a miraculous and holy Indian gem hidden in the mountains, the chemist confesses that he is eager to take this holy gem apart by chemical means in order to learn its elemental composition by destruction. From destroying one's own health to destroying holy things is only the first step in the transformation of the 'mad alchemist'. The next step of 'madness', the step towards moral perversion, is hurting or killing other people as a result of one's scientific obsession and hubris, on which Hawthorne later wrote at least two stories.

The Birth-mark (1843)[46] features an 'al-chemist' of the late eighteenth or early nineteenth century.[47] Alluding to contemporary Romantic philosophies of nature, Hawthorne let this 'al-chemist' temporarily exchange his love for alchemy with the love for his new wife, who is described as the ideal of beauty, save for a small birthmark on her cheek. After a while, the birthmark, in the view of the 'al-chemist', grows to an intolerable symbol of material imperfection. Eventually, he revives his old chemical laboratory and brews a remedy to remove the spot. However, at the end of the story, it turns out that his wife's birthmark is the only bond of her "angelic spirit" with the "mortal frame" of her body, such that the successful removal results in her death. The moral of this fable is easy to grasp: material perfectionism by chemical means, *i.e.* the hubris of improving the divine creation, results in destruction and death. As with other 'mad scientist' stories, in order to make the moral plausible, Hawthorne requires surreal elements (here, the bond of her angelic spirit with her mortal frame) such that the story turns into a fable at the very end.

In *Rappaccini's Daughter* (1844),[48] Hawthorne introduced a new component that changed the 'mad alchemist' into the full-fledged 'mad

---

[46] First published in *Pioneer*, I (March, 1843): 113-19; repr. in *Mosses from an Old Manse* (New York, 1846), vol. I, 32-51.

[47] Hawthorne wrote, "when the comparatively recent discovery of electricity, and other kindred mysteries of nature, seemed to open paths into the region of miracle." Since 'amber electricity' was already known in antiquity, I suppose that he referred to either Galvani's experiments (1786) or Volta's pile (1799).

[48] First published in *United States Magazine and Democratic Review*, XV (December, 1844): 545-60, as 'Writings of Aubépine'; repr. in *Mosses from an Old Manse*, 85-118.

scientist'. Dr. Rappaccini is a physician at the University of Padua "very long ago", who is experimenting with vegetable poisons – as chemical physiologists actually did in France at that time. According to his colleague Professor Baglioni, "he cares infinitely more for science than for mankind. His patients are interesting to him only as subjects for some new experiment. He would sacrifice human life, his own among the rest, or whatever else was dearest to him, for the sake of adding so much as a grain of mustard seed to the great heap of his accumulated knowledge." In the story, Rappaccini's main experimental subject is his daughter, whom he has fed with poison from an early age, to the effect that the touch of her body is poisonous to any other living being. Owing to a misunderstanding, she takes an antidote prepared by Baglioni and, because she somehow embodies the poison, the antidote kills her. The hubris theme plus moral perversion is still important in the story, since Rappaccini's so-called "experiment" is an effort to "improve" the physical nature of his daughter according to his own ideals of perfection and power, *i.e.* "to be endowed with marvelous gifts against which no power nor strength could avail an enemy [...] to be able to quell the mightiest with a breath [...] to be as terrible as thou art beautiful." However, the hubris theme is combined with moral criticism of the obsessed and unscrupulous scientist who knowingly runs the risk of doing harm to other people. Unlike in the examples discussed above, the harm is no longer superimposed clumsily or in fable-like manner, but is presented, without too many surreal elements, as the plausible outcome or risk of narrow-minded research. From Dr. Cacaphodel's self-destructive obsession via the 'al-chemist's hubris in *The Birth-mark* to the unscrupulous and hubris-driven Dr. Rappaccini, Hawthorne transformed the 'mad alchemist' step by step into the 'mad scientist'.[49]

---

[49] Taylor Stoehr (1978) has argued that Hawthorne's mad scientist stories reflected the contemporary rise of "pseudosciences", such as mesmerism, homoeopathy, and phrenology, rather than that of science. However, Stoehr's distinction between science and pseudoscience is, like the term 'pseudoscience', rather an ex-post-facto projection onto early nineteenth-century popular American culture. As the reference to Dr. Cacaphodel's "researches in chemistry and alchemy" illustrates, Hawthorne combines rather than distinguishes between traditions. In 'The New Adam and Eve' (1842), he even goes as far as to equate the entire Harvard University library with "the fatal apple of another Tree of Knowledge". Stephanie P. Browner (2005, chap.

Nineteenth-century writers established a firm link between chemistry and hubris that was already prepared by the Faust tradition, which also flourished at the time. A reliable method to prove that the link had become a literary cliché is to look for stories featuring chemists who commit the 'sin of hubris' without any direct reference to chemistry or alchemy. Such an instance is *The Haunted Man and the Ghost's Bargain* (1848)[50] by Charles Dickens (1812-70).[51] Although the main character of that novel, Redlaw, is a chemistry professor and although most of the plot takes place at his university "in his inner chamber, part library and part laboratory", Dickens avoided any further mention of chemistry. Instead, since poor Redlaw is haunted by his memory of awful personal affairs in the past, he makes a "bargain" with a ghost. In that Faust-like pact, he receives the gift of forgetting all wrongs in the past as well as the capacity to pass on the same gift to everybody with whom he gets in touch. Playing "the benefactor of mankind" by freeing other people from the burden of their memory, Redlaw makes great use of his new capacity. Contrary to what he expects, this has disastrous effects, however, because all the infected people turn into heartless and selfish persons. As the ghost explains to the chemist in chapter 3, "you are the growth of man's presumption" that overthrows "the beneficent design of Heaven".

Did all nineteenth-century writers consider chemistry the embodiment of hubris? Of course not, but many from various countries did. German writers, usually quick with moral complaints, were relatively quiet about hubris in that period, which was probably due to the absorbing power of German idealism and the romantic philosophy of nature as an effort to

---

2), argues that "Hawthorne's repeated use of the trope [of the mad medical scientist] suggest that the evil medical man was not just a stock figure for him. Indeed, Hawthorne wrote again and again about medical ambition because he was genuinely troubled by the increasingly confident claim to somatic mastery that medicine was making in those years" (p. 40).

[50] The Haunted Man and the Ghost's Bargain: a Fancy for Christmas-time (London: Bradbury & Evans, 1848).

[51] Baldwick (1987), who, for some reason, sees *The Haunted Man* in the Frankensteinian rather than in the Faustian tradition (p. 115), suggests another interesting method to prove the stereotypical connections between chemistry and villainy. In his criminal story *The Woman in White*, Wilkie Collins "laid a false trail for us" by introducing a character as "being 'one of the first experimental chemists living' – which is almost enough for us to condemn him in advance as a murderer," says Baldwick (p. 184).

reconcile science, religion, and the arts. However, I know only one literary example that took the opposite stand and ridiculed the hubris motif with respect to chemistry, which is from the American novelist Herman Melville (1819-91). In his picaresque satire *The Confidence-Man: His Masquerade* (1857),[52] this confidence-man, scene-by-scene, transforms into various pseudomoralistic figures. One is a herb doctor who lectures at length in front of a very sick man about the wrongs of chemistry-based medicine as opposed to his own natural herbs. Here, I quote only a small part (chap. 16):[53]

> Oh, who can wonder at that old reproach against science, that it is atheistical? And here is my prime reason for opposing these chemical practitioners, who have sought out so many inventions. For what do their inventions indicate, unless it be that kind and degree of pride in human skill, which seems scarce compatible with reverential dependence upon the power above? Try to rid my mind of it as I may, yet still these chemical practitioners with their tinctures, and fumes, and braziers, and occult incantations, seem to me like Pharaoh's vain sorcerers, trying to beat down the will of heaven. Day and night, in all charity, I intercede for them, that heaven may not, in its own language, be provoked to anger with their inventions; may not take vengeance of their inventions. A thousand pities that you should ever have been in the hands of these Egyptians.

Eventually the sick man, unable to listen to the chatter of the quack any longer, buys a few of his herbs to get rid of him.

In the metaphysical battle against the emergence of modern science, which chemistry embodied for nineteenth-century writers, the hubris theme was the weakest argument, but became the strongest blow. It was weak not only because the actual research, such as the rudimentary steps of medicinal chemistry and the synthesis of some organic substances, gave little reason to compare chemists with the Christian creator; also, based on any of the ethical theories of the time, there was simply no moral objection to the improvement of medical or other material conditions of life. Moreover, the whole idea of hubris, which is rooted in and

---

[52] First published New York: Dix, Edwards & Co., 1857.
[53] On the herb doctor, see Browner 2005, pp. 91-101; for related biographical anecdotes, see Cook 1996, pp. 91f., 106-9.

prompted by the peculiarities of Christian theology, is neither an ethical idea nor a theologically consistent one. In order to make hubris a morally convincing accusation for their readers, nineteenth-century authors created the 'mad scientist'. Transformed from the 'mad alchemist' already established in the medieval literature, the 'mad scientist' combines hubris with all the moral perversion that nineteenth-century writers could imagine. Borne out of the need for serious arguments, this literary figure has dominated the public view of science ever since. Although the 'mad scientist' later moved on to other disciplines, such as biology and nuclear physics,[54] the figure continued to bear characteristics of the medieval alchemist, thereby revealing its chemical legacy.

7. Conclusion

Since the late eighteenth century, the notion of science has changed drastically with regard to its institutions, methods, and the content and structure of its knowledge. Formerly places for preliminary education before rising to the 'higher faculties' of theology, law, and medicine, the philosophical faculties at the European universities became centers of discipline formation with PhD programs, and with laboratories and research institutes for each of the emerging disciplines. The traditional form of chemical research, laboratory experimentation, became the prevailing research method in most of the sciences, including medical branches such as physiology and pharmacy. Scientific knowledge, produced by experimentation and published in the newly founded journals, proliferated and became increasingly fragmented due to the formation of separate disciplines that defined their own cognitive and practical goals. Unlike in the earlier period of natural philosophy, there was no longer a

---

[54] See Haynes 1994. Most influential for the shift to biology and 'biological hubris' was H. G. Wells's *The Island of Doctor Moreau* (1896), which became the basis for many films. However, Wells continued to use 'mad chemists', as in *The Food of Gods, and How it Came to Earth* (1904) and *The World Set Free* (1914). The latter novel is interesting not only because it was an apocalyptic call for World War I, but also because it narrates a history of chemistry that culminates in the development of a kind of nuclear fission bomb. Whereas this appears to anticipate the discovery of nuclear fission by the chemists Hahn and Strassmann in 1939, later mad scientist stories featured physicists as bomb-makers.

metaphysical system to provide an overall framework and orientation, and nor was it any longer acceptable for religious ideas to interfere in scientific matters. Furthermore, compared to the rapid growth of the sciences, the humanities considerably lost influence and reputation.

Many nineteenth-century writers, frequently with a background in the humanities, in law, or in theology, observed these tremendous changes with great concern. Not only were the approaches and methods of the new sciences alien to most of them, but they also worried particularly about the fragmentation of knowledge and the loss of any unifying metaphysical, moral, or religious framework. The more they considered their profession as public moral education, the more they felt obliged to compensate for the growing independence of the sciences and their goals and to warn the public of misleading hopes and promises resulting from preliminary successes of the sciences.

In this chapter I have distinguished between four kinds of literary response, which all picked up the alchemist from the medieval and early modern literature and transformed the figure for their own purposes. Some writers, particularly of the earlier period, considered the sciences altogether useless and recommended instead a spiritual and religious life that refrained not only from the temptations of the material world but also from the curiosity of any scientific investigation. Following up a medieval debate, they praised their own way as the true alchemy. A second group of writers, well aware of the contemporary success of the experimental sciences, particularly of chemistry and its applications, pointed out their narrow-minded goals and their reduced view of the world. In their writings, they refurnished the obsessed 'mad alchemist' with some ingredients from modern chemistry and let him, after some preliminary successes, fail overall. A third group responded more aggressively, as if modern science was undermining the fundamentals of their culture. Their 'al-chemists' are atheists, materialists, and nihilists, who reject any moral or spiritual values and who, in their blind obsession with science, are presumptuous and destructive fools. Of all these accusations, many writers considered the sin of hubris to be the most important one, since they elaborated on it to form a fourth response that featured the powerful figure of the 'mad scientist', which resulted from a transformation of the 'mad alchemist'. Whereas the 'mad alchemist' in his obsessive search for the philosophers' stone harmed primarily himself (his health, wealth, and social status), the new 'mad scientist' did harm primarily to other people through his obsession with playing God. Because the actual literary instances of 'playing God' were largely confined to research into pharmaceutical cures, which writers considered the hubris of assuming 'God-like control over life and death', the accusation of hubris alone was hardly convincing. To compensate for the lack of ethical or theologically consistent arguments, writers equipped their 'mad scientists' with moral perversion or satanic elements.

These literary responses to the rise of modern science are scattered throughout Western literature, including that of Russia. In addition to the mentioned works, they can be found in hundreds of other pieces of literature. Far from being only a topic of Romanticism or *Bildungsromanen*, they appear in all kinds of literary styles and genres, in novels, plays, short stories, fables, poems, and even operas. All these responses, from the modest to the most radical, tried to separate out science from the authors' own understanding of culture and thus prepared the much-debated split into 'the two cultures' (Snow 1959). Since chemistry was the main target of nineteenth-century authors, it is not surprising that chemistry became particularly alienated from the humanities.

In this cultural battle, the most effective blow was the creation of the 'mad scientist', a stigma that is still cultivated today, if only for entertaining reasons. In retrospect, one might be inclined to see early warnings of possible scientific misconduct in 'mad scientist' stories. Yet such an ahistorical reading overlooks the fact that in the nineteenth century the main issue was not professional ethics but the organization of knowledge, the relationship between science and religion, and the reputation of science versus the reputation of the humanities.

References

Ambrière, M.: 1999, *Balzac et la Recherche de l'Absolu*, Paris: Presses Universitaires de France.

Baldick, C.: 1987, *In Frankenstein's Shadow: Myth, Monstrosity, and Nineteenth-century Writing*, Oxford: Clarendon.

Benedict, B.: 2004, 'The Mad Scientist: the Creation of a Literary Stereotype', in: R.C. Leitz & K.L. Cope (eds.), *Imagining the Sciences: Expressions of New Knowledge in the "Long" Eighteenth Century*, New York: AMS Press, pp. 59-107.

Botting, F.: 1991, *Making Monstrous: Frankenstein, Criticism, Theory*, Manchester: Manchester University Press.

Browner, S.P.: 2005, *Profound Science and Elegant Literature: Imagining Doctors in Nineteenth-century America*, Philadelphia: University of Pennsylvania Press.

Clack, R.A.: 2000, *The Marriage of Heaven and Earth. Alchemical Regeneration in the Works of Taylor, Poe, Hawthorne, and Fuller*, Westport: Greenwood Press.

Cook, J.: 1996, *Satirical Apocalypse: An Anatomy of Melville's The Confidence-Man*, Westport: Greenwood Press.

Crichton, M.: 1999, 'Ritual Abuse, Hot Air, and Missed Opportunities', *Science*, **283**, 1461-63 (repr. in *AAAS Science and Technology Policy Yearbook 2000*, Washington, DC: AAAS, 2000, pp. 397-404).

Deghaye, P.: 2000, *Paracelse à Thomas Mann. Les Avatars de l'Hermétisme Allemand*, Paris: Dervy.

Döbling, H.: 1928, 'Die Chemie in Jena zur Goethezeit', *Zeitschrift des Vereins für Thüringische Geschichte und Altertumskunde*, Jena, Beiheft 13.

Gierlich, S. 1972, *Jean Paul: "Der Komet oder Nikolaus Marggraf, eine komische Geschichte"*, Göppingen: Kümmerle.

Hahn, O.W.: 1988, *Jung-Stilling zwischen Pietismus und Aufklärung: sein Leben und sein literarisches Werk 1778 bis 1787*, Frankfurt/M.: Lang.

Haynes, R.D.: 1994, *From Faust to Strangelove: Representations of Scientists in Western Literature*, Baltimore: John Hopkins University Press.

Hirzel, M.: 1998, *Lebensgeschichte als Verkündigung: Johann Heinrich Jung-Stilling – Ami Bost –Johann Arnold Kanne*, Göttingen: Vandenhoeck & Ruprecht.

Krätz, O.: 1990, 'Chemie im Spiegel der schöngeistigen Literatur zur Zeit Leopold Gmelins', in: W. Lippert (ed.), *Der 200. Geburtstag von Leopold Gmelin*, Frankfurt/M.: Gmelin Institut, pp. 73-112.

Krätz, O.: 1991, 'Die Chemie im Spiegel der Literatur des 20. Jahrhunderts', *Chemie in unserer Zeit*, **25**, 44-50.

Krätz, O.: 2004, 'Mad scientists und andere Bösewichter der Chemie in Literatur und Film', in: K. Griesar (ed.), *Wenn der Geist die Materie küsst*, Frankfurt: Harri Deutsch, pp. 131-47.

Kuhn, D.: 1972, 'Goethe und die Chemie', *Medizinhistorisches Journal*, 7, 264-78.

Lembert, A. & Schenkel, E. (eds.): 2002, *The Golden Egg: Alchemy in Art and Literature*, Berlin-Cambridge: Galda & Wilch.

Linden, S.J.: 1996, *Darke Hierogliphicks. Alchemy in English Literature from Chaucer to the Restoration*, Lexington: University Press of Kentucky.

Marteau, R.: 1995, *La Récolte de la Rosée. La Tradition Alchimique dans la Littérature*, Paris: Belin.

Meakin, D.: 1995, *Hermetic Fictions: Alchemy and Irony in the Novel*, Keele: Keele University Press.

Newman, W.R.: 2004, *Promethean Ambitions: Alchemy and the Quest to Perfect Nature*, Chicago: University of Chicago Press.

Nobis, H.: 1976, *Phantasie und Moralität: das Wunderbare in Wielands "Dschinnista" und der "Geschichte des Prinzen Biribinke"*, Kronberg: Scriptor.

Noble, D.F.: 1997, *The Religion of Technology: the Divinity of Man and the Spirit of Invention*, New York: A.A. Knopf.

Pollin, B.R.: 1970, *Discoveries in Poe*, Notre Dame: University of Notre Dame Press.

Read, J.: 1947, *The Alchemist In Life, Literature and Art*, London: T. Nelson.

Rothfield, L.: 1992, *Vital Signs: Medical Realism in Nineteenth-century Fiction*, Princeton: Princeton University Press.

Schaffner, A.: 1996, *Honoré de Balzac, La Peau de Chagrin*, Paris: Presses Universitaires de France.

Schuler, R.M. (ed.): 1995, *Alchemical Poetry: 1575-1700; from Previously Unpublished Manuscripts*, New York: Garland.

Schummer, J.: 2003, 'The Notion of Nature in Chemistry', *Studies in History and Philosophy of Science*, **34**, 705-36.

Schwedt, G.: 1998, *Goethe als Chemiker*, Berlin: Springer.

Seeley, F.F.: 1991, *Turgenev: a Reading of His Fiction*, Cambridge: Cambridge University Press, 1991.

Skal, D.J.: 1998, *Screams of Reason. Mad Science and Modern Culture*, New York: Norton.

Snow, C.P: 1959, *The Two Cultures and the Scientific Revolution*, Cambridge: Cambridge University Press.

Stableford, B.: 1979, 'Scientists', in: P. Nicholls (ed.), *The Encyclopedia of Science Fiction*, London: Granada, p. 533.

Stein, W.B.: 1953, *Hawthorne's Faust: a Study of the Devil Archetype*, Gainesville, FL: University of Florida Press.

Stiasny, K.: 1997, *E.T.A. Hoffmann und die Alchemie*, Aachen: Shaker.

Stoehr, T.: 1978, *Hawthorne's Mad Scientists: Pseudoscience and Social Science in Nineteenth-century Life and Letters*, Hamden, Conn.: Archon Books.

Toumey, C.P.: 1992, 'The Moral Character of Mad Scientists: a Cultural Critique of Science', *Science, Technology, and Human Values* , **17**, 411-37.

Tracy, A.B.: 1981, *The Gothic Novel, 1790-1830: Plot Summaries and Index of Motifs*, Lexington: University Press of Kentucky.

Tropp, M.: 1976, *Mary Shelley's Monster*, Boston: Houghton Mifflin.

Tudor, A.: 1989, *Monsters and Mad Scientists. A Cultural History of the Horror Movie*, Oxford: Blackwell.

Urdang, G.: 1921, *Der Apotheker im Spiegel der Literatur*, Berlin: Springer.

Urdang, G.: 1926, *Der Apotheker als Subjekt und Objekt der Literatur*, Berlin: Springer.

Vasbinder, S.H.: 1984, *Scientific Attitudes in Mary Shelley's Frankenstein*, Ann Arbor: UMI Research Press.

CHAPTER 3

CHEMISTS AND THEIR CRAFT IN FICTION FILM

Peter Weingart

*Department of Sociology, Institute of Science and Technology Studies,
University of Bielefeld, 33501 Bielefeld, Germany; weingart@uni-bielefeld.de*

The chapter presents results from a quantitative analysis of some 200
fiction films. Chemistry is the iconic discipline of the 'mad scientist'
reflecting the alchemical imagery that was prevalent until recently (and
can still be identified) in the depiction of science in films. Other results
show the ambivalence with which primarily the natural sciences are
represented in popular movies.

1. Introduction[*]

Michael Crichton, well-known author of bestsellers dealing with science,
is a wanderer between the worlds of fact and fiction. Crossing the
boundary towards 'science fiction' and combining thrilling action with
plausible accounts of scientific advances, his books have frequently been
turned into movies, the most famous being *Jurassic Park*. In a talk before
the *American Association for the Advancement of Science* he presented
himself as an educated scientist who could boast of degrees in
anthropology and medicine as well as of publications in the renowned
New England Journal of Medicine. Later he assumed the position of a
movie producer and explained to his academic audience that they should
not be worried about the negative representation of science in movies,

---

[*] Parts have been taken from a German version 'Von Menschenzüchtern, Weltbeherr-
schern und skrupellosen Genies: Das Bild der Wissenschaft im Spielfilm' in Weingart 2005. The material has been extracted from an analysis of 220 fiction films the
results of which were published in Weingart *et al.* 2003.

reasoning that since 'all professions are depicted negatively why should one expect scientists to be treated differently?' Since there is no match between social reality and the reality presented in movies there is no reason to be concerned about the depiction of science in movies (Crichton 1999, p. 1461).

Crichton is certainly right that the reality content of movies should not be taken too seriously. In particular, the depiction of scientific activity does not lend itself well to story telling because abstract thought or the pursuit of knowledge as such is difficult to represent in images. It is no accident that filmmakers show scientists in adventure or love, or both if they use them in plots. One could assume, therefore, that science is a much too esoteric subject to play any role in a popular medium such as fiction film. However, even a superficial search of movies about science or scientists yields over 400 titles. A study of the representation of science on television has shown that viewers are confronted to a remarkable degree with science, technology, and medicine. Contrary to what could be expected, this does not happen in news magazines or documentaries like NOVA in the US, but in fictional portrayals in the evening program (Gerbner 1987, p. 110). A larger share appears in 'dramatized entertainment', *i.e.* fiction films, be it science fiction movies, hospital series, mystery, or espionage stories. Science and its protagonists are evidently suitable subjects of the dream factory after all.

Crichton is too simplistic if he believes that the way science is represented in movies can only be explained through its particular entertainment value. The clichés and stereotypes about science, especially those regarding the 'mad scientist', were neither invented in Hollywood nor by the UfA-producers of the Weimar period. They have much deeper historical roots, and their exceptional stability and continuity qualifies them as products of the popular culture that express a deeply seated ambivalence toward science.[1] Above all, the 'mad scientist' stories are an enduring genre of the anti-rationalist critique of science that has found its way from literature into movies (Toumey 1992, p. 434).

---

[1] Two years after the publication of the first results of this project I came across Crichton's article and a manuscript by Joachim Schummer raising the same points vis à vis Crichton. I also owe other information to him that had been unknown to me before (Schummer 2006).

Although we have little doubt that movies and TV are exceptionally powerful media, we know next to nothing about their actual impact on the people's opinions and attitudes toward science. It is an open question if the form of popular critique of science to be found in films is really "extremely effective", as Toumey suggests. Crichton, on the other hand, argues reassuringly. The mass media, he claims, have lost their influence. The film reaches only a fraction of the entire population (*Jurassic Park* was seen only by 8-15% of the American people), and the Hollywood version of science is not to be taken more seriously by the public than other media contents (Crichton 1999). Apart from the fact that we know very little about the reception of movies in general and of horror films in particular, it is out of the question to assume a linear causality between watching a movie and believing its contents. It is more relevant that all the many versions of the Frankenstein and Jekyll-and-Hyde stories appeal to audiences again and again, that they represent relatively stable stereotypes and are evidently icons of popular culture.

At a time when science in all Western societies is increasingly concerned about its image, because it has lost the unconditional support of the public (or at least of policy makers) that it used to have in the late nineteenth and throughout the better part of the twentieth centuries, one could assume a focused attention on the media that presumably shape the image of science most effectively. The limited evidence we have shows that the depiction of science in TV entertainment cultivates a less than positive picture (Gerbner 1987, p. 112). The same is true for fiction films. Science administrators and policy makers would have ample reasons to be concerned about the image of science that is daily diffused on TV and film screens, even more so as they employ modern media formats and instruments of mass entertainment to raise interest and enthusiasm for science. The mad scientist of the movies is their natural opponent, and they would be well advised to acknowledge his historical presence.

The interest in the image of science portrayed in the many 'moving pictures' cannot be limited to the immediate PR effects on the well-being of the institution. Scientific knowledge and research as the activity to bring it about are problematic elements of popular culture. It is a kind of knowledge whose legitimacy has been established and even broadened since the Renaissance but continues to remain controversial.

Examples of attacks on the legitimacy of science are legend. The present generation has little reason to look down upon the irrationalities of earlier generations. The battle of *creationism* against evolutionary theory in the US or the banning of Western science by radical fundamentalists of different religions readily demonstrate forces that question the rationality of scientific methods and the superiority of scientific knowledge or openly fight against it. The conflict over the boundaries of science, about what methods of knowledge production and what forms of knowledge use should be legitimate, is an inherent element of Western culture. More recent debates over the boundaries of molecular medicine are just further illustrations of the conflict.

2. Popular Myths of Scientific Knowledge

Since antiquity scientific knowledge and its technical applications have been associated with both liberation and enslavement, with the power to exert control as much as with the threat to be controlled, with welfare for the people and with destruction. Gerbner notes that the "popular market for science is a mixture of great expectations, fears, utilitarian interests, curiosities, ancient prejudices, and superstitions", and "mass media appeal to all of these" (Gerbner 1987, p. 110). This fundamental ambivalence associated with science suggests that communicators have to deal with crystallizations around specific issues that seem to recur again and again and are cast into popular myths, while only the specific details change along with new knowledge. One of these myths, probably the most powerful of all, is the creation of artificial human life or its alteration by intervening in hereditary material, *i.e.* the creation of hybrids, monsters, and the like. The prototypical figure of this myth is the alchemist Dr. Faustus whose apprentice Wagner Goethe has create a 'homunculus'. His most famous literary successor is Dr. Frankenstein, who has inspired a chain of further stereotypes: Dr. Jekyll, Dr. Moreau, Dr. Caligari, Dr. Strangelove, and others (Haynes 2003). The creation of life appears as the ultimate goal and achievement in the production of knowledge. As the ongoing debate over the moratorium on cloning humans illustrates, the limits to that hubris, however fragile they may have become under the assault of progress, still "exert their power and arouse a certain dread of what will be found beyond these limits" (Back 1995, p. 328). Thus, it can be expected that this myth plays an important role in popular culture in general, and in films in particular.

If one wants to gauge how deep the roots of the critical myths of science actually reach, one needs to go back to their origins and trace their changes through time. Then it becomes understandable how the representation of science in film follows certain patterns.[2] The persistence of the figure of the alchemist as the embodiment of the scientist is best explained with the deep conflict between modern science and religion. Alchemy is foremost a metaphor for the pursuit of material goods and immortality. Authors of the late Middle Ages and early modernity contrast the 'crazy alchemist' with admonitions for a frugal life guided by moral and religious values. In the Christian romantic literature of the eighteenth century criticism was directed against the amoral pursuit of mere knowledge about nature. The true alchemy of the search for God is contrasted with the false alchemy of modern science. Goethe's *Faust* represents the limitations of the new experimental science whose far-reaching abilities empower it to manipulate nature but which then loses control over its own products because it lacks a deeper understanding of a holistic natural philosophy.

The division of science into 'two cultures' has its origin in this romantic contrast, the core of which is the religiously motivated critique of materialism, nihilism, and hubris. The critique of materialism in modern science is directed against the fact that it no longer needs a God as creator. Materialist science is atheist. To commit the sin of hubris means to give in to the ambitions of modern science to unravel the secrets of divine creation. Mary Shelley's *Frankenstein* marks the birth of the mad scientist, whose hubris not only leads himself into ruin, as was the case with his precursors, but now above all also the people in his environment. In the course of the nineteenth century the critique of modern science's hubris coincides with the moral critique of the obsessed scientist

---

[2] For the following I rely on Schummer 2006 for some detailed references to literary figures as well as on Haynes 1994.

who unscrupulously pursues his goals and knowingly risks the endangering of other people.

Schummer (2006) reconstructs the genealogy of the mad scientist that I have briefly sketched here, from contemporary literary works and focuses primarily on the religious roots of the critique of science. Toumey, on the other hand, explains why in his view the character of the *mad scientist* grows increasingly amoral as time passes. He sees the main causes in the artistic process of transferring texts into films and the commercial exploitation of characters through the production of sequels. This development, which he illustrates with film examples, takes place outside and independent of real science. It is foremost due to the unavoidable simplification that characterizes the film vis-à-vis the written text (Toumey 1992, p. 423). Even if one sees the direct influence of the degenerated picture of the scientist conditioned by the medium a bit more skeptically than he does, the dynamics inherent in the movie business is nevertheless an important explanation for the independence of the medium film. It adds to the stabilization and continuity of the myths that determine the social embedding of science.

That these myths are themes of movies does not come as a surprise. In the great majority of films the depiction of science reveals a deep uneasiness, distrust, and even mystification of science on the part of the filmmakers, which mirrors the sentiment of their audience. The images, clichés, and metaphors employed by filmmakers are the mirror image of science in popular culture. At the same time the movies enforce these images and provide them with imaginative detail and decorum. The film as one of the most influential media interacts in complex ways with its audiences, reflecting, shaping, and reinforcing images and identities. It can safely be assumed that science as one of its subjects is no exception to this (Turner 1999, pp. 100, 144).

Whether or not the position of science is now more precarious than in the past is a matter of judgment that is regularly skewed by the short memory of the media and their focus on the present. The many attempts by science administrators and policy makers to increase the public interest, understanding, and even 'engagement' in science seem to suggest that science is experiencing a crisis of acceptance. However, the suspicion is that criticism of particular lines of research (*e.g.* stem cell research, cloning of human embryos) or of the implementation of knowledge in certain technologies (*e.g.* the genetic manipulation of food) are time-bound expressions of media attention, and that they reflect a much more profound ambivalence toward 'new knowledge'. Thus, it is worth exploring the more stable patterns and stereotypes that are reproduced by the popular media in order to put present debates into perspective and to arrive at realistic expectations about the possibility of changing the public's attitudes by short-winded PR campaigns.

3. Chemists and Chemistry in Fiction Films – Patterns and Stereotypes

3.1 Note on methodology

The following is based on the analysis of 222 films ranging over eight decades of movie making. The selection of films is not representative in a statistical sense but based on a search for films depicting science and scientists. Out of some 400 identified films the selection of the sample was primarily guided by the availability of the films. However, an attempt was made to have a roughly equal share of examples in each decade corresponding to the distribution of the 400 films over the decades. As can be expected the number of recent films is much higher than that of older films.

The films were analyzed on the basis of a code sheet with about 120 categories. The results are based on the coding by several people. Due to severe limitations of resources and time (the project was carried out in the context of a research seminar with students doing the majority of screening and coding) only in very few cases the inter-rater reliability of the codings was tested. In order to keep the unavoidable impact of subjective judgments small, only results that could be established with some confidence are presented. For the same reason we refrained from further statistical analysis of the data since that would suggest a precision that cannot be sustained by the actual methodology used. All this implies that the percentages given cannot be seen as reliable representative figures. Rather they refer to our selection of movies and should not be interpreted as absolute figures but as relative ones. In the original analysis of the data no particular attention was paid to specific disciplines (Weingart *et al.* 2003). For the present analysis of the depiction of chemistry, the same film material was used and data for chemistry were extracted where appropriate. However, because of that some overlap with the results already published is inevitable.

The items that were selected provide an initial picture of the representation of chemistry in fiction film.

3.2 Popular disciplines

The assumption is that the relative frequency with which certain fields or disciplines appear in movies reflects most likely the degree of public concern associated with the knowledge produced by them. Chemistry ranks third in the sample after 'medical research', on the same level as psychology. If one assumes that disciplines with an image of being potentially life threatening and/or being involved in experiments with human identity receive particular attention in film scripts, chemistry is clearly in a prominent position. This is especially true considering that chemistry is often involved in medical research and to some extent even in psychology. After all, Dr. Jekyll is a chemist who tries to solve a psychological problem, *i.e.* the separation of the 'good' part of man's soul from the 'bad' one. The archetypical Frankenstein in Mary Shelley's novel seems to use "chemical instruments" to bring his creature to life, and it is only in James Whale's movie (*Frankenstein,* 1931) that an electrical process is used.

3.3 Settings of research

One of the most characteristic aspects of alchemy that distinguish it from modern science is its secrecy. Likewise, the most characteristic feature of the 'mad scientist' film is the secret basement laboratory, usually ornamented with gothic elements of medieval castles. Secrecy is involved even where these stylistic elements are missing (modern type basement laboratories can be found, for example, in *The Brain That Wouldn't Die* [1963] and *The Fly* [1958]). The secret laboratory is also typically the *private* laboratory of an *individual* scientist who works at most with one assistant. It is the place in which illegitimate experiments are carried out. This implies that dangerous research is taking place outside of public institutions such as university laboratories and government facilities (although, in fact, such institutions house their share of dangerous practices). Scientists working in their home basements are outsiders. They have isolated themselves from the critical observation of the scientific community because they feel misunderstood, often because they are obsessed with research of questionable goals and methods which they see justified, however, by the success they expect to have.

A fifth of all films in the sample portray science as a secret activity carried out in private basements. In contrast, over 40% of the movies that deal with chemistry are in the alchemist tradition, *i.e.* showing research being carried out at home. Next to chemistry, no other field except medical research stands out for being associated with this characteristic. Other fields are more likely to be associated with research taking place either as field work (anthropology, zoology, biology, psychology) or at universities (humanities). Chemistry as a discipline depicted in movies has the second highest share of secrecy (behind robotics!) as a feature.

On the level of disciplines we may conclude, albeit with some simplification, that fields that are generally considered socially and/or ethically problematic are also associated with research taking place in secrecy and in places isolated from the critical eyes of scientific peers or the lay public. The unproblematic disciplines typically operate outdoors or in public settings such as universities and government laboratories (Weingart *et al.* 2003, p. 285).

3.4 How knowledge is gained

The activity of 'doing science', of research, is usually hidden from the public eye. Precisely because the laboratory is a strange world, because the instruments used by scientists are foreign, and above all, because the methods used are both obscure and powerful, the ways in which scientists gain their knowledge are of particular interest. They arouse suspicion like the methods of jugglers at country fairs who were, after all, the eighteenth-century traveling demonstrators of electricity in public places (Hochadel 2003, ch. 4).

The major categories that arouse suspicion are 'experimentation on humans and animals', which represents a certain problematic type of research, and 'field research and expeditions', which are associated with the adventurous sciences. Our analysis shows that movie portraits of medical research and psychology, chemistry, biology, and genetics emphasize experimentation on living objects as the dominant method for gaining knowledge. Chemistry, again, is second only behind 'medical research' in being involved in experimentation on humans and animals.

But it is not just the methods and instruments that are suspicious, it is also the scientists' intellectual power that surpasses that of ordinary lay people, or at least so it seems. The 'genius' of scientists as a source of knowledge arouses a certain amount of suspicion because it sets scientists apart from ordinary lay people, and discovery 'by accident' also suggests their extraordinary capability to read the 'book of nature'. Both categories are in accord with the stereotype of the individualist nature of scientific discovery and are prejudices that are held by the lay public and supported by scientists.

3.5 Dangerous discovery/invention

One of the most common stereotypes about science is that scientists generate dangerous knowledge, through discoveries and inventions, which is associated with hubris. To a large degree, associations with that kind of knowledge determine the images of the different disciplines. In the case of chemistry only a quarter of the films in the sample shows discoveries in chemistry that are not dangerous. More than half are depicted as unintentionally dangerous, the remainder being depicted as the dangerous results of ill will. This prompts the question of who is depicted as the victim of dangerous research. It turns out that in half of the movies the discoveries and inventions affect uninvolved people. In roughly a third the victim of the discovery is the scientist himself. If one includes colleagues and assistants this share increases to about half of all the films. This reflects the (alchemist) tradition of solitary research and heroic self-experimentation.

3.6 Chemistry and ethical values

The ambivalence and potentially threatening nature of scientific knowledge and the technical inventions that accrue from it is expressed in a conflict between scientific knowledge and ethical values. In just more than half of the films (51%) ethical values are challenged, undermined, and in direct conflict with the science portrayed in the respective story (Weingart *et al.* 2003). If one breaks down the overall result for the different disciplines, the previous picture emerges once again: The discipline that is ethically problematic is above all medical research, to be followed by physics, chemistry, genetics, psychology, and biology. Astronomy, anthropology, and the humanities are mostly regarded as outside of this concern. If one looks at films in which chemistry is a subject, the largest single segment of them shows the discipline being in conflict with ethical values.

3.7 Depictions of scientists' characters

In view of the notoriety of the 'mad scientist' as the icon of a movie character one might expect that whenever scientists appear in film plots they tend to be descendants of Victor Frankenstein. Here we have compiled a slightly more complex picture that needs some explanation. On the one hand, results from a host of opinion polls show, time and again, that science as an institution is highly trusted by society. This is reflected in a large number of figures indicating scientists as being 'benevolent' and 'good'. However, our category of the 'benevolent' scientist already includes traits of ambivalence. The benevolent scientist can be naive when dealing with powerful interests, can mean well but sees his or her discoveries being put to some perverted use and the like. The 'ambivalent' scientists are easily manipulated, idealistic but progressively corrupted, ambitious, lose sight of the consequences of their work, and, most importantly, they grow willing to violate ethical principles for the sake of gaining new knowledge.

If one looks at the distribution of profiles by field it is quite obvious that medical research, physics, chemistry, and psychology are the disciplines that are portrayed with the greatest ambivalence. In these fields the audience is most likely confronted with 'mad scientists', the Faustian who trespasses ethical boundaries in order to gain forbidden knowledge and fame. Anthropology, astronomy, zoology, geology, and the humanities, on the other hand, are the fields that seem to have an unchallenged image of trust. The large majority of scientists from these fields are depicted as 'good' and 'benevolent'.

3.8 Scientific misconduct by discipline

The misconduct of scientists without any specification of the type of misconduct may be seen as an aspect of the dubious or at least ambivalent nature of science. If science is identified with misconduct this suggests distrust. Again, certain fields are more than others associated with questionable conduct. Chemistry is among them, together with genetics and pathology, even above medical research, biology, and the computer sciences. In literary studies and generally in the humanities misconduct is comparatively rare.

3.9 Utopias and dystopias of science – objects of fictional science

Fictionalization is one of the means by which some media, above all film, deals with the problem of representing abstract subject matters to a larger audience whose attention is fleeting. In particular, science and scientists are relatively abstract subjects to be represented by a medium that is normally focused on narrative and action. The world of knowledge has to be adapted to the rules and constraints of visual drama. This is done by representing it in different stages of development that reach beyond contemporary research fronts and technological achievements, and by projecting it onto either utopian or dystopian realms. By doing so films not only reinforce the mystique of the production of new knowledge. They also participate in the process of 'embedding' new knowledge in societies to become part of popular culture. In fact, scientists themselves are engaged in this process whenever they project future developments of their research in order to gain acceptance, especially when that appears problematic with respect to dominant values. Their utopian promises (*e.g.* new medication, cure of illness, longevity) are opposed by dystopian projections from opponents (*e.g.* dangers like the moral degeneration of society, genetic selection, and the loss of individuality). In the subsequent discourse the new knowledge and social values are gradually accommodated to each other.

In 39% of the films in our sample, real scientific fields are depicted at a fictional level of development; in additional 14% of the films, fictional fields of science are shown. Only less than half (47%) of the movies deal with a non-fictional area of science. For chemistry this is by and large the same.

If one looks at the kinds of subject matters of the fictional or semi-fictional sciences, it is apparent that the projections of the future associated with them are mostly dystopias or at least highly ambivalent utopias. Roughly a third of the movies in the sample deal with artificial, supernatural, human, animal, or extraterrestrial life forms, cloning, reanimation, or immortality. If illness and cure are added to this category the share is even larger (by 5%). The utopian or dystopian views about science are clearly dominated by concerns about the manipulation of human and animal life. These concerns are focused primarily on medical research, as we saw above. But we can infer that chemistry has its share of attention.

3.10 Authenticity

Films are made to capture the imagination of the audience. Illusion is the essence of fiction film, and yet filmmakers mostly try hard to create plausible plots and representations, to render their products authentic in order to have impact on the public. Just a little more than a quarter of all chemistry movies are depicted as non-authentic, only about a fifth are comedies and satires. A look at *The Nutty Professor* shows that not even these are just funny.

The authenticity is obviously enhanced when gadgets and technologies are shown that look familiar to the viewer. Chemistry is often presented in conjunction with familiar instruments. As Schummer and Spector have shown some of these are iconographic for the representation of science as a whole like the chemist holding up a flask and gazing at it (Schummer & Spector 2007).

The overwhelming majority of chemists in movies are represented as knowing the truth. This portrays scientists as authoritative, and thus credible, and therefore contributes to authenticity.

And yet, most films dealing with chemistry in one way or another are meant to frighten their viewers. Roughly a quarter of all chemistry movies are horror movies (Table 1).

Table 1: Chemistry in movies by genre	
Action (4.4%)	Adventure (3.3%)
Animation (3.3%)	Comedy (13.3%)
Crime (4.4%)	Drama (8.8%)
Family (4.4%)	Fantasy (0%)
Film-Noir (0%)	Horror (24.4%)
Musical (0%)	Mystery (2.2%)
Romance (0%)	Science Fiction (8.8%)
Satire (0%)	Thriller (13.3%)
War (3.3%)	Western (0%)

3.11   *Preoccupation with the past – alchemy*

There is no doubt that the legacy of alchemy had its impact on film makers throughout the twentieth century as a selection of film titles reveals (Table 2), and probably will continue to do so in the twenty-first century.

The continuity of the occurrence of alchemy raises the obvious question of what if anything has changed in the representation of chemistry in movies over the last century. Our material does not provide a definitive answer to that question, not least because the disciplinary focus did not guide the selection of films. Not surprisingly movies dealing with science change the appearance of characters and the decorum of their research laboratories following the fads and fashions of the different genres. The creation of life by means of a cumbersome fictitious assortment of steaming and glowing chemicals that dominated the movies until as late as the 1990's is slowly being replaced by the clean microscopic techniques of molecular biology. Cloning has entered the movie scene rather late, with the exception of very few films like *Boys from Brazil* (1978). But the basic stereotypes, the fears associated with the creation of life like the ill meaning scientist and/or the experiment going out of control can be found just the same way in recent productions like *Godsend* (2003), *Blueprint* (2003), and *The Sixth Day* (2000). The impression is that the underlying anxieties about new knowledge reflected in the products of popular culture are much more fundamental than the images which link them to the respective worlds familiar to their audiences.

Table 2: Alchemy movie titles from the twentieth century

- *The Hallucinated Alchemist* (1897, USA)
- *The Clown and the Alchemist* (1900, USA)
- *The Alchemist* (1913, USA)
- *Homunculus* (1916, Germany)
- *Der Alchimist* (1918, Germany)
- *The Alchemist's Hourglass* (1936, USA)
- *Alchimie* (1952, France)
- *Une Alchimie* (1966, Belgium)
- *Alchimisten* (1968, GDR)
- *Alchemik* (1990, Poland)
- *Des alchimistes / Alchemists* (1991, Canada)
- *Alchemy* (1997, USA, TV)

---

4. Conclusions

To stress once again: these results are impressionistic and cannot claim statistical representativeness. But they are stable enough to allow the general conclusion that chemistry is among the fields of science that, in spite of all the benefits that it may have brought to mankind or perhaps because of them, has difficulties communicating with the lay public if the anxieties and ambivalences expressed in popular fiction movies are being taken as an indicator. Chemistry is not alone in this position. Medicine fares worse, and physics not much better. It may be concluded that the most powerful scientific disciplines – powerful in terms of shaping our environment and thus ourselves – are also those that are seen with the greatest suspicion. As far as the immediate PR needs of the discipline are concerned, the crucial question for the chemistry community is if the images of the field communicated through movies do have an impact in particular on young people, and what this impact is like.

References

Back, K.W.: 1995, 'Frankenstein and Brave New World: Two Cautionary Myths on the Boundaries of Science', *History of European Ideas*, **20**, 1-3, 327-332.

Crichton, M.: 1999, 'Ritual Abuse, Hot Air, and Missed Opportunities', *Science*, **283**, 1461-1463.

Gerbner, G.: 1987, 'Science on Television: How it Affects Public Conceptions', *Issues in Science and Technology*, Spring, 109-115.

Haynes, R.D.: 1994, *From Faust to Strangelove: Representations of the Scientist in Western Literature*, Johns Hopkins UP, Baltimore & London.

Haynes, R.D.: 2003, 'From alchemy to artificial intelligence: stereotypes of the scientist in Western literature', *Public Understanding of Science*, **12**, 243-253.

Schummer, J.: 2006, 'Historical Roots of the ‹Mad Scientist›: Chemists in nineteenth-century Literature', *Ambix*, **53**, 99-127 (reproduced in this volume as Chapter 2).

Schummer, J. & Spector, T.: 2007, 'Popular Images versus Self-Images of Science: Visual Representations of Science in Clipart Cartoons and Internet Photographs', in: P. Weingart & B. Hüppauf (eds.), *Images of the Sciences in Public Media*, Routledge, London & New York (forthcoming).

Toumey, C.P.: 1992, 'The moral character of mad scientists: A cultural critique of science', *Science, Technology and Human Values*, **17**, 411-437.

Turner, G.: 1999, *Film as Social Practice*, 3rd ed., Routledge, London & New York.

Weingart, P.: 2005, *Die Wissenschaft der Öffentlichkeit*, Velbrück, Weilerswist.

Weingart, P., Muhl, C. & Pansegrau, P.: 2003, 'Of power maniacs and unethical genius: science and scientists in fiction film', *Public Understanding of Science*, **12**, 279-288.

CHAPTER 4

CHEMISTRY AND POWER IN RECENT AMERICAN FICTION

Philip Ball

Nature, 4-6 Crinan St., London N1 9XW, U.K.; p.ball@nature.com

Writers of fiction have always held up a mirror to the world around them. The perspective they typically present is not one gathered from polls of public opinion, nor is it culled from the way issues are presented in the media. Yet in retrospect, the personal attitudes and views expressed in good literary fiction frequently prove to offer a revealing snapshot of trends in thought and topics of debate in the writer's milieu. With this in mind, I shall explore some of the themes on chemistry and society developed in the fictional works of three modern American writers. I believe that these examples provide food for thought, and possibly a little encouragement, to those who despair at the tarnished image that chemistry commonly seems to have in broader public discourse today. For while all of the texts I consider examine some of the fears often expressed about the chemical industry, they show a willingness to engage with issues of risk (real and perceived), social benefits, changing patterns of consumer behavior, and responsibility that is not always present in more conventional modes of ecocriticism.

1. Introduction

What strikes one first about chemistry in twentieth-century literature is that, in comparison to physics, biology and mathematics, there is so little of it. I do not think it is hard to understand why this is so. Chemistry is largely absent from our contemporary literature for the same reason that it is largely absent from any public discussion and dissemination of science, whether that be in popular science writing, television programs, or cultural debates. Fiction writers have always, by and large, sought to explore big themes: that is surely as true of Cervantes, Swift, Hugo, and

Dostoevsky as it is of Martin Amis, Margaret Atwood or Kazuo Ishiguro, to pick out just three contemporary writers who have drawn on ideas from science. Physics and biology appear to explore the major questions that a work of fiction might also explore: What does it mean to be human? What is the nature of existence? Amis used the post-Einsteinian plastic notion of time to run the Holocaust in reverse in his book *Time's Arrow* (1992), while both Atwood (*Oryx and Crake*, 2003) and Ishiguro (*Never Let Me Go*, 2005) project genetic engineering into a dystopian future.

Chemistry, in contrast, seems to have little to offer in the way of grand themes. In fact, it often seems today not to be asking any questions about the world at all: it is primarily a synthetic science, a science bound up with making things. Even many scientists, if they have no real knowledge of chemistry, seem unable to find a way to fit this discipline into their vision of what science is about, namely the process of discovering how the world works. Most current distinctions that are drawn between science and technology will place today's chemistry squarely within the realm of technology, or at least applied science, concerned as it is much more with invention than with discovery.

That was not always so. When far less was known about the material constitution of the world and the nature of its elemental building blocks, chemistry became temporarily a 'discovery science' *par excellence*. This was why, when chemists were trying to understand what made elements join in some combinations but not others – to understand what they called the notion of affinity – Wolfgang von Goethe famously found in chemistry an appropriate metaphor for the study of human relationships in his novel *Elective Affinities* (1809).

Now things are different. The 'big questions' of chemistry – what the elements are and how they unite in the material world – have been more or less answered. Today the vast majority of publications in the chemical literature are concerned with synthesis (Schummer 2004), which can look like, and indeed is sometimes practiced as, more of a craft than a science.

That is not, however, an *a priori* reason why it should lack appeal to modern writers. To say that chemistry is neglected in fiction because it poses no big questions is not to offer a necessary truth; rather, it is to say that we live in a particular kind of intellectual climate. It is a climate that we have inherited from antiquity, one in which the abstract and theoretical are valued above the manual and practical. Classical Greek philosophers were often careful observers of nature, but they rarely engaged in experiment, and even then it would not be to learn about the world but merely to demonstrate the validity of their ideas. It was only when this philosophical strand mingled with the practical skills of the Middle East in Hellenistic Alexandria that the great experimental Greek scientists such as Archimedes and Hero appeared (Multhauf 1993). That blend, of course, gave rise to the proto-science of alchemy; but alchemy, as well as practical chemical arts such as dyeing, pottery, metallurgy, cooking, and brewing, was never deemed a subject worthy of scholarly study at the medieval universities, where astronomy, geometry, and music were the pre-eminent 'sciences'. Although medicine was taught academically, the doctors typically never laid a finger on a human body – manual medical operations such as cautery, bone-setting, and blood-letting were left for lowly surgeons to perform.

Yet chemistry *could* have become a rich source of inspiration and metaphor for everyone interested in the puzzles and dilemmas of human existence. In the chemical philosophies that flourished in the sixteenth and early seventeenth centuries, it was precisely that: these theories, now seemingly so arcane and indeed occult, can be considered the first proto-scientific 'theories of everything'. This aspect of Renaissance science, which drew in particular on the ideas of the Swiss alchemist and physician Paracelsus and left its mark on the notion of science developed by Francis Bacon, has been discussed by the American historian of science Allen Debus (1978). It came sometimes into explicit conflict with the mechanistic view of science initiated by René Descartes and his followers, and which of course ultimately triumphed in the form of the deterministic mechanics of Isaac Newton.

I am not saying that this was a mistake, and that we should instead have chosen to embrace Paracelsian chemical philosophy, which typically veered towards a rather nebulous mysticism. I am simply pointing out that these developments in science were not independent of our culture as a whole, and that they continue to shape it.

2. Levi's Legacy

The British biologist Peter Medawar, one of the most perceptive commentators on the practice of science in the mid-twentieth century, has expressed very cogently where this preference for the abstract over the practical has led us:

> Francis Bacon was not the first to distinguish basic from applied science, but no one before him put the matter so clearly and insistently, and the distinction as he draws it is unquestionably just [...] Bacon's distinction is between research that increases our power over nature and research that increases our understanding of nature [...] Unhappily, Bacon's distinction is not the one we now make when we differentiate between the basic and applied sciences. The notion of *purity* has somehow been superimposed upon it, and in a new usage that connotes a conscious and inexplicably self-righteous disengagement from the pressures of necessity and use. The distinction is not now between the empirically founded sciences and those whose axioms were supposedly known a priori; rather it is between polite and rude learning, between the laudably useless and the vulgarly applied, the free and the intellectually compromised, the poetic and the mundane.[Medawar 1984]

Understandably, writers of fiction want the poetic, not the mundane. That is to say, they have been led, like our culture as a whole, to expect to find the poetic in the so-called pure sciences, the sciences of 'how the world works': in physics and biology. It has required a genuine insider, someone who knew chemistry intimately, to show that in fact there is plenty of poetry in chemistry too. That person was, of course, the Italian chemist and writer Primo Levi.

Inevitably one *must* mention Primo Levi in the context of this chapter's topic. But I confess that I intend to say rather little about him, since I rather feel that to dwell on Levi would be to cheat on my aim here. He had a privileged perspective in that he *was* a chemist, whereas I want to look at how chemistry has impacted on writers who did not have that training, or indeed that specific focus in their oeuvre. But I do wish to point out that Levi's classic book *The Periodic Table* (published in Italian in 1975) grasps the essence of chemistry's allegories in a manner that is very much akin to the chemical philosophies of centuries earlier, where the transformations that are conducted in the chemical laboratory are perceived as reflecting the processes of human life. In Paracelsian chemical philosophy these correspondences were seen as much more than a metaphor; but I think it is fair to say that they were rather more than metaphors for Levi too, who was clearly moved by a profound empathy for chemical science. He writes, for example, with something like reverence about the process of distillation:

> Distillation is beautiful. First of all, because it is a slow, philosophic, and silent occupation, which keeps you busy but gives you time to think of other things, somewhat like riding a bike. Then, because it involves a metamorphosis from liquid to vapour (invisible), and from this once again to liquid; but in this double journey, up and down, purity is attained, an ambiguous and fascinating condition, which starts with chemistry and goes very far. And finally, when you set about distilling, you acquire the consciousness of repeating a ritual consecrated by the centuries. [Levi 1985]

Levi also found ways to expound the *synthetic* nature of chemistry, the fact that it was about making things. In his novel *The Monkey's Wrench* (1978) he points out that chemistry has in fact much in common with the profession of the engineer. The narrator, talking to a construction worker named Faussone who assembles bridges, says

> The profession I studied in school and that has kept me alive so far is the profession of a chemist. I don't know if you have a clear idea of it, but it's a bit like yours; only we rig and dismantle very tiny constructions [...] I've always been a rigger-chemist, one of those who make syntheses, who build structures to order, in other words.

And he goes on to explain what that entails – how difficult it is to assemble a structure using atoms:

> [...] when you come down to it, we're bad riggers. We really are like elephants who have been given a closed box containing all the pieces of a watch: we are very strong and patient, and we shake the box in every direction and with all our strength. Maybe we even warm it up, because heating is another form of shaking. Well, sometimes, if the watch isn't too complicated, if we keep on shaking, we succeed in getting it together; but, as you can imagine, it's more reasonable to proceed a bit at a time, first attaching two pieces, then adding a third, and so on. It takes more patience, but actually you get there first. And most of the time that's the way we do it. [Levi 1987]

Chemistry has been fantastically lucky to have Levi's advocacy – not so much because he is a chemist who can write beautifully (that is simply the recipe for a good science writer) but because he is first and foremost an artist who, to our good fortune, happened to take up the profession of chemistry.

3. Home Truths about Chemistry

But Levi's almost spiritual response to chemistry is unusual now. The writers on whom I want to focus here are distinguished in having understood that, rather than standing remote from the realities of human existence, chemistry has become central to it. Their interest in chemistry is materialistic, for the simple and obvious, although generally overlooked, reason that our lives are materialistic. Increasingly, we live in a synthetic environment, a world of new and unfamiliar materials, in which our foods and clothes and medicines are manufactured in factories and laboratories. I am aware that this is a perspective usually voiced as a criticism, a lament about a world in which 'artificial' and 'synthetic' are terms of derogation, to be contrasted with the goodness that inheres in 'natural' things. But it was not always so. For Francis Bacon, synthesis and artifice were the primary aims of science, and his scientific agenda, which imposed a strong influence on the founders of the Royal Society in London, was pre-eminently a practical one. Scientists, he said, should be like bees. "The bee", he wrote,

> extracts matter from the flowers of the garden and the field, but works and fashions it by its own efforts. The true labour of philosophy resembles hers, for it neither relies entirely nor principally on the powers of the mind, nor yet lays up in the memory the matter afforded by the experiments of natural history and mechanics in its raw state, but changes and works it in the understanding. [Bacon 1620, p. 349]

The three writers I wish to discuss here – Don DeLillo, Richard Powers, and Thomas Pynchon – do not exactly celebrate artifice in the way that Bacon does, but neither, I think, do they present a simple-minded critique of it. I am unapologetic about the fact that they are all American writers, because I think that is no coincidence: few national cultures have embraced the synthetic to the extent that America has, and DeLillo and

Powers in particular phrase their analysis of what we might call 'everyday chemistry' with a seemingly conscious cultural specificity. Moreover, these three authors are commonly bracketed together – Powers, for instance, has been described as "one of the few younger American writers who stake a claim to the legacy of Pynchon and DeLillo", while DeLillo in turn has been said to share the 'mad willfulness' of Pynchon – and I feel that part of the reason for this is the way that they are able to engage in an informed way with the immediacy of our chemical and material world.

DeLillo's take on this issue is illustrated most clearly in his 1984 novel *White Noise*. This, the eighth of his novels, is widely regarded as his 'breakthrough' work, an accessible and highly entertaining satire on the fears and myths of contemporary American life. It exemplifies what critic Charles Molesworth has identified as DeLillo's recurrent themes:

> No other contemporary novelist could be said to outstrip DeLillo in his ability to depict that larger social environment we blandly call everyday life. Brand names, current events, fads, the society of the spectacle, and the rampant consumerism that has become our most noticeable, if not our most important, contribution to history, all are plentifully and accurately recorded throughout DeLillo's work. [Molesworth 1991]

Yet *White Noise* divided critics and reviewers. Some saw it as a straightforward critique of the American way of life: a 'liberal' attitude that infuriated conservative commentators. For others, it was almost a celebration of that same post-modern perspective, in which high art is mixed with consumer culture and the philosophy of Nietzsche is no more or less valid than the philosophy of the breakfast-cereal packet. "DeLillo has been read both as a denouncer and as a defender of post-modern culture", says Mark Osteen (2000), who feels that neither interpretation really fits *White Noise*.

From the very first paragraph, which describes the return of students to college after the summer vacation, DeLillo makes it clear that he is pre-occupied with the material and specifically the synthetic aspects that pass unquestioned in modern American life:

> As cars slowed to a crawl and stopped, students sprang out and raced to the rear doors to begin removing the objects inside; the stereo sets, ra-dios, personal computers; small refrigerators and table ranges; the car-

tons of phonograph records and cassettes; the hairdryers and styling irons; the tennis rackets, soccer balls, hockey and lacrosse sticks, bows and arrows; the controlled substances, the birth control pills and devices; the junk food still in shopping bags – onion-and-garlic chips, nacho thins, peanut crème patties, Waffelos and Kabooms, fruit chews and toffee popcorn; the Dum-Dum pops, the Mystic mints. [DeLillo 1984, p. 3]

This, DeLillo implies, is the complete kit you need for modern life in America, all of it essential, including – perhaps especially – those brand-named items that remain an utter mystery to non-Americans: the Waffelos and Kabooms. The book is a fantastical grotesque, Rabelais transferred to the late twentieth century – for it was Rabelais who introduced such absurd, comical lists into the novel (Rabelais 1532, 1534). And he too wrote satire with serious intent.

DeLillo's narrator, Jack Gladney, teaches at the College-on-the-Hill in a town called Blacksmith, where he is chairman of the department of Hitler studies, a discipline he invented in 1968. Jack has subsequently been concealing the fact that he actually does not know the German language, while making ineffectual and clandestine attempts to learn it. Thus Jack's professional life is every bit as superficial and synthetic as his material life, a world of strange and unfamiliar substances which he and his family wear and use and ingest without question. "We began quietly plastering mustard and mayonnaise on our brightly colored food", he says. They sense something is not right about this, but the culture in which they are embedded renders them powerless. "This isn't the lunch I'd planned for myself", Jack's wife says. "I was seriously thinking yoghurt and wheat germ."

This is a life that is pharmaceutically sustained. Everyone is on medication. When Jack's daughter asks him "What do you take?", he tells her, "Blood pressure pills, stress pills, allergy pills, eye drops, aspirin. Run of the mill." But some medication is not described by function; it simply has a medical-sounding name. Jack's wife is on a drug called Dylar, and he can discover nothing about what it is supposed to do. All he knows (at first) is that it makes her absent-minded.

Jack Gladney's world is full of these trade names for synthetic chemicals and materials, and they serve the dual purpose of comforting and alienating. People recite the names because that is all they have by way of understanding or describing these substances: a meaningless, superficial, invented label. If you use the label, it sounds as though you have taken command of the substance, it makes it something familiar and casually appropriated – even though you have absolutely no idea what it is. Jack starts to see or hear about teams of men in protective clothing who appear around Blacksmith, and in every case he specifies that the garments are made from Mylex, although it is clear that this means nothing to him. 'Mylex' sounds technical, it sounds as though he knows what he is talking about, although there is (so far as I know) no such substance. There is a knowing, post-modern irony at work here. It is widely recognized that the sloppy fictional mode particularly prevalent in movie scripts tends to employ scientific words without any notion of what they mean, simply to add a patina of apparent scientific credibility (if not merely to signpost supposedly scientific content). DeLillo has Jack Gladney do the same thing, and now the author is not inadvertently showing his ignorance but pointing out how this tendency has become a stock aspect of modern life.

But there is no doubt that Jack's identification of the protective material as Mylex has another implication. If he had simply said 'plastic', the effect would not be the same. Mylex has a corporate aura – it suggests that the men in protective clothing are part of an operation as inscrutable as the fabrics they wear, an organization shrouded in the mysterious trappings of power. And as the tale proceeds, this operation becomes more ominous. The Mylex men are clearly involved in some kind of clean-up procedure, and eventually this literally spills out into the open when a train carrying some chemical agent is derailed, creating a fire or explosion that sends a cloud of toxic material to threaten Blacksmith. When Jack tries to establish the nature of the spill, he is faced with a similar blank, forbidding label: his son Heinrich tells him that "It's called Nyodene Derivative or Nyodene D." When Jack finally sees this so-called 'airborne toxic event', again he seeks refuge in names that he has heard but not understood: "It was a terrible thing to see, so close, so low, packed with chlorides, benzines [*sic*], phenols, hydrocarbons, or whatever the precise toxic content."

Nyodene, Mylex, Dylar: clearly names from the same stable as Nylon, Kevlar, Mylar, the ubiquitous synthetic products of the chemical industry, presented to us without explanation or justification. At one point, DeLillo simply lists them, à propos of nothing in particular: "Dacron, Orlon, Lycra Spandex", one of his recurring little mantras to the modern world. He calls such labels "supranational names, computer-generated, more or less universally pronounceable. Part of every child's brain noise, the substatic regions too deep to probe."

It might be tempting to read all of this as standard knee-jerk paranoia in response to our 'chemical world', a reiteration of the popular notion that all 'chemicals' are bad and the chemical industry is inevitably polluting. Some critics have indeed interpreted *White Noise* as, in part, a cautionary fable about such ecological and toxicological human-made hazards. Perhaps that was not surprising in view of the context in which it was first published in January 1985 – just a month after the leakage of methyl isocyanate gas from Union Carbide's chemicals plant at Bhopal in central India, which claimed thousands of lives. Tom LeClair argues that the toxic substances in the airborne toxic event "were engineered to kill and thus give man control over the Earth; instead, they threaten their inventors and nature". *White Noise*, he says, is an expression of DeLillo's "rage at and pity for what humankind does to itself" (LeClair 2003).

But I think DeLillo's fable is more subtle than that. Jack does not regard the toxic cloud as the inevitable product of humankind's hubris in making these awful substances; rather, he is perplexed at how the prosaic process of synthesis and artifice can generate something that resembles a *natural* hazard:

> This was death made in the laboratory, defined and measurable, but we thought of it at the time in a simple and primitive way, as some seasonal perversity of the earth like a flood or tornado, something not subject to control. Our helplessness did not seem compatible with the idea of a man-made event. [DeLillo 1984, p. 127f.]

The synthetic chemicals that pervade Jack's life are regarded by him as benign, or at least as necessary. He is bewildered when they seem to turn on him. Yet he experiences no conversion to any sort of back-to-basics environmentalism in the book, despite acquiring a potentially fatal condition from the toxic airborne event and despite discovering unwholesome truths about his wife's Dylar, a drug created to suppress overwhelming fears of mortality.

Indeed, there is a good case to be made that *White Noise* is a discourse on the irrational and obsessive fear of death in modern middle-class America, and that the airborne toxic event is just a symbol of that. When Jack finally sees the deadly cloud, it is described in mythological terms: "The enormous dark mass moved like some death ship in a Norse legend, escorted across the night by armoured creatures with spiral wings." Its appearance spawns folk tales among the awed inhabitants of Blacksmith: it "had released a spirit of imagination. People spun tales, others listened spellbound".

This, I think, brings us to the crux of *White Noise*. Its true subject seems, above all else, to be the mythology that underlies suburban American life: the way that feelings of disempowerment and helplessness engendered by a dependence on commodities and services provided by faceless corporations and invisible forces create their own superstitions, belief systems, and legends. "The genius of the primitive mind", Jack acknowledges, "is that it can render human helplessness in noble and beautiful ways." According to critic Mark Conroy (2003), "If anything, the scientific advance chiefly on display in this world [...] reduces the people further to infantilism, primitive fantasy, and dependence upon the system as if upon a deity [...] the products of modern technology become themselves fetish objects".

This theme is made explicit through the character of Murray Jay Siskind, an ex-sportswriter and now a colleague of Jack's at the College-on-the-Hill who wants to explore the mythology and mystique of Elvis in the same way that Jack does with Hitler. Siskind studies packaging in the supermarket and scans the advertisements in trashy magazines like *Ufologist Today*. "I want", he says, apparently voicing DeLillo's intentions, "to immerse myself in American magic and dread."

Within this pantheon of contemporary occult forces, technology, like the old gods, holds both the threat of damnation and the promise of salvation. "Give yourself up to it", Siskind urges Jack. "Believe in it." Jack himself recognizes that these forces are at play, and that our response to them is primeval. "The greater the scientific advance", he tells his wife, "the more primitive the fear." But these primitive fears are now mediated through brand names, advertising, television. The recurring triads of names are a part of Siskind's 'American magic': they are like incantations, with echoes of a recitation of the Holy Trinity that are not simply ironic. Fetish objects, indeed. Even the airborne toxic event is presented in this way: the authorities seize on various euphemisms for it before alighting on this one, seeking the right balance of gravity and distance. Dealing with the crisis becomes a question of finding the right slogan. The deadly cloud, Jack notes, is presented to them in consumerist terms, like an advertising campaign for death. *"White Noise"*, says critic Michael Valdez Moses,

> is DeLillo's exploration of an America in which technology has become not merely a pervasive and mortal threat to each of its citizens, but also, and more importantly, a deeply ingrained mode of existing and way of thinking that is the characteristic feature of the republic. [Moses 1991]

Where, we might reasonably ask, does DeLillo himself stand in all of this? That it is hard to answer that question contributes to the book's richness. As Thomas DiPietro writes,

> In DeLillo's truly Swiftean satire, we're never sure what he himself believes or what he thinks of his characters. As in Swift, we're instead forced to rely on ourselves, to measure literary experience against our own sense of reality. [Lentricchia 1991]

This refusal to provide a neat message, this offering of a range of perspectives, some of them only half-glimpsed, is a characteristic of much post-modern fiction, and certainly it can be found in the other two books I discuss below. However, Ursula Heise offers one particularly intriguing interpretation of DeLillo's stance that has a special resonance from the point of view of the book's attitudes to technology in general and to chemical technology in particular. She suggests that DeLillo has found a way to explore the complex and in some sense irresolvable issues of risk with which modern life confronts us. "In *White Noise*", Heise (2002) says, "DeLillo is concerned with the way in which new kinds of risk have invaded the lives of even those citizens that might earlier have had reason to believe themselves safe from their most dire consequences." We are bombarded daily with health scares, and not just from synthetic chemicals with obscure, futuristic names but from the ingredients in familiar foods and drinks that we never even knew were there. One day red wine is good for you; the next, it is a hazard. Beware sugar; beware salt. These oils are good; those are bad. New pollutants are being detected as fast as new methods are devised to detect them (and, of course, because of those very innovations). Old drugs prove to have unforeseen side effects; can we trust the new alternatives any better?

Jack Gladney's family is surrounded by such vague and incomprehensible dangers, of which the airborne toxic event is just the most concrete example. His son Heinrich's hairline is receding, although he is just fourteen. "Did his mother consume some kind of gene-piercing substance when she was pregnant?" Jack wonders. His stepdaughter Denise tells her gum-chewing mother "That stuff causes cancer in laboratory animals in case you didn't know." At one point, the children's school is evacuated because of toxic fumes, which could be coming from

> the ventilating system, the paint or varnish, the foam insulation, the electrical insulation, the cafeteria food, the rays emitted by microcomputers, the asbestos fireproofing, the adhesive on shipping containers, the fumes from the chlorinated pool, or perhaps something deeper, finer-grained, more closely woven into the basic state of things. [DeLillo 1984, p. 35]

In other words, everything is a potential hazard. And Heise argues that, just as DeLillo's characters cannot be sure what to believe, so in *White Noise* he creates a narrative structure in which the *reader* does not know what to believe either. (We will later see precisely the same device used by Thomas Pynchon.) Not just the half-familiar names of products – Mylex, Dylar, and so forth – but also the seemingly wilder comic inventions have an air of plausibility: Siskind's academic quest for a mythology of Elvis, college courses on the study of car-crash scenes in movies, drugs for suppressing irrational fears. Even the story in a supermarket tabloid that "From beyond the grave, dead living legend John Wayne will communicate telepathically with President Reagan to help frame U.S. foreign policy" starts to sound horribly possible. Thus, says Heise (2002), "the novel's narrative mode, which exacts decision making [about what is real and what is not] from the readers, mirrors in its form the fundamental uncertainties that beset risk assessments in the 'real world'."

It would be simplistic, then, to interpret *White Noise* as a warning about the dangers of chemical industry. It is, among other things, a mediation on the tragicomedy of our (which is to say, America's) simultaneous dependency on and ignorance of the products of that enterprise. The book ends with a description of people in a supermarket, thrown into agitation and panic when the shelves are rearranged without warning. "They walk in a fragmented trance", says Jack, "trying to figure out the pattern, discern the underlying logic, trying to remember where they'd seen the Cream of Wheat."

4. Corporate Gain, Public Loss?

In his 1998 novel *Gain*, Richard Powers presents a rather more somber analysis of this same dilemma. This is a fiction of almost unprecedented chemical sophistication. It tells two stories, shifting sequentially between them every few pages. One is concerned with the genesis of the fictional chemicals company Clare, which begins as a candle- and soap-making business run by two Irish immigrants in Boston in the nineteenth century and grows to share the stage with Lever, Colgate, and Procter and Gamble in manufacturing domestic products, foods, and agrochemicals. The other story is the tale of Laura Bodey, a real-estate agent living in modern-day Lacewood, Illinois – a town that owes its existence to the presence of Clare's factories and headquarters. Laura discovers she has ovarian cancer, which her ex-husband Don thinks was induced by proximity to the Clare chemical works.

Powers has a remarkable understanding of industrial history generally and of how the chemicals companies arose in particular. He quotes William Cullen, professor of chemistry at Glasgow and Edinburgh, who made one of the most eloquent defenses of chemistry as an applied science:

> Chemistry is the art of separating mixt bodies into their constituent parts and of combining different bodies or the parts of bodies into new mixts [...] for the purposes of philosophy by explaining the composition of bodies [...] and for the purposes of arts by producing several artificial substances more suitable to the intention of various arts than any natural productions are. [Powers 2001, p. 35]

Cullen was in fact quite insistent on chemistry's role as handmaid to industry – in this same article he went on to say:

> Does the mason want a cement? Does the dyer want a means of tinging a cloth of a particular colour? Or does the bleacher want the means of discharging all colours? It is the chemical philosopher who must supply these. [Cullen c.1766, quoted in Donovan 1975, p. 107.]

Powers points out how industry provided both the means and the motives for fundamental chemical research, in particular with the aim of finding out how to synthesize the molecules that were extracted at considerable cost and hazard from natural sources, and how they might be modified and improved:

> Chemistry was not the means to soapmaking. Soapmaking was, rather, a means toward the consummate chemical end. To that goal, the elements moved from one incarnation to the other the way that the seasons, variously advantageous, moved through the eternally renewing year. If Nature were no more than eternal transformation, Man's meet and right pursuit consisted of emulating her. [Powers 2001, p. 79]

And just as, in *The Monkey's Wrench*, Primo Levi exploited the fact that he was writing a novel rather than a textbook to show us a molecular diagram that no popular science writer would dare place before the reader, so Powers can risk displaying the most extraordinary chemical detail in describing the activities of the Clare company. He gives us in all its stoichiometric glory the Leblanc process for making soda from salt:

$$2NaCl + H_2SO_4 = Na_2SO_4 + 2HCl$$

$$Na_2SO_4 + 2C = Na_2S + 2CO_2$$

$$Na_2S + CaCO_3 = CaS + Na_2CO_3$$

Or, as an illustration of how the company made economies and at the same time diversified by recycling by-products as raw materials, we are shown on page 171 a diagram of the various uses of Glauber's salt.

What, one might ask, is this textbook material doing in a novel? Well, novels can do that kind of thing. Readers will tolerate it today because learned asides have become part of the modern novelist's technique. In a novel, unlike a non-fiction book, you do not feel you have to *understand* this stuff; you merely absorb it as a signifier of authenticity. Powers reminds us of this with a suitably flowery, cod-Victorian explanation of his chemical equations:

> The symbols traipsed across the page, as cryptic as the skittering beetle code in that story by Mr. Poe from the *Philadelphia Dollar Weekly*. The first equation was a cotillion, a quadrille of decoupling and recoupling. Na and Cl parted amicably, grabbing the split partners of 2H and SO_4 to forge new squares while still balancing beautifully across the equal sign. The second spun a sprightly Roger de Coverley, the terpsichorean set-and-a-half breaking down longways in the winding hey, SO_4 cracking into two new dancers of its own right, with never a leg being gained or lost. [Powers 2001, p. 131]

The bottom line of all the technical details is clear enough: "Man now spun worth from worthlessness, gold from dross." The dream, in other words, of the chemical philosophy.

So fluent does Powers become in this chemicalization of culture that he can even toss us a (rather good) chemical joke or two, as when Laura Bodey's daughter admits to having provoked a fight with another girl at her school: "She says", Laura tells Don, "that she asked the girl how many viscoses died to make her blouse."

But Laura Bodey is, seemingly, there to remind us of the consequences of it all. In the light of the book's title, it could appear to take the shape of a morality tale: the business begun by the upright, honorable Clare brothers becomes transformed over the years into a greedy multinational that ends up endangering the citizens unfortunate enough to live close to its toxic, carcinogenic effluent, or who use its chemical products. Inevitably perhaps, if rather depressingly, Powers was accused by some reviewers of taking an anti-industrial stance in which he mounts "an assault on corporate America" (Caldwell 1998). As with *White Noise*, such crude readings tell us more about the preoccupations of the reader than about the novel.

Powers himself is much more careful to balance his equation. For a start, it is never clear in *Gain* whether Laura's ultimately terminal illness is really connected to Clare products at all. As Don presses Laura to sue, she insists that there is no reason to believe that her cancer has environmental causes. When Don tells her that she is part of a cluster centered on Lacewood, she points out that "ovarian cancer doesn't cluster". She is due nothing, she thinks. "No more than anyone else with a body. No more than anyone who will get sick, which is everyone." Don's insistence comes to look like a part of the culture of compensation, a symptom of the modern need to find someone to blame (and to sue) for our misfortune.

As Don explains the case for the prosecution, it is apparent that he has striven manfully to grasp the science behind the issue – he does not accept this potential danger with the barely comprehending fatalism of the Gladneys:

> The theory is that certain ring-shaped molecules [...] ones with chlorine in them, get taken up into the tissues of women. The body turns them into something called xenoestogen. Very long-lasting. These fake estrogens somehow trick the body, signal the reproductive system to start massive cell division [...] The thing is, these ring-chlorine things are found in certain pesticides. [Powers 2001, p. 319]

But the truth of the matter never becomes clear. Expert witnesses contradict one another's claims. Clare buys in some of its fertilizer feedstock from another firm, causing confusion about liability. Laura dies, but there is never any Hollywood-style payoff whereby the chemicals company is revealed to be the Machiavellian villain.

And even more pertinently, Laura realizes that establishing some kind of culpability with Clare would make no difference anyway. For this is how she and her fellow citizens have chosen to live. They use Clare's chemical products because they genuinely make life easier. More synthetic, perhaps, more manufactured – but easier. The famous DuPont slogan – Better Living Through Chemistry – is shown to live up to its promise. When Powers mimics DuPont by quoting from advertisements from the Industrial Processes Group of Clare Material Solutions, he is not indulging in some heavy-handed irony:

Life After Chemistry

> No, there's nothing wrong with this picture. There's nothing wrong with your magazine or printers either. We just thought you'd like to see what life would look like without those life-threatening chemical processes you read so much about these days [...] Life without chemistry would look a lot like no life at all.

Less knowledge is not the answer. Better knowledge is. Chemical processes are not the problem. They're the rules of the game.

It's elementary: your life is chemistry. [Powers 2001, p. 153]

And whatever the cause of Laura's cancer, chemistry is a big part of the attempted cure. She is given taxol, manufactured by Bristol-Myers Squibb – "but Clare sells them cheap materials", her doctor tells her. "I thought the stuff was made with tree bark", Laura says. The doctor replies,

It used to be. Now they use artificial tree bark. Used to take six mature hundred-year-old Pacific yew trees to treat you. Pretty expensive, when you figure yew trees can only be harvested by clear-cutting [...] that's exactly where the science comes in. One of our home-team chemists has figured out how to make, in a test tube, what used to cost an arm and a leg and half a dozen yew trunks. The molecule that does all the good work is so complex that synthesizing an imitation was supposed to have taken years. But so many people were willing to pay so much for it that science has produced a substitute in record time [...] If you just get out of people's way, they'll figure out how to make what people need. [Powers 2001, p. 151f.]

Thus taxol becomes the analogue of DeLillo's Dylar, the "benign counterpart of the Nyodene D menace" as Jack Gladney puts it. More than this, even – for Laura's son Tim comes to see that 'better chemistry' is the solution as well as the problem. He changes gradually from a college drop-out who stages annual hunger vigils in front of the Clare headquarters to a computer scientist at MIT who writes a program that predicts protein folding from sequence data. With that capability at their disposal,

people might create molecules to do anything. The team found itself staring at a universal chemical assembly plant at the level of the human cell. Together with a score of other machines just then coming into existence, their program promised to make anything the damaged cell called out for. [Powers 2001, p. 355].

And in the exhausted depths of her terminal illness, Laura herself sees that, even if Clare products did cause her condition, that is not ultimately where the problem lies. She is one of the millions who have willed companies like Clare into existence. These companies do no more and no less than make things, and this is what everyone wants them to do.

"People want everything", she whispers. "That's their problem." Even when Don suggests that one of the products being scrutinized in the legal proceedings is a Clare herbicide that she used on her garden, she sees that the dispute has no real meaning.

> It makes no difference whether this business gave her cancer. They have given her everything else. Taken her life and molded it in every way imaginable, plus six degrees beyond imagining. Changed her life so greatly that not even cancer can change it more than halfway back. [Powers 2001, p. 320]

Is Powers promoting anti-capitalist dissent, or fatalism? It seems more likely that he is advocating no simple polarities; rather, Heise (2002) argues that his position is informed by modern commentaries on risk that present it as an inseparable component of the techno-economic system. According to sociologist Ulrich Beck (1992), "in advanced modernity, the social production of *wealth* is systematically associated with the social production of *risks*". Not only are such risks inevitable and pervasive, but they are uncertain and unpredictable even to specialists. Heise cites the work of historian of technology Thomas Hughes (1989), who, she says, argues that "these large-scale systems into which technologies are embedded have become so complex that they can no longer be easily understood or controlled, and therefore they give rise to risks whose origins and outcomes are extremely difficult to trace and to manage" (Heise 2002). While DeLillo explores the unnerving effects of such a cultural environment on its hapless inhabitants, Powers confronts more directly the question of who is to blame for it. His conclusion appears to be that blame becomes itself an outdated and meaningless notion. The industrialized world has its own ecology, its own food chains through which materials and energy are processed (as Powers illustrates with a dissection of the components of a disposable camera and their provenance), its own inevitable dangers and lines of defense. This ecosystem is self-sustaining: even Tim Bodey's protein-drug technology becomes, at the very end of the book, the foundation for a new corporation, a future pharmaceuticals company. 'Plastic' stands proxy for all our technologies when Powers says that "Plastic happens; that is all we need to know on earth" (Powers 1998, p. 771).

Does this mean that corporations and chemicals companies are not responsible for the ailments that their products and by-products may induce – that we are *all* somehow 'responsible' for them? Powers avoids that kind of evasive, anodyne conclusion. For one thing, we cannot but feel the injustice of Laura Bodey's fate. Moreover, corporate malpractice in chemical companies unquestionably does occur, as the thalidomide and Bhopal incidents reveal; and the public-relations blandishments of Clare, regardless of whether or not the reader thinks their products have caused Laura's cancer, are all too reminiscent of the responses to such cases. But *Gain* succeeds in showing how a simplistic 'little guy against big business' narrative does us no favors either. And most of all, it illustrates the error and indeed the danger of imagining that the hazards of chemical manufacturing somehow stem from an intrinsic malignity within chemistry itself.

5. Portentous Polymers

If Richard Powers seems to have done his homework, that is because he started it early. He says that as a child he always felt "destined to be a scientist", and he read Darwin's *Voyage of the Beagle* in fourth grade. He began studying at the University of Illinois as a physics major, but then switched to literature. He worked as a computer programmer after graduating, and continued to read about science. His other novels have also explored scientific themes: *Prisoner's Dilemma* (1988), as the title suggests, took in the game theory of nuclear conflict, while his most well-known work, *The Gold Bug Variations* (1991) used metaphors from genetics and computer science.

A similar background of scientific training informs *Gravity's Rainbow*, the book that made Thomas Pynchon a cult figure. Pynchon is famously reclusive, to the extent that there are no publicity photographs of him and the few facts that are known about his life have been gleaned only through the detective work of his obsessively curious fans. He studied engineering physics at Cornell in the 1950s before serving in the navy. He then returned to Cornell to study English, during which time he was taught by Vladimir Nabokov. But like Powers, he returned to technical work before his writing career took off, and in the early 1960s he was employed as an 'engineering aide' at Boeing. He worked on *Gravity's Rainbow* for seven years, completing it in 1973. It is said (although we should always be cautious about the Pynchon legend) that the novel was unanimously selected for the 1974 Pulitzer prize, but was turned down by the advisory board, who considered it not only 'turgid' and 'overwritten' but also 'obscene'.

No doubt the same charges (and worse) were leveled at Rabelais in the sixteenth century, whose *Gargantua* and *Pantagruel* are again the obvious literary forebears of Pynchon's extraordinary, sprawling work. Peppered with songs, scatology, science, and mathematical formulae (it is the only book I have ever seen with an *algebraic* joke), *Gravity's Rainbow* is impossible to categorize or to summarize. It is a text of Joycean complexity which eschews the conventions of traditional narrative even to the extent of allowing the central character to fade from the stage many pages before the end. For the present purposes, we need to know only that the events the book describes take place towards and immediately after the end of the Second World War, and that they are concerned with the development of the rocket program that began with the German V2 flying bombs, the arcing trajectory of which is alluded to in the book's title. What emerges is that the tail end of the war begins to look less like a conflict of nations and more like a business enterprise orchestrated by a conglomerate of companies within which the German chemicals cartel IG Farben looms large.

As in *White Noise*, the reader is thrown off balance, uncertain what is 'real' and what is 'fantasy'. Whereas DeLillo used such a narrative mode to mirror the vague forebodings of risk and danger in the minds of his characters, Pynchon recreates in this way a sense of the paranoia felt by his protagonist Tyrone Slothrop – Pynchon's equivalent of Joseph Heller's Yossarian, the wise-cracking, sympathetic yet helpless everyman – who is thrown this way and that by forces beyond his control or understanding. "Pynchon gives the impression of a politico-economic process taking place which can only be glimpsed and which seems to baffle logic", according to literary theorist David Seed (1988).

IG Farben is (or at least seems to be) the prime mover in this grand, behind-the-scenes plot. It is, of course, the ideal choice for such a villain, for the cartel manufactured Zyklon B poison gas and ran the Buna-

Werke concentration camp on the outskirts of Auschwitz, comparable to the rocket-building labor camp at Peenemünde that hosts one of Pynchon's set-pieces in *Gravity's Rainbow*. Seed says that Pynchon "concentrates on IG as a process, a steady relentless agglomeration of power through mergers, takeovers and contracts [...] IG becomes the model of the totalitarian state". It is, indeed, the prototype of the modern military-industrial complex; but one in which the tentacles of power are entwined with elements of the occult and chthonic.

This again could be interpreted as a kind of ecological 'rage against the machine', and indeed the critic J.D. Black has, in Seed's words, "located Pynchon in a tradition of anti-technological dissent which presents man as the destroyer of a vitalistic earth" (Seed 1988). According to Black (1980), Pynchon "describes a Nature which has been ruthlessly violated, quantified, and technologically transformed by the irreversible, exhaustive process of history."

But again this seems simplistic. It is true that Pynchon expresses a profound distaste for the military-industrial complex: he has said that,

> As well-known President and unintentional Luddite D.D. Eisenhower prophesied when he left office, there is now a permanent power establishment of admirals, generals and corporate CEO's, up against whom us average poor bastards are completely outclassed, although Ike didn't put it quite that way. We are all supposed to keep tranquil and allow it to go on, even though, because of the data revolution, it becomes every day less possible to fool any of the people any of the time. [Pynchon 1984]

But that is a complaint about power structures, not technology *per se*. And in *Gravity's Rainbow* Pynchon is more interested in exploring the genealogy of this structure than in formulating an anti-technological stance.

A mysterious but central role in the nascent rocket technology is played by an ominous polymer called Imipolex G, which was developed in 1939 for IG Farben by Professor Laszlo Jamf. Jamf was taught by a pupil of August Wilhelm Hofmann, the German chemist whose student William Perkin triggered IG Farben's original line of business in dye manufacture with his discovery of the mauve coal-tar dye in 1856. (It is hinted darkly that there is some deep symbolic significance in that 'unfolding' of a new color from the molecules of long-dead organisms in coal-tar.) Jamf is Pynchon's Faust figure, whom he explicitly links in the novel to the character of Rothwang in Fritz Lang's *Metropolis*, and to Lang's diabolical Dr Mabuse, a psychologist who seeks world domination. Like the archetypically mad scientist, Jamf wants to cross forbidden boundaries, to blur the distinction between the living and the lifeless. And characteristically, Pynchon's chemistry borders on the sinisterly plausible:

> 'Silicon, boron, phosphorus [says Jamf] – these can replace carbon, and can bond to nitrogen instead of hydrogen [...] move beyond life, towards the inorganic. Here there is no frailty, no mortality – here is Strength, and the Timeless.' Then in his well-known finale, as he wiped away the scrawled C–H on his chalkboard and wrote, in enormous letters, Si–N. [Pynchon 1995, p. 580]

Which of course spells out also: sin.

In tracing the origins of Imipolex G, Pynchon takes us deep into the early history of polymer science. The material is, he says,

> traceable back to early research done at du Pont. Plasticity has its grand tradition and main stream, which happens to flow by way of du Pont and their famous employee Carothers, known as the Great Synthesist. His classic study of large molecules spanned the decade of the twenties and brought us directly to nylon, which not only is a delight to the fetishist and a convenience to the armed insurgent, but was also, at the time and well within the System, an announcement of Plasticity's central canon: that chemists were no longer to be at the mercy of Nature. They could decide now what properties they wanted a molecule to have, and then go ahead and build it. At du Pont, the next step after nylon was to introduce aromatic rings into the polyamide chain. Pretty soon a whole family of 'aromatic polymers' had arisen: aromatic polyamides, polycarbonates, polyethers, polysulfanes. [Pynchon 1995, p. 249f.]

Notice again this listing of names that will mean nothing to the average reader: a list that serves to say '*You* might not have a clue what these things are, but someone else does, and that's why they have more power than you do.' And to rub this point in, Pynchon describes Jamf's chemical accomplishments in terms technical enough to suggest that again there is an intellect behind all of this that far exceeds the poor reader's:

Jamf, among others, then proposed, logically, dialectically, taking the pa-
rental polyamide sections of the new chain, and looping *them* around into
rings too, giant 'heterocyclic' rings, to alternate with the aromatic rings.
This principle was easily extended to other precursor molecules. A desired monomer of high molecular weight could be synthesized to order,
bent into its heterocyclic ring, clasped, and strung in a chain along with
the more 'natural' benzene or aromatic rings. Such chains would be
known as 'aromatic heterocyclic polymers.' One hypothetical chain that
Jamf came up with, just before the war, was later modified into Imipolex
G. [Pynchon 1995, p. 250]

One might imagine that Pynchon could have got away with making this
stuff up; but I am not sure that he could have made it sound authentic
unless it really was (as, in essence, it is).

What is so special about Imipolex G? True to the nature of the narrative, Pynchon succeeds brilliantly in uniting the scientifically plausible,
indeed even the prescient, with the wickedly sensual:

Imipolex G is the first plastic that is actually *erectile*. Under suitable
stimuli, the chains grow cross-links, which stiffen the molecule and increase intermolecular attraction so that this Peculiar Polymer runs far
outside the known phase diagrams, from limp rubbery amorphous to
amazing perfect tesselation, hardness, brilliant transparency, high resis-
tance to temperature, weather, vacuum, shock of any kind [...] Evidently
the stimulus would have had to be electronic. [Pynchon 1995, p. 699]

It was, in other words, what we would now call a smart material, the re-
sponsive skin of a deadly, almost sentient and all too phallic smart bomb.

For those not already familiar with Pynchon's style, these extracts,
even though considerably edited, will perhaps serve to indicate the difficulty of summarizing what he means to say. His method is, in a Joycean
manner, to work with allusion, to be constantly cross-referencing and
hinting at broader themes. In *Gravity's Rainbow*, everything is part of a
murky plan, everything refers to something else. Entire lexicons have
been composed to help the reader navigate through the book's complex
pathways.

But what must surely concern us here is that Pynchon has chosen to
place the chemical industry at the core of his Great Scheme. His implication is that, if Knowledge is Power, then knowledge of how to *synthesize*
things offers the greatest power of all. In a rather different idiom and cer-

tainly with a rather different setting than either DeLillo or Powers, Pynchon anticipates their conclusion that applied (that is, industrial) chemistry has more to tell us about the way modern life is structured than does any other applied science.

But it takes real understanding of the science to realize this, and to be able to express it in a literary context. Understanding; but also something more – something that I can only think of as a kind of materialist aesthetic, a delight in the smells and sights and textures and responsiveness of the substances and fabrics that make up our lives. This, I suspect, is a rather rare attribute today, and the conjunction of that with the skills needed to articulate it is rarer still. It is perhaps no surprise, then, that the writers I have discussed are exceptions in contemporary literature; and moreover they seem likely to remain so while chemistry continues to be seen as an unfashionable, even a moribund science. If that is a discouraging note on which to close, let us nevertheless note that these three texts offer a far richer basis than is typically found in today's mass media for discussing the impacts, origins, benefits, and dangers of technology in modern life. That debate is being prompted in particular by the emergence of biotechnology and nanotechnology, and fictional explorations of both these topics have tended to be predicated on lurid extrapolations into the future. In *White Noise, Gain* and *Gravity's Rainbow* we find instead perspectives on chemical technology that are clearly rooted in the past and the present; it is surely from here that any debate should begin.

References

Bacon, F.: 1620 (1944), *Novum Organum*, Wiley, New York.

Beck, U.: 1992, *Risk Society: Towards a New Modernity*, trans. M. Ritter, Sage, London.

Black, J.D.: 1980, 'Probing a post-Romantic palaeontology: Thomas Pynchon's *Gravity's Rainbow*', *Boundary*, **2**, 8ii, p. 233.

Caldwell, G.: 1998, 'On the soapbox' (book review), *Boston Sunday Globe*, 7 June, C4.

Conroy, M.: 2003, 'From tombstone to tabloid: authority figured in *White Noise*', in: H. Bloom (ed.), *Don DeLillo's White Noise*, Chelsea House, Broomall, Philadelphia, p. 153.

Debus, A.G.: 1978, *Man and Nature in the Renaissance*, Cambridge UP, Cambridge.

DeLillo, D.: 1984, *White Noise*, Viking Penguin, New York.

Donovan, L.A.L.: 1975, *Philosophical Chemistry in the Scottish Enlightenment*, Edinburgh UP, Edinburgh.

Heise, U.K.: 2002, 'Toxins, drugs, and global systems: risk and narrative in the contemporary novel', *American Literature*, **74**, no. 4.

Hughes, T.P.: 1989, *American Genesis: A Century of Invention and Technological Enthusiasm, 1870-1970*, Viking, New York.

LeClair, T.: 2003, 'Closing the loop: *White Noise*', in: H. Bloom (ed.), *Don DeLillo's White Noise*, Chelsea House, Broomall, Philadelphia, p. 5.

Lentricchia, F. (ed.): 1991, *New Essays on White Noise*, Cambridge UP, Cambridge.

Levi, P.: 1985, *The Periodic Table*, Abacus, London.

Levi, P: 1987, *The Monkey's Wrench*, Penguin, London.

Medawar, P.: 1984, 'Two conceptions of science', in: *Pluto's Republic*, Oxford University Press, Oxford, p. 35.

Molesworth, C.: 1991, '*Don DeLillo's Perfect Starry Night*', in: F. Lentricchia (ed.), *Introducing Don DeLillo*, Duke University Press, Durham, pp. 143-57.

Moses, M.V.: 1991, 'Lust removed from nature', F. Lentricchia (ed.), *Introducing Don DeLillo*, Duke UP, Durham, p. 63.

Multhauf, R. P.: 1993, *The Origins of Chemistry*, Gordon & Breach, Langhorne, Pennsylvania.

Osteen, M.: 2000, *American Magic and Dread*, University of Pennsylvania Press, Philadelphia.

Powers, R.: 2001, *Gain*, Vintage, London.

Pynchon, T.: 1984, 'Is it O.K. to be a Luddite?', *The New York Times Book Review*, 28 October, pp. 40-1.

Pynchon, T.: 1995, *Gravity's Rainbow*, Penguin, London.

Rabelais, F.: 1532, 1534 (1955), *Gargantua and Pantegruel*, Penguin, Harmondsworth.

Schummer, J.: 2004, 'Why do chemists perform experiments?', in: D. Sobczynska, P. Zeidler & E. Zielonacka-Lis (eds.), *Chemistry in the Philosophical Melting Pot*, Peter Lang, Frankfurt, pp. 395-410.

Seed, D.: 1988, *The Fictional Labyrinths of Thomas Pynchon*, Macmillan, Basingstoke.

CHAPTER 5

POPULARIZING CHEMISTRY: HANDS-ON AND HANDS-OFF

David Knight

Department of Philosophy, University of Durham, 50 Old Elvet, Durham DH1 3HN, U.K.; d.m.knight@durham.ac.uk

Hands-off people appreciate, enjoy, and support chemistry, recognizing it as a useful and illuminating activity; hands-on people practice or are going to practice chemistry. Popularizing aims to increase the number in the first group, and also to recruit for the second. Chemistry at present enjoys low esteem: to whom then, and how, should it be popularized; how was this done in its golden age in the nineteenth century; and how is popularizing related to the coming of professional science during that period? Looking at nineteenth-century examples may give us hints today about what has gone wrong, and how chemistry (which is clearly useful, and relevant to today's problems) might again be made exciting and respectable in our culture of suspicion.

1. Introduction[*]

Linus Pauling said, "Chemistry is wonderful. I feel sorry for people who don't know anything about chemistry. They are missing an important source of happiness" (Gaither & Cavasos-Gaither 2002, p. 118). Most people do not feel that. What might be done, and what used to be done, to make chemistry popular? I had thought that 'hands-on' might distinguish those active in chemistry from 'hands-off' supporters, interested but not participating: but now I am not sure.

---

[*] This chapter was first presented at the 5th International Conference on the History of Chemistry, Lisbon, Portugal, 6-10 September 2005.

I happen to sit on the Royal Society of Chemistry's Committee for Promoting Chemistry to the Public. I have been a member of the society since I was a student reading chemistry forty-five years ago (before it was Royal), but was invited (I suppose) to join that committee in the hope that an historian might advise on restoring the reputation of the science to where it was in the long-distant past. The traditional model of popularizing was that one took a little chemistry, diluted it, and added sugar to make it go down: but this has not worked. There is a famous book-review by a child: 'this book told me more about elephants than I wanted to know'. That is how many people feel about being told what professors and academicians are up to: but with chemistry they may also feel alarm. They think of pollution, slow poisoning, and weapons of mass destruction.

I am (like that committee) puzzled about the nature of 'the public' – no doubt they are and were really publics. Recently the 'SciPer' project at Leeds and Sheffield has been sampling the science in popular periodicals, mostly from Britain, in the nineteenth century – and this has resulted in three books,[1] in which chemistry duly features (though not very largely). So I hope now to share some uncertainties, hoping for clarification.

There seem to be three questions that we can profitably have at the back of our minds:

1. Who is chemistry being popularized to, and perhaps why and where?
2. How was it done in some supposedly heroic better past?
3. How do popularizing and professionalizing fit together?

2. Who are the Public?

On the first one, the RSC committee tried to identify publics. One was the elite: graduates, opinion formers, journalists, members of parliament. This was a group not unlike the Cambridge undergraduates who flocked to Bishop Watson in the eighteenth century (Archer & Haley 2005), or

---

[1] Cantor & Shuttleworth 2004, Cantor *et al.* 2004, Hensen *et al.* 2004, and my essay-review (Knight 2005b).

the wealthy intelligentsia who heard Michael Faraday at the Royal Institution in the nineteenth. The problem is that these are a critical group, with interests and preconceptions, looking perhaps for a good story rather than sober science.

Then there are children. School science is difficult and dogmatic (Thomas Kuhn [1963] thought necessarily so) and chemistry is not very excitingly taught in these days of 'health and safety' legislation. Such manual skills as boring corks, bending glass, and handling concentrated acids, the experience of smelling and tasting (on purpose or by accident) unpleasant gases and fluids, and making flashes and bangs are denied to children today. So ways are needed to arouse enthusiasm and direct curiosity, so that some will become chemists, hands-on people, and others sympathetic, hands-off adults.

The interested but unsophisticated are another group, reading newspapers that avoid long words and long sentences, and who may pick up the personal rather than the abstract. They should not be despised as unfit to learn about so arcane a science as chemistry, which can and has been made accessible through obituaries and biographies, and the writings of great communicators, like Justus Liebig in his *Familiar Letters*. And finally there are the taxpayers and the consumers, who pay one way or another for chemistry; and are thus essential for its future.

3. What Used to Happen?

So to the next question: what happened in the past? In the nineteenth century, chemistry was in the useful category of 'entertaining knowledge'. Public lectures attracted big audiences, Antoine Fourcroy in Paris and Humphry Davy in London being notable – they made professing a performance art, competing with metropolitan theatres and concert halls (Knight 2002). There were black markets in tickets and one-way traffic arrangements to ease congestion. Chemistry could appeal to body, mind, and spirit (Knight 2004): an experimental science, it was a craft or 'art' that required manual skills (Faraday's only formal book was *Chemical Manipulation*, 1827), an exciting body of knowledge in the throes of theoretical upset, and momentous in its promise to cast light on matter and mind, elective affinities (Goethe 1971, Richards 2002), God and nature. Chemistry like surgery was both hands-on and hands-off, a science of the secondary qualities (colors, tastes, and smells), where thinking had to be done with fingers, nose, and eyes as well as in the armchair. It was a part of high culture, making Davy in great demand at salons and dinner parties; but also promised to be useful, for example in cleaning up smoky London:[2]

> O Chemistry, *attractive* maid,
> Descend in pity to our aid!
> Come with thy all-pervading gasses,
> Thy crucibles, retorts, and glasses
> Thy fearful energies and wonders,
> Thy dazzling lights and mimic thunders!
> Let Carbon in thy train be seen,
> Dark Azote, and fair Oxygene,
> And Woolaston, and Davy guide
> The car that bears thee, at thy side.
> If any power can any how
> Abate these nuisances, 'tis thou.

Audiences, men and women, watched for the most part, as the lecturer (often very near the front row) did the experiments, which might be spectacular – as when potassium, and miners' safety lamps, were the subject. Anna Laetitia Barbauld, in her poem '1811', wrote how, for American tourists in decayed London, some future antiquarian might (Barbauld 1995):

> Call up sages whose capacious mind
> Left in its course a track of light behind;
> Point where mute crowds on Davy's lips reposed,
> And nature's coyest secrets were disclosed;
> Join with their Franklin, Priestley's injured name,
> Whom, then, each continent shall proudly claim.

In 1811 the coyest secret was that chlorine was an element, but the sexy imagery takes up some of Davy's pantheistic rhetoric about Nature.

---

[2]   Luttrell 1993, pp. 530-1; 'Woolaston' was William Hyde Wollaston, metallurgist.

4. Hands-off to Hands-on?

Some of these audiences went into hands-on chemistry. S.T. Coleridge wrote to his friend Davy (Knight 2005a) for advice about setting up a laboratory in the Lake District with his fellow-poet William Wordsworth, and for anybody thus tempted 'portable laboratories' were available, wooden boxes fitted up with apparatus, used in schools and at home, suitable for both serious and recreational chemistry. John Dalton's friend William Henry sold various sizes, at fifteen, eleven, or six and a half guineas – James Watt junior bought one of the expensive ones.[3] They might be devised to accompany a chemistry book. Then photography became a craze by the middle of the nineteenth century, requiring expertise in handling apparatus and chemicals. Hands-on chemistry included the spice of danger. But for those who remained hands-off, it was the dynamical character of chemistry that seemed most attractive. Priestley had prophesied that natural philosophers working in chemistry, optics, and electricity would eclipse Newton himself, getting below the surface, and exploring the underlying forces (Priestley 1966, p. xv). This excited poets and artists, as we see in recent studies of Percy Shelley and of Coleridge, both well-read in chemistry and medicine (Ruston 2005, Vickers 2005), and of Joseph Turner (Hamilton 2001); chemistry, the leading science of the day, was moving away from a clockwork universe.[4]

Working men (skilled artisans and craftsmen rather than laborers) could also get to lectures, at Mechanics' Institutes lit (chemically) by gas making evening classes possible, and at peripatetic meetings of organizations like the British Association for the Advancement of Science, founded on a German model, and itself the model for societies in the USA, France, and Australia. Gradually museums, originally intended for ladies and gentlemen, were opened to a more general public – even on Sundays, after a struggle, in Sabbatarian Britain. Exhibitions illustrating science, technology, and general progress attracted huge audiences and

---

[3]   Henry, 1801, pp. 3, 14; 3rd ed., 1803, p. vi. A guinea was one pound, one shilling (£1.05), the unit used for gentlemen's fees, prizes, and luxuries.

[4]   William Paley's *Natural Theology* (1802), the classic statement of the clockwork metaphor, will be published in a new edition, ed. M.D. Eddy and D.M. Knight, Oxford UP, 2006.

generated vast enthusiasm. Sometimes, as in London's 'Crystal Palace' in 1851, the building housing the exhibition was itself a marvel of high technology. Many of the exhibits there were broadly chemical, and international juries compared them in various classes and awarded prizes. Davy had been the apostle of applied science, making big promises (blank checks on the future); by the mid century, science (especially chemistry) was delivering utility. Ballyhoo was appropriate.

5. Publications

Reading remained the major way into chemistry for those fired by lectures or displays. Jane Marcet, excited by Davy's lectures but needing something more systematic, wrote for girls in the same position her *Conversations on Chemistry,* 1806, a best-seller which turned the young Faraday (a bookbinder's apprentice) towards the science. Hers was not a chemistry of 'separate spheres'; the girls do experiments, doubtless with a portable laboratory, and learn the latest science. In the second quarter of the nineteenth century, the price of books in Britain dropped sharply by about a half, so that they ceased to be a luxury – new technology, longer print runs, and (temporary) collapse of the copyright system all played a part (St Clair 2004). Categories of chemistry books were fuzzy: there were some formal textbooks, for students of medicine and pharmacy, but in the first half of the century many were aimed at general readers keen on self-help (Lundgren & Bensaude-Vincent 2000). They had to be accessible and attractive, unlike textbooks efficiently and systematically covering the syllabus for an examination that students had to pass.

There were from the late eighteenth century informal scientific journals, in Britain published by Alexander Tilloch *(Philosophical Magazine),* William Nicholson *(Journal of Natural Philosophy)*, and Thomas Thomson *(Annals of Philosophy):* Nicholson and Thomson were both chemists with substantial publications in the science. 'Taxes on knowledge', which inhibited periodicals, were not lifted until the mid century, and postage was expensive until then also. But nevertheless in their heyday these journals, offering speedy publication, had published some original papers, reprinted papers from elsewhere, reviewed books and meetings, and included correspondence (sometimes contentious). The editors sought to build up a community of regular readers, who could feel that they were part of the great enterprise of advancing knowledge. They were predominantly, but not exclusively, concerned with chemistry: Thomson wrote that "our *Annals* must contain a greater proportion of Chemistry, which is making a rapid progress, than of those sciences which are in a great measure stationary" (*Annals of Philosophy,* 1 [1813], p. iv).

They were with others all swallowed up in due course by the increasingly formal *Philosophical Magazine,* as science became more specialized and less widely attractive, and the scientific community more self-conscious. In the second half of the century we have William Crookes' *Chemical News* and his *Quarterly Journal of Science,* Norman Lockyer's *Nature,* the *Mechanics' Magazine,* and *Science Gossip,* which despite its promising title was mostly a sober work of natural history – but chemistry was much less prominent in these last four. By 1900 it had become forbidding rather than accessible. Original papers were in a compressed style, full of equations, and written for experts. There was no longer room for the interested experimenter with his portable laboratory to make a serious contribution fit to appear in print alongside serious researchers' work.

6. Professions, Specialization, and Popularizing

That brings us to our third question, for chemistry had become professionalized and this had a powerful and continuing effect on its popularity. Undergraduate degrees in chemistry were on offer by the middle years of the nineteenth century, and the Prussian victory over the French Second Empire in 1870 was seen as a vindication of the German educational system. It had an effect comparable to the Sputnik of 1957 in promoting scientific education. In England a Royal Commission headed by the Duke of Devonshire promoted Scientific Instruction in a series of reports. Such things can be an excuse for inaction, but in this case they were acted upon. An unintended consequence was the rise of what have been called 'two cultures', scientific and humanistic, poorly communicating with each other because they have had different and specialized educations (Knight 2004b).

When two or three historians of chemistry are collected together, the conversation tends to turn to 'profession' and what it means in different times and places. For us it is enough that it involves education, jargon, self-regulation, and recognized status and expertise. That seems to have happened to chemists in the later nineteenth century. Professions thus serve the public, but they can also be conspiracies against the public; as the longstanding jokes about, and doubtful popularity of, lawyers, clergy, and doctors indicate. A naval historian (Rodger 2004, p. 201) remarks of officers in Britain's 'Glorious Revolution' of 1688/9 that most "seem to have taken a professional attitude to the revolution, in the sense that they thought first of their careers". We live in a culture of suspicion, where experts are seen as self-interested and pompous and are distrusted. 'Alternative' therapies, religions, and beliefs about 'chemicals' continue to abound; confusion about the 'organic' is as bad as it ever was in previous centuries.

Suspicion is not new. A journal[5] aimed at artisans, *The Chemist,* was rude about Davy, for whom chemistry had been a vehicle for social mobility, propelling him from provincial poverty into the Presidency of the Royal Society and a baronetcy:

> he professes a sort of royal science [...] he has no appearance of labouring for the people. He brings not the science which he pursues down to their level; he stands aloof amidst dignitaries, nobles and philosophers; and apparently takes no concern in the improvement of those classes for whom our labours are intended, and to whom we look for support. Amidst all the great efforts which have been lately made to promote scientific instruction among the working classes, and amidst all the patronage which these efforts have found among opulent and clever men, it has been with regret that we have sought in vain to trace one exertion or smile of encouragement bestowed on such efforts by the President of the Royal Society. [*The Chemist,* 1 (1824), pp. vi-vii]

Davy was indeed snobbish and alarmed at the 'March of Mind', but distaste for pundits on the one hand, and for plebeians and their popularizers

---

[5]   The editor's name was Montgradieu (possibly Montgradien); Martyn Berry, personal communication, 19/8/05.

on the other, was to become a feature of the science of the later nineteenth century, and lead to the 'dilution' model of getting chemistry across.

Faraday, Davy's disciple and successor at the Royal Institution, lectured brilliantly to children, notably on 'The Chemical History of a Candle', in a tradition that still continues and is now more democratically available, on television. He did not feel that it was in any way beneath him to popularize, but the next generation did often think that way, and their successors often do. Serious science, to be noted in university promotion committees, does not include popular writing or lecturing.

We can ask what did interest people who went to hear Faraday or his contemporaries, and it was clearly not only ideas but also facts. Lectures at the Royal Institution included much on explosives and weapons – the 'military-industrial complex' of Eisenhower's famous speech went back a hundred years or so. Poisons, like explosions, have also always drawn audiences, who might not have gone to hear August Hofmann talk about molecular structures, even though he had croquet balls and rods as his visual aids. In the mid twentieth century, young Oliver Sacks delighted in chemistry, practical and factual, which helped him focus his life in wartime London (Sacks 2001). He, and people like me a little later, learned chemistry not so very different from that of the late nineteenth century, and often in laboratories of that date; definitely hands-on.

In the professionalizing Victorian age, popularizers also began to be professionals, people with a foot in both camps, of science and of journalism and other writing; and like other Grub Street hacks, made a living out of it (Fyfe 2005). But they were tolerated rather than much admired by the scientific community; and indeed popularizing science (and its history) is still problematic – we see it as simplifying, dumbing-down, sensationalizing, and often simply misreporting (Laszlo 2005), and all too often that is what it is. We must have all groaned over amateurish histories which ignore recent scholarship.

7. The Unpopularity of Chemistry

This applied to all the sciences, and yet chemistry now writhes beneath popular dislike to a greater degree than other sciences. This is partly because, as Lavoisier hoped, its language looks like algebra, but with jaw-cracking long names – the jargon is hard to break into, and nowadays proficiency in mathematics has become more important than manual dexterity. Then, the conflict of 1914-18 was 'the chemists' war', where poison gas particularly struck the public imagination as a horrifying manifestation of the science. At the same time, with Einstein and his contemporaries, chemistry was displaced from its elite and fundamental position. It was plausible to say that it was reduced to physics (though really no truer than to say that architecture is reduced to physics), and that the new Newton would be found among physicists. Chemists had an essential role to play in the new teams and groups which in the twentieth century came to replace the lone genius like Faraday, but in physics or biology it seemed everyone's essential service-science – not very glamorous.

Chemistry seemed to have the cure for pollution like London's, where *Punch* commented in 1862 upon hopes for a clean-up:

> The passenger of Chelsea boat
> Unwonted salmon shall admire,
> Where dogs and cats he used [to] note,
> Defunct that on thy breast did float,
> Emitting exhalations dire. [*Punch,* 15th November 1862, p. 198]

In the event, it was engineers laying a new sewage system rather than Faraday's experiments with chlorine that brought improvement. Chemical industry has since acquired a reputation for polluting, and the pharmaceutical industry for profiteering.

8. Conquering or Worshipping Nature?

What could be done, if like King Canute we hope to turn this tide? Chemistry was a problematic science for natural theologians, because while astronomers wonderingly contemplated the starry heavens, and natural historians the eye of a fly, chemists busily sought to improve on nature (Brooke & Cantor 1998, Knight 2004c). This led to a rhetoric of conquest (Schummer 2006), deeply unpopular in our 'green' days. The rhetoric of chemistry has long been macho (Knight 2000a), full of images from warfare, but it might be wiser to return to a dynamical picture of revealing the powers inherent in nature so that we can use them, rather than torturing Nature ('putting her to the question', like a suspected witch), or conquering her.

In his published inaugural lecture of 1802, which Mary Shelley picked up and used in writing *Frankenstein* (Shelley 1999, pp. 17-24), Davy used a sexy rhetoric in which chemistry was a branch of sublime philosophy, and the chemist:

> Not contented with what is found upon the surface of the earth, [...] has penetrated into her bosom, and has even searched the bottom of the ocean for the purpose of allaying the restlessness of his desires, or of extending and increasing his power. [Davy 1839-40, vol. 2, pp. 318, 320; Woof et al. 1997]

Once conquered, Nature could be put on a pedestal and worshipped:

> Oh, most magnificent and noble Nature!
> Have I not worshipped thee with such a love
> As never mortal man before displayed?
> Adored thee in thy majesty of visible creation,
> And searched into thy hidden and mysterious ways
> As Poet, as Philosopher, as Sage? [Knight 1998, p. 9]

In our post-Freudian age, we probably could not, with a straight face, write quite that way about the scientific urge, though we should note that Davy's lectures and writings were very popular with women – this was before the prudish Victorian era. But we might be able to make chemistry less down-to-earth and prosy than we often do, maybe giving a new frisson to hands-on and hands-off.

Chemists were culturally active, Davy analyzing colors used in ancient wall-paintings from Pompeii and elsewhere (through his friendship with the sculptor Antonio Canova [Knight 2000b]); while Wollaston wrote, also for the Royal Society's *Philosophical Transactions,* on 'fairy rings' in the grass, and with Sir Thomas Lawrence, President of the Royal Academy, a paper on why the eyes in portraits follow you around. In conservation and restoration, the role of chemists remains essential, and that should be good for the reputation of the science. And we still, like Goethe, use the idea of personal chemistry in analyzing human relationships.

Boundaries between sciences are certainly social constructs, and the science we call 'chemistry', with its inorganic, organic, and physical branches, in institutes and departments is only one way of exploring and describing the world. It might come to an end, as some fear: though materials science, nanotechnology, molecular biology *etc.* would continue under different umbrellas. What if it did come to an end? We might be perturbed, but as historians we need not worry – the Roman Empire still supports a small army of historians investigating its affairs, and there are much fuller records for the Empire of Chemistry.

References

Archer, M. & Haley, C. (eds.): 2005, *The 1702 Chair of Chemistry at Cambridge: Transformation and Change*, Cambridge UP, Cambridge.

Barbauld, A.L.: 1995, 'Eighteen hundred and eleven', in: A. Ashfield (ed.), *Romantic Women Poets, 1770-1838*, Manchester UP, Manchester, p. 25.

Brooke, J.H. & Cantor, G.: 1998, *Reconstructing Nature: the Engagement of Science and Religion*, Clark, Edinburgh.

Cantor, G. & Shuttleworth, S. (eds.): 2004, *Science Serialized: Representations of the Sciences in Nineteenth-century Periodicals*, MIT Press, Cambridge MA.

Cantor, G.; Dawson, G.; Gooday, G.; Noakes, R.; Shuttleworth, S. & Topham, J.R.: 2004, *Science in the Nineteenth-century Periodical*, Cambridge UP, Cambridge.

Davy, H.: 1839-40, *Collected Works*, Smith Elder, London.

Fyfe, A.: 2005, 'Conscientious Workmen or Booksellers' Hacks? The Professional Identities of Science Writers in the Mid-Nineteenth Century', *Isis*, **96**, 192-223.

Gaither, C.G. & Cavasos-Gaither, A.E. (eds.): 2002, *Chemically Speaking: a Dictionary of Quotations*, Institute of Physics, Bristol.

Goethe, J.W.v.: 1971, *Elective Affinities* (1809), ed. and trans. R.J. Hollingdale, Penguin, London.

Hamilton, J. (ed.): 2001, *Fields of Influence: Conjunctions of Artists and Scientists, 1815-1860*, Birmingham UP, Birmingham.

Henry, W.: 1801, *Epitome of Chemistry*, Johnson, London (3rd ed. 1803).

Henson, L.; Cantor, G.; Dawson, G.; Noakes, R.; Shuttleworth, S. & Topham, J.R. (eds.): 2004, *Culture and Science in the Nineteenth-century Media*, Ashgate, Aldershot.

Knight, D.M.: 1998, *Humphry Davy: Science and Power*, 2nd ed., Cambridge UP, Cambridge.

Knight, D.M.: 2000a, 'Why is Science so Macho?', *Philosophical Writings*, **14**, 59-65.

Knight, D.M.: 2000b, 'Theory, Practice and Status: Humphry Davy and Thomas Thomson', in: G. Emptoz & P. Achevez (eds.), *Between the Natural and the Artificial: Dyestuffs and Medicines*, Brepols, Tyrnhout, pp. 49-58.

Knight, D.M.: 2002, 'Scientific Lectures: a History of Performance', *Interdisciplinary Science Reviews*, **27**, 217-24.

Knight, D.M.: 2004a, 'The 2003 Edelstein Address: Making Chemistry Popular', *ACS Bulletin for the History of Chemistry*, **29**, 1-8.

Knight, D.M.: 2004b, 'Trabalhando à luz de duas culturas', in: A.M. Alfonso-Goldfarb & M.H.R. Beltran, *Escrevendo a història da ciência: tendencias, propostas e discusões historiográficas*, EDUC, São Paulo, pp. 147-163.

Knight, D.M.: 2004c, *Science and Spirituality: the Volatile Connection*, Routledge, London.

Knight, D.M.: 2005a, 'Humphry Davy the Poet', *Interdisciplinary Science Reviews*, **30**, 356-72.

Knight, D.M.: 2005b, 'Snippets of Science', *Studies in History and Philosophy of Science*, **36**, 618-25.

Kuhn, T.S.: 1963, 'The Function of Dogma in Scientific Research', in: A.C. Crombie (ed.), *Scientific Change*, Oxford UP, Oxford, pp. 347-369.

Laszlo, P.: 2005, 'Unfortunate Trends in the Popularisation of Science', *Interdisciplinary Science Reviews*, **30**, 223-30.

Lundgren, A. & Bensaude-Vincent, B. (eds.): 2000, *Communicating Chemistry: Textbooks and their Audiences, 1789-1939*, Science History, Canton MA.

Luttrell, H.: 1993, 'Letters to Julia, in Rhyme' (1820), in: J.J. McGann (ed.), *The New Oxford Book of Romantic Period Verse*, Oxford UP, Oxford, pp. 530-1.

Priestley, J.: 1966, *The History and Present State of Electricity* (1775), Johnson, New York, vol. 1.

Richards, R.J.: 2002, *The Romantic Conception of Life: Science and Philosophy in the Age of Goethe*, Chicago UP, Chicago IL.

Rodger, N.A.M.: 2004, *The Command of the Ocean: a Naval History of Britain, 1649-1815*, Penguin, London.

Ruston, S.: 2005, *Shelley and Vitality*, Palgrave Macmillan, London.

Sacks, O.: 2001, *Uncle Tungsten: Memories of a Chemical Boyhood*, Picador, London.

Schummer, J.: 2006, 'Providing Metaphysical Sense and Orientation: Nature-Chemistry Relationships in the Popular Historiography of Chemistry', in: I. Malaquias, E. Homburg & M.E. Callapez (eds.) *Proceedings of the 5th International Conference on the History of Chemistry, Lisbon, Portugal, 6-10 September 2005*, Aveiro: Sociedade Portuguesa de Química, 2006, pp. 166-175.

Shelley, M.: 1999, *Frankenstein: the original 1818 text*, ed. D.L. Macdonald & K. Scherf, 2nd ed., Broadview, Peterborough, Ontario.

St Clair, W.: 2004, *The Reading Nation in the Romantic Period*, Cambridge UP, Cambridge.

Vickers, N.: 2005, *Coleridge and the Doctors*, Oxford UP, Oxford.

Woof, R.; Hebron, S. & Tomalin, C.: 1997, *Hyenas in Petticoats: Mary Wollstonecraft and Mary Shelley*, Wordsworth Trust, Grasmere.

CHAPTER 6

LIEBIG OR HOW TO POPULARIZE CHEMISTRY

Marika Blondel-Mégrelis

CNRS, Institut d'Histoire et de Philosophie des Sciences et des Techniques, 13 rue du Four, 75006 Paris, France; marika.blondel@club-internet.fr

The popularization of chemistry was one of Liebig's major tasks. I examine why one of the most famous theoreticians and experimenters of organic chemistry came to this new and rather unusual project in the mid-nineteenth century, and how he managed to create a new image of chemistry: no longer the servant of pharmacists and physicians, it must be considered the most useful of all sciences and the most popular.

1. Introduction

Justus Liebig (1803-73) became famous as early as 1831 notably for his *Fünf-Kugel-Apparat*. The great number of his organic analyses, his theory of organic radicals, his personal and scientific battles, and the extraordinary activities in his international laboratory contributed altogether to make him one of the founders of the new organic chemistry, in opposition to Berzelius and in competition with Dumas and Laurent. Moreover, being a chemist his name was an exceptionally well-known throughout the world, and to this day. Even the European housemaid knew Liebig's soup! Although Laurent and Liebig worked in the same years, mostly on the same materials, thought about the same questions, stumbled on the same difficulties, Laurent's name is much lesser known than that of Liebig.

On his return from Great Britain in 1837, and in association with the project of writing a book on agriculture, Liebig suddenly started an energetic campaign. His idea was to communicate a new image of chemistry throughout the world. By studying texts, memoirs, and correspondence, I analyze the reasons for such a change in Liebig's preoccupation, from doing pure chemistry to constructing a new image of chemistry. I evaluate the implication of such a campaign to understand why his policy eventually worked out. An analysis of his overall approach shows Liebig as a very modern person. He was engaged in advertising, even marketing, and used his scientific reputation to impose non-scientific assertions; and he discussed the relationships between pure and applied science, teaching and research, science and industry, and finally science and power.

2. A Break in Liebig's Trajectory

By the end of the 1830s, Liebig was considered one of the major chemists of the century. He had published great memoirs, including a series of papers in collaboration with Wöhler on bitter almond oil, benzoic acid, and the benzoic radical, which was considered as the dawn of a new period for vegetal chemistry;[1] the famous theoretical memoir on the constitution of organic acids, which questioned the interpretation of organic compounds prevailing since Lavoisier and adapted by the electro-dualistic system. And he continued working with Wöhler on uric acid, "which is beginning to solve the mystery of living substance chemistry"[2] and which announced the chemistry of artificial matters.[3]

Through the invention of his *Fünf-Kugel-Apparat* Liebig was also an established analyst. The apparatus permitted quick and easy measurements of the relative mass of carbon in small organic samples even by non-skilful chemists; a large number of organic analyses were published, which profoundly impressed Berzelius. These analyses were different from the French analyses, from those of Dumas, who made everything only to "glance"; from those of Dumas and Pelletier, who improved their

---

[1]   Berzelius to Liebig and Wöhler, 2 Sept. 1832. For manuscripts and unpublished letters, the following archives have been consulted: Archives de l'Académie des Sciences, Dossier Liebig, and Archiv der Justus Liebig Gesellschaft, Giessen.

[2]   Berzelius to Liebig, 14 Aug. 1839.

[3]   "It must be viewed not only as probable but as certain that we shall produce organic substances in our laboratories. Sugar, salicin and morphine will be artificially produced." (Wöhler & Liebig 1838).

results "with the pen"; and from those of "poor Henry and Plisson who are using bad methods of beginners".[4] Although Liebig's method of organic analyses was only an improvement upon the works of many previous chemists, his laboratory quickly became a place to which many chemists from around the world traveled.[5]

The publication of his *Anleitung zur Analyse organischer Körper* (1837) pushed Liebig to the center of the international stage and made him on par with the most eminent chemists of the time, Berzelius and Dumas. Liebig took over the fifth edition of P. Geiger's *Handbuch der Pharmacie*, which became the *Handbuch der Chemie* (1843), he edited the *Handwörterbuch der reinen und angewandten Chemie* (1842ff.), and since 1832 the *Annalen der Pharmacie*, which he used to make his own ideas widely known.

However, with the two violent pamphlets, 'Der Zustand der Chemie in Österreich' ('The State of Chemistry in Austria', 1838) and, particularly, 'Der Zustand der Chemie in Preussen' (1840, 'The State of Chemistry in Prussia'), Liebig began to act as a propagator of chemistry, a science that had to be known, to be taught, and to be valued. Up to then, chemistry "had been the servant of the physician, because it provided purgatives and emetics [...] it did not exist in the universities apart from medicine and pharmacy". Useful to make soda and soap, to improve iron and steel, to prepare dyes for cotton and silk, it was not considered an element of intellectual education or research of nature (Liebig 1840). "Chemistry proceeds by answering questions, just as physics does. It teaches the way to know the various substances of which the crust of the earth consists, the constitution of animal and vegetable organisms." (Ibid., p. 112)

From 1840 on, Liebig's occupations began to change as reflected in the titles of his publications: *Organic Chemistry in its Applications to Agriculture and Physiology, Animal Chemistry or Organic chemistry in its Applications to Physiology and Pathology, Familiar Letters on Chemistry and its Relation to Commerce, Physiology and Agriculture, Chemische Briefe*, and *Nouvelles Lettres sur la Chimie*, while his scien-

---

[4] Berzelius to Liebig, 8 Jan. 1831, 8 May 1831.
[5] *Cf.* Wöhler to Liebig, 8 May 1839.

tific memoirs became less numerous. In addition, he traveled extensively to meetings and conferences and he became involved in many close correspondences. Since then, Liebig would describe chemistry as a universal science and the source of innumerable precious applications.

3. 1837: The Crucial Year

In 1837, five young foreign students were working in Liebig's Giessen laboratory. Three of them were English: T. Richardson, W. Eatwell, and T. Thomson, the son of the Glasgow professor of chemistry who invited Liebig to attend the meeting of the British Association for the Advancement of Science (BAAS), which took place in Liverpool in September 1837. The travel to Great Britain seems to have played an important role in changing Liebig's mind.

Liebig had an early interest in technology. During his study in Paris, he was impressed by Nicolas Clément's lectures and the applications of chemistry to the arts.[6] In 1832, on Liebig's insistence, Vieweg accepted the idea of publishing the *Handwörterbuch der reinen und angewandten Chemie* ('Dictionary of Pure and Applied Chemistry'), which would become of great help to technological chemists and manufacturers.[7] Liebig also pushed Vieweg to manufacture his own paper "as beautiful as English paper" and, after visiting the most important paper mills of Ireland, Scotland, and England, he advised Vieweg about the manufacturing technologies.[8]

On his way to the Liverpool meeting, Liebig took the opportunity to visit many factories of soda, sulfuric acid, soap, steel, and paper. He became more aware of the importance of chemistry in every sector of industry and of its crucial importance to the prosperity of a country, "chemistry, the real mother of every industry" (Liebig 1838). He considered chemistry the most worthy science and the most useful matter of education: "If a person well trained in pure chemistry, but completely inexperienced, happens to manage soda, sulfuric acid, or sugar factories,

---

[6] Liebig to Schleiermacher, 17 Feb. 1823, in Brock 1997, p. 29.
[7] Liebig to Vieweg, 3. Nov. 1832.
[8] Liebig to Vieweg, 1837-8.

dying industries or any other industry, he will be familiarized with the methods of fabrication within half an hour; and he will allow substantial improvements within the first hour." Thanks to the knowledge of the bases and laws of science, applications were easy and would automatically follow (ibid.).

His visits of factories and his discussions with men such as W. Crum, J. Muspratt, Ch. Macintosh, and Trueman made Liebig more concerned with industrial problems than before. He became convinced that developing the teaching of chemistry and making it more popular at the state level as well as in the common mind, was the primary aim. Just after Liebig's return to Giessen, Thomas Graham wrote to Liebig, "my ambition and the object of my life will be to raise something like a chemical school in London, and your example of success is my most efficient stimulus".[9]

Another outcome of Liebig's travel was the enthusiastic reception of his memoir on uric acid, read by Faraday himself. This made him conscious that he had to play a prominent role in the chemical scene in Europe. He was ensured of the alliance of "all the northern chemists". Although "England was not the country of science", he had to promote chemistry in this country where "the chemists are ashamed to be called chemists" and where the druggists, who are called chemists, are despised.[10] The acclamation of the English chemists, who asked him to write a Report on organic chemistry, made Liebig even more a leader in organic chemistry, which "exercises an immense influence over medicine, over manufactures, and over common life" (Liebig 1837).

Back in Giessen at the end of 1837, Liebig was convinced to play an important role in popularizing chemistry in Europe. Part of this project was to unite Dumas and Graham as co-editors of the *Annalen*: "Your grand idea of a chemical journal to be published in the three languages delights me. I see no other means so likely to revive an interest in true Chemistry in my own country."[11] In 1840, the *Annalen der Pharmacie* became the *Annalen der Chemie und Pharmacie*.

---

[9] Graham to Liebig, 17 Oct. 1837.
[10] Liebig to Berzelius, 26 Nov. 1837.
[11] Graham to Liebig, 25 Nov. 1837.

The other leader of organic chemistry and another opponent of Berzelius' school was Dumas, whom Liebig met on his way back to Germany. After an attempt to unite their forces, whether real or pretended, Liebig decided that he would start alone the campaign to make chemistry more popular. "You are powerful in Paris, but you have no influence elsewhere in the world as long as you are not at the head of a journal. Paris influence is little, to my opinion, regarding Europe."[12] Back in Giessen, Liebig was determined to become the leader and servant of chemistry worldwide.

4. 1840: The Turning Point

In 1837, Liebig was still vigorous and enterprising in developing a new fruitful system of organic chemistry, but this slightly changed in 1840. His struggles became increasingly intense, leading to a rupture with Dumas and damaged relations with Berzelius. His attempts to create a new system based on radicals turned out to be impossible. "I am really afraid of theoretical discussions."[13] The first volume of his the *Traité* (1840), where compounds were studied and classified according to their radicals, were followed by an outdated approach: acids, fatty compounds, and dyes (Liebig 1840-44). The revolution that Liebig intended to start in organic chemistry seemed impossible for the present. "The more I am thinking about the constitution of organic compounds, the more I become convinced that all our efforts are in vain to establish strong bases for a theory.[14] He would "turn to a completely different side of the science".[15]

In 1840 he published two important publications of another type: 'Der Zustand der Chemie in Preussen' and *Die organische Chemie in ihrer Anwendung auf Agricultur und Physiologie* ('Organic Chemistry in its Applications to Agriculture and Physiology', henceforth called *Agricultural Chemistry*). First published in the *Annalen*, the first publication would also be published as a booklet by Vieweg, on Liebig's demand: *Über das Studium der Naturwissenschaften* (1840, 'On the Study of Sci-

---

12 Liebig to Dumas, 18 March 1838.
13 Liebig to Berzelius, 28 July 1839.
14 Liebig to Berzelius, 10 March 1839.
15 Liebig to Berzelius, 26 Apr. 1840.

ence'). Likewise for the second publication, a booklet that was in fact the Introduction to his French *Traité de Chimie organique*, and imposed by Liebig on Vieweg, as a personal gift: "It will excite a great sensation."[16]

Already in 'Der Zustand der Chemie in Österreich' (1837), Liebig had harshly criticized the teaching of chemistry, this real mother of every industry, and denounced professors of chemistry as no real chemists (Liebig 1838). Yet, 'Der Zustand der Chemie in Preussen' was his first official attempt to popularize chemistry.[17] Chemistry could no longer be considered the servant of physicians,[18] nor less important than mathematics, which was unable to verify the exactness of its assertion. Instead, chemistry answered questions about nature in the same way as physics did, using the language of phenomena. Chemistry was a 'mother science' because it was necessary for progress in physiology and medicine; it was a central science because it was necessary for the improvements of industries and trades and, particularly, agriculture. And chemistry was an important training of the mind, unlike *Naturphilosophie* that abused the mind and falsified reasoning. Liebig wanted to make clear that chemistry was a fundamental science. Thanks to chemical methods, the problems of agriculture, physiology, and medicine could be solved by nourishing the people and restoring their health. "As you know, my intention is to make the nation see the real nature of chemistry."[19]

Introduced to Vieweg as the "most appropriate prospectus to announce the publication of the *Agricultural Chemistry*", 'Der Zustand...' began popularizing chemistry in a polemic tone. Liebig asked for 2-3000 copies to be sent "to all the kingdoms of the world".[20] He announced that he would also try to publish it in major newspapers, as *Morgenblatt* and *Allgemeine Zeitung*, in order to "make more noise about it, if possible". His *Agricultural Chemistry* tried to demonstrate that chemistry could explain every transformation in the living bodies and, therefore, could help

---

[16] Liebig to Vieweg, 17 March 1840, see also Blondel-Mégrelis 2005.
[17] Regine Zott (1993) has discussed the relationship between the two famous publications of 1840.
[18] Liebig kept on writing that chemistry could no longer be considered a servant, that it had to be considered in its own right (*e.g.* Liebig 1840, p. 102; Liebig to Linde, 26 Apr. 1840).
[19] Liebig to Wöhler, 3 July 1840.
[20] Liebig to Vieweg, 28 May 1840.

improve a field if natural laws were respected. That should be possible by using a simple language and images comprehensible to everyone and without any chemical formulas and tables. Moreover, He aimed to show that between modern agriculture based on chemistry and the most traditional ones, like little farms or Chinese and Japanese agriculture, there was no hiatus. This tendency would intensify through the successive editions of the *Agricultural Chemistry*. There would be no matter of mistrust or fear about chemistry, as phenomena were neither mysterious nor irrational.

In fact, Liebig wanted everybody to believe that chemistry commanded every phenomenon in living nature: "Alles ist Chemie." ('Everything is chemistry.') Knowing the laws of chemistry, everyone would be able to understand and improve. The first task was to prioritize the teaching of chemistry, particularly pure chemistry that he considered as the trunk of a tree. A prospectus that advertised the *Handwörterbuch* summarized Liebig's points: "Nobody is able to do completely without chemistry, nobody has been studying chemistry without any profit at all: chemistry is closely related with trade and industry, with medicine and the natural sciences, with everything connected with life".[21]

Liebig's original *Organic Chemistry in its Application to Agriculture* did not promote agricultural chemistry as the title suggests; only the seventh edition of 1862 became the birth of the myth of Liebig, the founder of modern agriculture (Blondel-Mégrelis & Robin 2001). Instead, the book developed a new image of chemistry (Jas 2001).

5. The Instruments of Popularization

Teaching was, of course, a major instrument to diffuse chemistry. Already in 1838, Liebig had severely criticized the Austrian professors of chemistry. Even in Prussia, H. Rose was in Liebig's view "the only man who gives practical scientific lectures" and enjoyed to educate chemists. Now Liebig sought for a larger and more general audience that would be attracted by his growing international fame. Half a century

---

[21] Vieweg, F. und Sohn: 'Prospectus: Handwörterbuch der reinen und angewandten Chemie', 1842.

before, Lavoisier already had a similar aspiration referring to the same sector of agriculture: "the experiences I am working on made me hope that I could contribute, one day, on the national prosperity, by acting on the public opinion with writings and facts" (Lavoisier 1792). This care for a larger audience became evident in the first months of 1840, when Liebig worked on his booklet for agriculturists.

In the middle of that year Liebig took care of every detail that could help the diffusion of his ideas: a tasteful print, an elegant type-foundry, a beautiful paper, and a well-composed dedication.[22] He insisted on being a Professor of Chemistry, a member of the Royal Society, and an honorary member of the city of Giessen.[23] And he carefully selected the priorities of his coveted audience.[24]

Of course writing was a major tool to popularize chemistry, which Liebig used by numerous editions. His friend and publisher Eduard Vieweg was a major aid in that regard. The multiple editions of Liebig's works, particularly after 1840 and with improved quality of paper and print, were a precious help in the popularization of chemistry. All the more since Liebig himself assisted in the diffusion. He requested that the *Agricultural Chemistry* be ready in the bookshops for the naturalists' meeting in Erlangen. When the agriculturists had a meeting in Brünn, Liebig managed to have the copies arrive in time. He went to Vienna to hand over copies to Metternich and Colowzat.

Liebig's pupils, especially foreigners, played an important role in the diffusion of his ideas. Although it is a matter of discussion whether he was a pupil of Liebig, C. Gerhardt translated into French most of Liebig's writings. In the English-speaking world, Liebig's pupils were extremely important. The *Agricultural Chemistry* was published in England as soon as 1840, translated in the Giessen laboratory by Playfair. W.

---

[22] For the choice of the dedication in the English version, see Gregory to Liebig, 25 May 1842.

[23] "On the title of the *Physiology* [Agricultural Chemistry], Professor of Chemistry has to be inserted, as well as honorary citizen of the town of Giessen; then, after membership of the Royal Society, must be written member of the British Association for the Advancement of Science." (Liebig to Vieweg, 25 July 1840).

[24] "Write above it: to Chemists (before that 1), Pharmacists (before that 5), Agronomists (before that 4), Physiologists (before that 2), and Botanists (before that 3), and Physicians (before that 6)" (Liebig to Vieweg, 3 July 1840).

Gregory, at the 1840 meeting of the BAAS, added, after Graham had read an abstract of the glorious book: "The object of the work was to show that, without a profound knowledge of chemistry, no real progress in Agriculture and Physiology was possible."[25] The first English edition was quickly introduced in America, pirated and sold very cheaply by an American editor. Liebig's views were popularized by the *Cultivator* as soon as 1841, and his theory of the fixation of ammonia quickly replaced Davy's (Rossiter 1975). In 1842, Gregory drew up a laudatory report on Liebig's *Physiology* pronouncing that chemical research had proved some facts, "which the boldest imagination dared not have ventured to conceive". He concluded that "there is no living philosopher to whom the Chemical Section could have more appropriately entrusted their investigation" (Playfair 1843).

Liebig frequently wrote articles for newspapers. In 1842 and 1843, he wrote a series of articles for the supplement of the *Augsburger Allgemeine Zeitung*. Some of them were united in a book on the suggestion of E. Dieffenbach, one of his first pupils, and published in 1843 in an English edition: "I hope that this little offering may serve to make new friends to our beautiful and useful science." Of course, a major impact made Liebig's *Chemische Briefe*, which he wrote "for the special purpose of exciting the attention of governments, and an enlightened public, to the necessity of establishing Schools of Chemistry, and of promoting, by every means, the study of a science so intimately connected with the arts, pursuits, and social well-being of modern civilized nations." (Paoloni 1968, p. 106) C. Paoloni (1968) has established the complete chronology of the multi-language editions of the *Familiar Letters*, as it was called in English: thanks to the services of his former pupils, it was translated into nine languages, with eleven editions in Italy alone. Brock (1998) has studied how this monument of German literature enlarged the public knowledge and raised a large interest in chemistry.

Another important means of propagating, if not popularizing, chemistry was the *Annalen*. In 1831 Liebig started as co-editor with P. Geiger the *Magazin für Pharmacie*, which in 1832 became the *Annalen der Pharmacie*. In 1838, he associated Dumas and Graham, which was only

---

[25]   Gregory to Liebig, 25 Sept. 1840.

a formal co-editorship, ridiculed by Wöhler,[26] but an attempt to attract a European audience. It was also an important step of the time to make the German pharmacists, "who are on such a high level of education", more involved in the advancement of chemistry: "This Journal will be preeminently devoted to the new chemistry, the organic chemistry, without excluding the most important discoveries in other parts of the science."[27] In 1840, the journal title changed to *Annalen der Chemie und Pharmacie*.

Liebig also used his personal influence, contacts, friendships, and fame to diffuse his ideas. By all means he tried to make everyone in every country be acquainted with chemistry, including the readers of the *Allgemeiner Anzeiger* (Gotha), the chancellor of Hessen-Darmstadt, and Napoleon III. Finlay (1998) has described how Liebig's international contacts and political connections helped him disseminate his ideas of chemistry across the world. Among the more curious means was an extract of meat that was marketed and branded 'Liebigs Fleischextrakt', which propagated his name and, consequently, the image of chemistry. In university policy, he used his connection to Linde, the chancellor of the University of Giessen, "to raise the Institute of Natural Sciences of Giessen to a higher level than at any other German University", by intervening into material and financial issues of the building and into new appointments.[28] For instance, he was influential in the appointment of Buff to the chair of physics with a decent salary, because "an education in chemistry is impossible without a former accurate knowledge of physics".[29]

Liebig was known as a polemicist seeking for quarrels and scandals, such that only a few chemists and friends escaped his quarrels. However, he deliberately used his scandals as a means to make himself and his ideas better known. For instance, his essay 'Der Zustand...' (Liebig 1840a) was meant to raise a scandal for the propagation of his new book ("The *Zustand* will be the best and most appropriate prospectus for our

---

[26]   Wöhler to Berzelius, 30 July 1838.
[27]   Liebig's 'Vorbericht' (1 Jan. 1838) in *Annalen der Pharmacie*. Note that his essay 'Der Zustand der Chemie in Österreich' was published in the same volume.
[28]   Liebig to Linde, 22 May 1839.
[29]   Liebig to Linde, Nov. and Dec. 1837.

Chemical Physiology"[30]), which turned out to be sucessful: "The essay made much more noise than I hoped. The mathematicians, professors, philologists were irritated because of the disdainful manner they are treated, as they say."[31]

Liebig also used simple words and clear sentences that anyone could understand, and thus contributed not only to the formation of the chemical language,[32] but also to the broader public education. In addition, he frequently used simple images and analogies drawn from ordinary life, particularly in his *Letters on Agriculture* and in the last editions of the *Agricultural Chemistry*. The first part of the first volume of the seventh edition of the *Agricultural Chemisty* was a model of simplicity and non-specialization, making clear to everyone the principles of his agriculture and the crucial importance of chemistry for improving crops without exhausting the earth. The farmer must respect the great principle of chemistry: nothing is left, nothing is created, everything changes. The prosperity of the ancient little farm, of Chinese agriculture, rested on the principle of restitution, the first law of the circulation of elements. Regarding manure as a magic remedy to save our exhausted fields was the same as seeking for the philosopher's stone.

6. Conclusion

During the second half of his life, Liebig worked as a propagator of chemistry, partly at the expense of his scientific activity. He was determined to make his science known to the general public, as a primary service to chemistry. In 1851, he dedicated to Dumas his *Nouvelles Lettres sur la Chimie*: "I have tried to popularize the doctrines for which you played such an important part." (Liebig 1852) However, he was never really in agreement with Dumas's doctrines. Rather than teaching doctrines, Liebig placed chemistry in the very center of everybody's daily life. Since '*alles ist Chemie*', everybody had to know chemistry. Without any of our modern means of mass communication, Liebig

---

[30] Liebig to Vieweg, May and June 1840.
[31] Liebig to Vieweg, 12 June 1840.
[32] Brock (1997, p. 223) quotes the Grimm brothers' homage in their *Deutsches Wörterbuch*: in Liebig's mouth, chemistry becomes '*Sprachgewalt*'.

managed to make his message heard beyond borders in space, time, and societies. As Brock (1997, p. 266) wrote, "Liebig worked to make chemistry the fundamental science to modern societies". Popularizing was part of the task, not the least important.

References

Blondel-Mégrelis, M., Robin, P.: 2001, 'Physiologie végétale et Chimie agricole, Liebig, une fondation à questionner', *Bibliothèque d'Histoire rurale*, **6**, 275-296.

Blondel-Mégrelis, M.: 2005, 'Die Veröffentlichung von *Chimie organique appliquée à la Physiologie végétale et à l'Agriculture* in Frankreich', *Berichte der Justus Liebig-Gesellschaft zu Giessen*, **8**, 13-55.

Brock, W.H.: 1997, *Justus von Liebig*, Vieweg, Braunschweig.

Brock, W.H.: 1998, 'Popularisierer der Wissenschaft: Liebig's «Chemische Briefe»', in: *Das Publizistische Wirken Justus von Liebigs*, Berichte der Justus Liebig-Gesellschaft zu Giessen, Giessen, pp. 77-101.

Felschow, E.M., Heuser, E.: 1992, *Universität und Ministerium im Vormärz, Justus Liebigs Briefwechsel mit Justin von Linde*, Ferber, Giessen.

Finlay, M.: 1998, 'Justus von Liebig and the Internationalization of Science', in: *Das publizistische Wirken Justus Liebigs*, Berichte der Justus Liebig-Gesellschaft zu Giessen, Giessen, pp. 57-76.

Hofmann, A.W.: 1888, *Aus Justus Liebig's und Friedrich Wöhler's Briefwechsel*, Vieweg, Braunschweig.

Jas, N.: 2001, *Au carrefour de la chimie et de l'agriculture: Les Sciences agronomiques en France et en Allemagne, 1840-1914*, Ed. des Archives Contemporaines, Paris.

Judel, G.K.: 2003, *Justus Liebig in Großbritannien*, Berichte der Justus Liebig-Gesellschaft zu Giessen, Giessen.

Lavoisier, A.L.: 1792, 'De quelques expériences d'agriculture, et réflexions sur leur relation avec l'économie politique', *Annales de Chimie*, **15**, 297-316.

Liebig, J., 1840-44, *Traité de Chimie organique*, 3 vols, Fortin, Paris.

Liebig, J.: 1837, 'On the products of decomposition of uric acid', *British Association Reports*, 38-41.

Liebig, J.: 1837, *Anleitung zur Analyse organischer Körper*, Vieweg, Braunschweig.

Liebig, J.: 1838, 'Der Zustand der Chemie in Österreich', *Annalen der Pharmacie*, **25**, 339-47.

Liebig, J.: 1840a, 'Der Zustand der Chemie in Preussen', *Annalen der Chemie und der Pharmacie*, **34**, 102-4.

Liebig, J.: 1840b, *Die organische Chemie in ihrer Anwendung auf Agricultur und Physiologie*, 1st edn., Vieweg, Braunschweig.

Liebig, J.: 1852, *Nouvelles Lettres sur la Chimie*, Masson, Paris.

Paoloni, C.: 1968, *Justus von Liebig: Eine Bibliographie sämtlicher Veröffentlichungen*, Winter, Heidelberg.

Playfair, L.: 1843, 'Abstract of Professor Liebig's Report on «Organic Chemistry applied to Physiology and Pathology»', *Report of the British Association*, 42.

Rossiter, M.W. : 1975, *The Emergence of Agricultural Science*, Yale UP, New Haven.
Schneider, M., W.: 1986, *Justus von Liebig, Briefe an Vieweg*, Vieweg, Braunschweig.
Wallach, O.: 1966, *Briefwechsel zwischen J. Berzelius und F. Wöhler*, Martin Sändig, Wiesbaden.
Wöhler, F; Liebig, J.: 1838, 'Untersuchungen über die Natur der Harnsäure', *Annalen der Pharmacie*, **26**, 241-340.
Zott, R.: 1993, 'The development of science and scientific communication', *Ambix*, **40**, 1-10.

CHAPTER 7

FROM CHEMISTRY FOR THE PEOPLE TO THE WONDERS OF TECHNOLOGY: THE POPULARIZATION OF CHEMISTRY IN THE NETHERLANDS DURING THE NINETEENTH CENTURY

Ernst Homburg

Department of History, University of Maastricht, P.O. Box 616, 6200 MD Maastricht, The Netherlands; E.Homburg@history.unimaas.nl

This chapter analyzes phases in the production of popular Dutch chemistry books in terms of their audiences and the character of the texts. While the first popular chemistry books (1809-1815), which were directed to women, youngsters, and common people, contained moralistic and physico-theological contemplations, these were absent in books that between 1830 and 1844 diffused 'useful knowledge' among the working classes. The next period (1845-1864) was a hey-day, which also marked the end of the old style of popularization of chemistry. After 1865 the number of popular chemistry books dropped considerably, as a result of (a) the professionalization of chemistry; (b) the introduction of chemistry as a school subject; and (c) the separation between science and religion. Until 1900 chemical technology became almost the exclusive focus of popular chemistry texts.

1. Introduction[1]

In August 1965, when half of the Dutch population was on holiday, a number of men gathered in The Hague, in the office of the Society of the Dutch Chemical Industry (Vereniging van de Nederlandse Chemische

---

[1] A longer version of this chapter appeared in Dutch (Homburg 1995). I thank the publisher of *Gewina* for permission to use parts of that article. I thank Ton Brouwers for translating those parts.

Industrie, VNCI). They were public relations officers from several large chemical companies and were faced with a problem. Since the publication of Rachel Carson's *Silent Spring* in May of 1962 and a large fire at a fertilizer plant near Rotterdam in 1963, the public image of chemistry in the Netherlands had noticeably deteriorated. Articles in the Dutch press began to use headings such as 'The poisonous cocktail of technology' and 'Is the Netherlands still inhabitable?' Something had to be done to counter this negative publicity. The Dutch population had to be made aware that chemistry had become an integral part of their life and that they better accepted it as such. It was decided to hire a communications representative who would be in charge of maintaining public relations with both the press and the public (Hoefnagels 1993, pp. 11, 30-31; De Galan 1965). Eibert H. Bunte, the man who was appointed, hit the ground running. In 1968, the year of the VNCI's 50th anniversary, he wrote the jubilee book *Leven met chemie* ('Living with chemistry') (Bunte 1968a/b). Since then the VNCI, together with its sister organization the Royal Dutch Chemical Society (Koninklijke Nederlandse Chemische Vereniging, KNCV), has been engaged in a consistent effort to improve the image of chemistry through information and popularization. In the 1990s this led to the establishment of the C_3 Foundation (Communication Center Chemistry).

Over the past four decades, science communication and the popularization of chemistry in the Netherlands have clearly been marked by this struggle to regain the favor of the public at large. The effort to improve chemistry's public image through the field's popularization was even so substantial that the uninformed might consider the genre of popular writings about chemistry to date back no further than the 1960s. For over two centuries, however, books and articles have appeared with the explicit aim of disseminating chemical knowledge in society, as well as promoting chemistry as a useful science. At times this specifically involved enhancing its public image, but this was certainly not always the case. When the Haarlem chemist and apothecary Martinus Nicolaas Beets (1780-1869) published his *Volks-Scheikunde* ('Popular chemistry, or Chemistry for the People') in 1815, chemistry was rather a fashionable field, a *Lieblingswissenschaft* about which many Dutch wanted to have more knowledge.[2] The wealthy educated gentleman who in Beets' book teaches his gardener the basics of chemistry is fortunate to encounter quite an eager student. When the gentleman tells him that in as much as he busies himself "with fertilizing and improving my soil, [he] also engages in the work of a chemist", the gardener is swiftly won over: "Ay, ay, Sir! Now I see: I should say I learned many a thing again." (Beets 1815, pp. 4-5) Chemistry allows one, Beets argued, to avoid specific harm, do away with superstition, while it also "promotes a sensible worship of God and produces utility and benefit for health and home economics" (Beets 1815, p. viii). If today chemistry popularization mainly serves the interests of chemical science and industry, in the early nineteenth century it was still part of a much broader effort aimed at social progress and the spread of a Christian civilization.

This difference between chemistry popularization then and now is not just revealing with respect to the development of the popular chemistry book; it also provides major insights into the social position of chemistry. Its popularization involves a set of activities that directly pertain to the interplay of chemistry and society. This is why a consideration of the popular literature about chemistry offers a surprising outlook on discipline formation, professionalization, and changing views of the function of chemistry education (*cf.* Meinel 1985, pp. 35-6). It is also from this angle that this chapter aims to provide a preliminary exploration of the relevant nineteenth-century popular chemistry literature.

Books devoted to popularizing chemistry come in many guises: textbooks, handbooks on doing experiments at home, texts devoted to spectacular new developments, apologetic books that promote the social significance of chemistry, popular chemistry histories (*e.g.* French 1937, Greiling 1938, Reichen 1964), novels and plays (*e.g.* Schenzinger 1937, see also Krätz 1991), and (auto)biographies of leading chemists (*e.g.* Curie 1938, Watson 1968). In this chapter I do not address the last three genres mentioned; while regarding the others my emphasis will be on their publication context rather than their content. During the nineteenth

---

[2] On chemistry as '*Lieblingswissenschaft*', and on the successful lectures by Humphrey Davy in London, see: Hufbauer 1982, pp. 13, 28-9, 145, 149; Golinski 1992, pp. 193-4.

century some 57 popular chemistry books (second and later editions included) appeared in the Netherlands: 1800-1815, 9; 1816-1829, 0; 1830-
1844, 8; 1845-1864, 30; and 1865-1899, about 10. My major objective is
to present a historical account that explains these different phases and
that shows how developments in popular literature on chemistry are
linked up with changes in the various interrelationships among learned
men, educators, chemists, publishers, and the general public.

2. Wonders of Nature

The first (text)books on chemistry for a broad audience appeared in the
closing decades of the eighteenth century. Up to that time, chemistry was
a subject that was taught only to physicians, apothecaries, and mining
engineers – to professionals, in short, who dealt with chemicals directly.
Yet for those interested among the well-to-do there were some alternative options to gain chemical knowledge. In the context of special
societies, but also outside of them, it was possible to follow lectures and
courses on the inquiry of nature in the broadest sense. Moreover, there
were a number of accessibly written books with facts and insights about
nature, some of which also treated chemistry topics. They had an evident
physico-theological bent, just like other eighteenth-century 'popular'
books on natural philosophy. Also the content's presentation in the first
popular books on chemistry – namely in the form of dialogues, letters, or
the catechism's question-and-answer structure – seems to be derived
from older popular books on natural philosophy.

   For the Netherlands, *Het regt gebruik der wereltbeschouwingen, ter
overtuiginge van ongodisten en ongelovigen* ('The right use of the world
view for the conviction of atheists and infidels', 1715) by Bernard Nieuwentijt (1654-1718) is the first in a long series of physico-theological
books that appeared throughout the eighteenth and nineteenth centuries
(Van Berkel 1985, pp. 78-9; Raichvarg & Jacques 1991, p. 47). As well
as fighting the views of Spinoza and his followers, Nieuwentijt also took
it upon him to explain the wonders of God's creation to 'the untrained'.
If God's existence had to be proven with the help of the 'wonders of nature', this argument would of course benefit from a clear and transparent

presentation of these wonders.[3] Thus Nieuwentijt paved the way to those who followed in his wake. Many later eighteenth-century books on natural philosophy were based on the notion that the spread of knowledge of nature would contribute to respect for the Creator and thus to devotion and virtue. An example is the 'physico-theological bestseller' *Katechismus der Natuur* ('Catechism of nature', 1777-1779), written by the teacher, clergyman, and natural philosopher Johannes Florentius Martinet (1729-1795) (Paasman 1971, pp. 47-9). Like Nieuwentijt's book, Martinet's *Catechism* was reprinted many times and came out in an abbreviated version for children, which like the original edition was reprinted and translated into several languages. Between 1790 and 1850 as many as 24 editions of *The catechism of nature for the use of children* appeared in the English-speaking world alone. Martinet's physico-theological doctrine continued to be influential through the middle of the nineteenth century in the Netherlands. The new edition of J.A. Uilkens' *De volmaaktheden van den Schepper* ('God's flawless creations'), which was revised and updated between 1852 and 1857 and contained only a few physico-theological passages, marked the end of an epoch (Paasman 1971, pp. 9-13, 61-5, 100-2). After 1860 the dominant influence of the thought of Nieuwentijt, Martinet, and their followers was definitively a thing of the past.

3. Science Popularization in the Eighteenth Century

The eighteenth century, thanks to its flourishing societies and the proliferation of works like those by Nieuwentijt and Martinet, is often seen as an era of 'science popularization' (Van Berkel 1985, pp. 77-84; Snelders 1992, pp. 309-12). Measured by the broad interest for the natural sciences among the bourgeoisie at that time, this characterization is certainly valid. Yet the term 'popularization' has one drawback; today we tend to associate it with rendering esoteric knowledge of experts accessible to a lay audience. In the eighteenth century, however, the practitioners of the natural sciences did not yet constitute a sharply

---

[3]   Cf. the French title of Nieuwentijt's work: *L'Existence de Dieu démontrée par les merveilles de la nature* (1725). On Nieuwentijt, see Vermij 1991.

delineated social group. They were part of a single learned and literate social elite within which new knowledge and insights involving nature circulated freely, even though on an individual level there were substantial differences in understanding, of course. In these societies, interested amateurs might have been at once 'consumers' of scientific knowledge and 'producers' of new facts and phenomena (*cf.* Golinski 1992). Popularization in the eighteenth-century sense, then, should not be merely conceived as the diffusion of knowledge within well-to-do male patrician circles, but primarily as the transfer of knowledge to social groups that because of their gender, age, or class did not belong to those circles: women, children and the common people.

From the mid-eighteenth century onward, it was far from unusual for upper class women to display a warm interest in the latest accomplishments of natural philosophy. They joined their husbands in society lectures, discussed natural science topics in salons, embraced Martinet's *Catechism of Nature*, and in 1785 established their own Natural Science Ladies Society (Natuurkundig Gezelschap der Dames) in Middelburg (Sturkenboom 2004). Books like Francesco Algarotti's *Il Newtonianismo per le Dame* (1737) and works by the abbot Nollet (1743) and Émilie du Châtelet (1738) were in high demand.[4]

After about 1770, influenced by Enlightenment pedagogues such as J.C. Rousseau, J.B. Basedow, C.G. Salzmann, and, later, J.H. Pestalozzi, children's education and the training and civilizing of the 'lesser classes' gained significant attention. This led to plans for education reforms and the start of courses for craftsmen and manufacturers, whereby the diffusion of knowledge of nature was one of the objectives pursued.[5] Martinet's 1779 *Catechism of nature for the use of children* offers a good example of this new phase in science popularization; *a fortiori* this also counts for the establishment, five years later, of the Maatschappij tot Nut

---

[4]   Marie Meurdrac's *Chymie charitable et facile en faveur des dames* from 1666 does not belong in this list, because it was not related to the socio-cultural movement from which the works of Algarotti and Du Châtelet emerged. It was a very practical book with home recipes (Raichvarg & Jacques 1991, pp. 31-4, 55-7; Van Berkel 1985, pp. 82, 87; Paasman 1971, pp. 41-2).

[5]   In France things occurred somewhat earlier. Pluche's *Le spectacle de la nature* (1732) was already specifically written for children (Homburg 1993a, pp. 100-13; Lenders 1988, pp. 21, 32-6, 132-48; Raichvarg & Jacques 1991, pp. 34-40).

van 't Algemeen. This 'Society for the Common Good', which sought to combine the diffusion of useful skills and sciences with the promotion of piety and morals among the general population, played a major role in the Netherlands in the diffusion of scientific knowledge throughout the nineteenth century (Mijnhardt 1988, pp. 104-5, 259-94; Lenders 1988, pp. 32-6).

4. Half a Century Too Late?

Regarding the field of chemistry, the popularization effort was marked by basically the same publication pattern: at first accessible works for an unspecified readership, which were followed by books that specifically catered to women, children, and enterprising members of the general public. But there was a striking delay of several decades. Why did the popularization of natural philosophy and natural history take off about half a century earlier than that of chemistry? Is it simply because Lavoisier's 'Chemical Revolution' occurred nearly a century after Newton's 'Scientific Revolution'? This is not very plausible. It is true that the latest discoveries by chemists such as Lavoisier and Davy were not absent in the first popular books on chemistry, but they played no central role. The basic tenet of the first chemistry works for a large audience was that the field, including the chemistry before Lavoisier, was important and useful anyhow; it would make an indispensable contribution to issues of health and disease, the growth of factories and production, and the advance of agriculture.

It seems more compelling, then, to assume that the popularization of chemistry took off comparatively late because the physico-theological genre and the nature of chemistry did not match very well. While the mechanics of planetary movements and the wondrous diversity of the three empires of nature could be linked up with God's creation in ways that were readily observable to everybody, chemical processes occurred in the laboratory's hidden world. This is why at that time chemistry was rarely counted as one of the *natural* sciences, but mostly as one of the *arts*, or technologies (Meinel 1983; Homburg 1993a, pp. 64-8; Roberts 1993). The phenomena and results of eighteenth-century chemistry ('schei-kunst' in Dutch, or 'the art of separation') were not so much exposed at the level of the divinely created cosmos or natural world, but in the industriousness of social life. For Beets, just like for Paracelsus three centuries earlier, chemistry revealed itself particularly in the work of bakers, gardeners, gin distillers, glass blowers, potters, water distillers, glue makers, and "so many others" (Beets 1815, p. 5; Homburg 1993a, pp. 58-61). This makes it understandable that the popularization of chemistry took off in the last four decades of the eighteenth century, when the Enlightenment got a more utilitarian character. In those years the need to improve agriculture and industry with the help of chemistry and mechanical engineering was emphasized again and again (*cf.* Lowood 1987). Furthermore, the integration of chemistry in the natural sciences opened up the possibility to interlace the subject matter's presentation with physico-theological lessons and considerations. The first popular scientific works on chemistry, however, did not denounce the field's separate character. If physico-theological considerations were rarely absent in the earliest popular chemistry literature, commonly their role was limited, at least in comparison to the repeated emphasis on the field's economic usefulness.

5. Chemistry for Women, Children, and the Common People

English and German authors took the lead in popularizing chemistry.[6] Starting in 1781, the *Chemical Essays* by the British bishop Richard Watson (1737-1816) conveyed "in a popular way, a general kind of knowledge" to "persons not so much versed in chemical inquiries". Apparently, this formula catered to a felt need because within 12 years six editions were published of this five-volume work, while it was soon translated in German as well (Watson 1793, preface).[7] Ten years later the prolific German author Jacob Andreas Weber (1737-1792) published *Leichtfassliche Chemie, für Handwerker und deren Lehrlinge*, and in the

---

[6] Apart from translations, the only French popular chemistry books I managed to track down are Ségur 1803 and Martin 1810 that aimed at female readers. That fewer popular works on chemistry appeared in France is probably caused by this country's more developed *regular* chemistry education that made such books less relevant. Parkes (1830, p. 3) explicitly refers to the French lead in this area.

[7] Watson's book was based on lectures he gave in Cambridge between 1764-1782 to students of all faculties; *cf.* Golinski 1992, p. 53.

ensuing years other textbooks by Scherer (1795), Parkinson (1799), Imhof (1802), and Wurzer (1806) came out. The wide distribution of these books in Germany gave the term *'populäre Chemie'* a common ring (Weber 1791, Scherer 1795, Parkinson 1799, Imhof 1802, Wurzer 1806).

Soon all these titles were overshadowed by two English works that appeared in 1806, the *Chemical Catechism* by Samuel Parkes (1761-1825) and the initially anonymously published *Conversations on Chemistry* by Jane Marcet (1769-1858). That these works explained chemistry in simple terms was hardly new; the way in which they did so was new however. Strategies like dialogue and catechism, deployed successfully by earlier popularizers like Pluche and Martinet, were now applied to chemistry for the first time. Until after the middle of the nineteenth century both works were repeatedly translated and republished. Parkes' *Chemical Catechism* subscribed to physico-theological views much more explicitly than Marcet. The book by Parkes was intended as a tool for parents to teach their children chemistry at home, but in a popular fashion "a body of incontrovertible evidence of the wisdom and beneficence of the Deity" was equally imparted. Fully in the tradition of Baconianism, Parkes assumed that only uncompromising attention for the experimental fact would offer a safeguard against "insidious sophistry [...] scepticism or superstition" (Parkes 1837, pp. vi-vii, 18-9; Knight 1986; *cf.* also Wurzer 1806, pp. vi-vii). Parkes' *Catechism*, then, had much more in common with Martinet's moralizing *Catechism of Nature* (which was very popular in England) than just the name and the didactic form.

Jane Marcet's *Conversations* was specifically aimed at women, which is why the dialogue in the book is between a female instructor and two girls. This book gained enormous popularity among English and, especially, American women. Until after 1850 over 50 editions (including illegal ones) appeared in both countries that were used in girls' schools and for self-study (Marcet 1841, Knight 1986, Lindee 1991). At the beginning of the nineteenth century the popular chemistry textbook definitively established a solid footing in England, Germany, and France.

Dutch publishers, translators, and authors were not lagging. About a quarter century after chemistry became fashionable with Dutch physicians, apothecaries, and entrepreneurs (Snelders 1992, pp. 314-6, 319-22;

Homburg 1993b, pp. 161-5), books came out that catered to youngsters, women, and the common people. In 1809 the Utrecht apothecary Pieter van Werkhoven (1772-1815) was the first with his translation of Wurzer's 1806 handbook. In 1810 the Dutch translation of Marcet's *Conversations* came out, followed the next year by a translation of Ségur's *Lettres élémentaires sur la chimie* of 1803.[8] In contrast to other countries, these books appear to have been unsuccessful in the Netherlands. The books by Wurzer and Ségur went through a second edition, but no more editions appeared. After the 1810s the interest in chemistry lost its momentum, efforts at educational reform lost strength, the national economy fell into a deep crisis, and, last but not least, the books were beyond reach to most people because of their high price (Homburg 1993b, pp. 165-6, 170, 173-4, 179; Verbong 1994, pp. 41-5, 47-9).[9] During this period, it seems, the Dutch popularization of chemistry was fueled not so much by public demand but rather by forces on the supply side.

The most prominent of these forces was the before mentioned Society for the Common Good, concerned with civilizing and educating the populace. According to this Society, the Dutch population's interest in modern natural science was poorly developed. "With regret" it noticed the "misunderstandings, prejudices, and superstitions that were still prevalent, and too much so, among those of little means", and therefore, in 1811, it published a textbook on natural knowledge written by Johannes Buijs "in the fashion of the very useful work by Helmuth published in Germany, *Naturlehre, zur Dämpfung des Aberglaubens*" (Buys 1811, preface). The same spirit also infused Beets' *Volks-Scheikunde*: the Society's prize competition explicitly asked for a chemistry book modeled after the example of Buijs (Beets 1815, pp. ix-xii). Supported by this influential Society with over 8,000 members, Beets' *Volks-Scheikunde* was much more widely distributed than the works by Wurzer, Marcet, and Ségur. At the same time, though, it symbolizes the end of an era. The Society for the Common Good turned away from its earlier utilitarian, science-based thinking modeled on the French tradition. Although chemis-

---

[8]   Wurzer 1809 (2nd Dutch edn. 1815), Marcet 1810, Ségur 1811 (2nd edn. 1817).

[9]   Wurzer's book came out in 1809; its price went up from 2.50 to 4 guilders by 1815. Marcet's book was priced at 3 guilders and Ségur's two-volume work at 5.50 (Holtrop 1842, pp. 326, 396, 412).

try and the other sciences continued to play a role in the activities of this Society, they no longer had a strategic function in the new, national civilization that this organization promoted with ever more zeal after the accession of King William I. Disciplines such as (Dutch) history, geography, and languages now received much attention, at the expense of a reduced interest in the sciences and the arts (Mijnhardt 1988, pp. 289-94).

6. Evening Schools and Sunday Schools

The boom of newly published chemistry books for beginners between 1795 and 1815 went hand in hand with criticism of traditional education in Latin schools. Various authors of popularizing works on chemistry ardently argued for its inclusion as a subject of general education. Every educated civilized man or woman needed to have knowledge of this field on account of its huge social utility and the wholesome influence it wielded on the intellectual faculties of students (Wurzer 1806, pp. vi-ix; Parkes 1837, vol. 2, pp. 18-9; Parkes 1830, vol. 3, pp. 21-3). Yet apart from a few exceptions very little came of the subject's introduction in secondary education, both in the Netherlands and the rest of Europe (Homburg 1993a, pp. 100, 113-4, 118, 128-9, 458 note 73, 464 note 157). When after 1815 the Restoration mentality gained the upper hand throughout Europe and the classic gymnasium education became the norm again, this killed all efforts to turn chemistry into a regular school subject. In the Netherlands it was introduced in the curriculum nationwide only after Thorbecke's Secondary Education Act of 1863. In the meantime, notably in the years before 1845, chemistry was taught exclusively for utilitarian reasons. Popularizing efforts regarding women and young people ceased for the time being. Only in combination with the training of craftsmen and manufacturers there continued to be a niche for popular chemistry books in the first few decades after 1815.

Although in the eighteenth century there were evening and Sunday courses for entrepreneurs and craftsmen (Homburg 1993a, pp. 107-12, 462 note 121), the breakthrough of this type of education occurred in England when between 1823 and 1826 the movement associated with the Mechanics' Institutes – under the banner of Bacon's 'knowledge is power' – achieved unprecedented successes (Russell 1983, pp. 139-46,

154-73; Shapin & Barnes 1977). The movement spread from England to the Continent. Henry Brougham's *Practical Observations upon the Education of the People, Addressed to the Working Classes and their Employers* (1825) was also very influential outside England.[10] In Germany, the *Polytechnische-* and *Gewerbe-Vereine* in various cities took charge of organizing evening and Sunday courses (Homburg 1993a, pp. 197, 233-6, 247, 400, 410, 414, 418), while in the Netherlands in 1825 King William I ordered the universities to deliver public lectures on the 'application of chemistry and mechanics to the useful arts' (Loschacoff-de Kanter 1970; Goudswaard 1981, pp. 33-5, 133-69). Shortly thereafter, on the initiative of the Society for the Common Good and the Maatschappij ter Bevordering van Nijverheid (Society for the Promotion of Industry), such education was also started up outside of university towns.[11]

In the second quarter of the nineteenth century, to serve those who attended evening and Sunday classes, various 'popular' chemistry instruction books were issued. In England this involved either practical guidelines for simple experiments with a 'portable laboratory' or 'chemistry chest', or traditional, not-too-difficult textbooks (Gee 1989, Homburg 1999). In 1836, under the direction of the Amsterdam professor of Mathematics, Physics and Chemistry W.S. Swart (1807-1847), who in 1830 had taught craftsmen and manufacturers, Erdmann's *Populäre Darstellung der neueren Chemie* was translated by two of his pupils. Eight years later a Dutch translation of Girardin's *Leçons de chimie élémentaire appliquée aux arts industriels* appeared (Erdmann 1836, Girardin 1851).[12] In addition, original Dutch instruction books for evening schools were published as well, such as Van der Boon Mesch's *Leerboek der scheikunde* (1831-35) and Meijlink's *Allereerste beginselen der scheikunde* (1836-38).

The differences between these new popular instruction books and those of the previous generation were substantial. Physico-theological

---

[10] There is also a Dutch translation, Brougham 1826.

[11] Physics and mechanical engineering were commonly the main subjects. Chemistry courses were given in Leiden (1826), Groningen (1826), Utrecht (1829), Amsterdam (1829, 1846), Maastricht (1838), Delft (1841) and, probably, Haarlem and Deventer (MacLean 1977; Goudswaard 1981, pp. 54-60, 93-5, 169-85).

[12] The first edition of Girardin appeared 1844-45, later editions in 1862-63 and 1867.

considerations, for one, vanished altogether, to be replaced by fervent arguments that highlighted the social usefulness of chemistry. Manufacturers could free themselves "from the old routine", and "a source of plenty for many" would come into being if one knew the basics of chemistry – this was the repeated message of the authors mentioned above (Girardin 1851, pp. i-ii). Didactically, too, there were striking differences to the popular chemistry books published between 1795 and 1815. Popularizing strategies such as the dialogue, the letter format, and the catechistic question-and-answer game were now absent. In their educational approach vis-à-vis industrialists and craftsmen all authors gave priority to the systematic nature of the science of chemistry. "Popularity, in the sense of comprehensibility for those without any education" was no longer the goal that had to be pursued at all cost (Erdmann 1836, pp. iii-iv). The treatment of the subject matter should avoid both overly systematic rigidity and overly indulgent popularity. In this respect, the popular chemistry books from that period were fairly conventional chemistry textbooks. Apart from a slightly larger concern for industry, their content hardly differed from the prominent standard work by Berzelius, which appeared in Dutch in that same period. But their approach was quite dissimilar, as is reflected in the use of language, the conciseness of the prose, and the emphasis on illustration and demonstration (Berzelius 1834-41; Verbong & Homburg 1994, pp. 248-9).[13]

7. Affordable and Illustrated Books for all Classes

The evening classes on technical chemistry in various Dutch towns and cities drew large crowds. An attendance of more than one hundred per evening was not unusual. Yet in view of the original aim of catering to craftsmen these courses were hardly successful. If manufacturers, officers, and other upper middle class members showed up regularly, it was much harder for workmen and craftsmen to have that same commitment because of their long working days and the cost of the books (Russell 1983, pp. 157-60). Prices of nearly three to seven guilders or more meant

---

[13] Some 'popular' authors explicitly compared their undertaking with the textbook by Berzelius (W.S. Swart, 'Voorrede', in: Erdmann 1836, pp. vi-vii).

that the purchase of books such as those by Meijlink and Girardin took up a full week's salary.[14] These were simply out of reach for workers.

Between 1845 and 1865 that situation changed dramatically, though. The popularization of chemistry entered a new phase, in which scientists, educators, and publishers sought to reach the common working man with new means and also broadened their effort (again) towards young people. Furthermore, as a by-product of the increasing professionalization of science, various scientists felt the need to legitimate their field vis-à-vis the public.

In this reemergence and broadening of science popularization, publishers played a major role.[15] From about 1830 enterprising publishers entered the stage, trying to open up a mass market by offering books at low prices and filling them with attractive illustrations. Thereby in innovative ways they combined the possibilities of a number of recent technical breakthroughs – such as the technique of wood engraving (ca. 1790), cheaper machine-made paper (ca. 1800), stereotype (ca. 1800), and the steam press (1811) – into the commercially successful product of the illustrated, affordable book.[16] French publishers, with their reasonably priced book series (ca. 1825), and their British colleagues, who first applied woodcuts on a large scale (ca. 1832), led the way (Simons 1915, pp. 15-8; Van Lente & De Wit 1993, pp. 190, 257-8). The launching of *Penny Magazine* in March 1832 by the English publisher Charles Knight, in collaboration with the Society for the Diffusion of Useful Knowledge, marked a definitive breakthrough. This magazine's success was overwhelming. Within a year its circulation rose to 200,000 copies, an unprecedented number. For the first time there was a magazine that was also widely read – and seen – by workers. If the popularization of science and technology was certainly a main aspect of the formula of Knight's maga-

---

[14] The book by Van der Boon Mesch was priced at approx. 4.80 guilders per volume (so 14.40 for the three volumes!), Erdmann at 3 (1 volume in 2 parts), Meijlink at 2.75, and Girardin at 7. For these prices, see Van der Meulen 1876.

[15] In the case of Liebig, see his fascinating correspondence with his publisher Vieweg (Schneider 1986).

[16] These innovations were introduced slightly later in the Netherlands: wood engraving approx. 1834, machine-made paper approx. 1834-38, and the fast press approx. 1828 (steam only after approx. 1850) (Van Lente & De Wit 1993, pp. 188-91, 205-10, 228-32, 256-60, 263-5, 276-81; Anderson 1994, pp. 2-3, 10-2, 72).

zine, its notion of *useful knowledge* had a much broader purport, referring to the total of the various knowledge areas dubbed *Realwissen* in Germany. It comprised science, technology, history, manufacturing, geography, modern languages, and, in particular, knowledge about the crafts – or basically all areas of knowledge except classic languages, pure mathematics, and religion.[17]

Innovative Dutch publishers such as Diederichs Brothers (Amsterdam), K. Fuhri (The Hague), A.C. Kruseman (Haarlem), and A.W. Sijthoff (Leiden), followed the British example (Van Lente & De Wit 1993, pp. 189-90, 232-3, 268-9, 271). They also belonged to the first Dutch publishers who marketed inexpensive popular books and magazines on chemistry and the other natural sciences. For instance, Diederichs, with its *Nederlandsch magazijn ter verspreiding van algemeene en nuttige kundigheden* ('Dutch magazine for the diffusion of general and useful skills') that appeared since 1834 and was modeled after a British example, also published Millard's cheap and illustrated *Scheikunde ten algemeene nutte* ('Chemistry for general use', 1842) and popular booklets on physics and physiology (Van Lente & De Wit 1993, pp. 264-5; Hemels & Vegt 1993, pp. 309-11).

More important for the popularization of the natural sciences in the Netherlands was the Haarlem apothecary son A.C. Kruseman (1818-1894), who in 1844 published a Dutch version of Liebig's *Familiar Letters on Chemistry*, and this was followed in 1852 by the first annual volume of the well-known popular science magazine *Album der natuur*.[18] Within a year 3,080 copies were sold, which suggests that the editors were right when in their preface of the first volume they posited that a fair and equal social distribution of knowledge of nature and its phenomena is "one of the basic needs of our times" (*Album der natuur*, 1 [1852], p. v). Although later on its circulation would drop, for years the *Album* was by far the main popular science magazine in the Netherlands (En-

---

[17]   On the *Penny Magazine* and Knight's view on educating the people voiced in it, see Anderson 1994, pp. 50-83.

[18]   *Album der natuur* (Haarlem, 1852-1909); on Kruseman, see Enschedé 1898.

schedé 1898, vol. 1, pp. 209-13; Coffeng 1994).[19] Still, this was not yet the end of Kruseman's science popularization efforts. In particular between 1853 and 1856, stimulated by the success of his magazine, he started publishing the *Practische volks-almanak* (1853-1862), an annual for the diffusion of "knowledge of the applied sciences among all social classes", and inexpensive magazines and book series for workers, farmers, and industrialists (Enschedé 1898, vol. 1, pp. 254-9, 264-6, 307-13, 320-9; Simons 1915, pp. 18-9; Van Lente & De Wit 1993, pp. 269-70; Hemels & Vegt 1993, pp. 154-5). These series included popular booklets on chemistry, but despite their moderate price (30 to 60 cents) the series was short-lived; probably, because Kruseman's competitors became more active in the same market and because, in terms of their content, Kruseman's books tended to be too popular for manufacturers and too difficult for workers (Enschedé 1898, vol. 1, p. 254).[20] By 1857 Kruseman in fact discontinued his activities in this area. He changed some of his popular science journals into family magazines and sold the others (Enschedé 1898, vol. 1, pp. 212, 258, 308-10, 325-6).

The publisher A.W. Sijthoff managed to have more lasting success. After having entered Kruseman's market in 1855 with his *Geïllustreerde almanak* (1855-65), which was supposed to compete with the *Practische volks-almanak*, in 1857 he began the popular science journal *Geïllustreerde familie-bibliotheek tot verspreiding van nuttige kennis* ('Illustrated family library for the diffusion of useful knowledge'). Strictly speaking this serial publication, which appeared in issues of 35 cents each, was no periodical, but a string of translated and adapted popular science books. For this series the enterprising publisher from Leiden had signed a contract with the German publisher Otto Spamer, who also supplied him with the indispensable plates for the illustrations. The quality of illustrations greatly influenced a series' commercial viability and Sijthoff had a nose for such details. With a circulation of 2,000, the *Boek der uitvindingen* ('Book of Inventions'), which comprised the first 48 is-

---

[19] Chemistry topics first played a modest role in the *Album*. This changed only after the Amsterdam chemistry teacher G. Doyer van Cleeff joined the editorial board in 1886; see *Chemisch Weekblad*, **13** (1916), 856-8.

[20] Examples of chemistry related works are Liebig 1855, Von Baumhauer 1855, Van Moorsel 1855a, Gunning 1857. For prices, see Van der Meulen 1876, p. 107.

sues of the new series, proved an extraordinary success. Before 1865 Sijthoff also published the series the *Boek der Natuur* ('Book of Nature') and the *Boek der Reizen* ('Book of Travels') (Van der Meulen 1891, pp. 56-9; Van der Meulen 1876, pp. 15-6; Enschedé 1898, vol. 1, pp. 257-8; Van Lente & De Wit 1993, pp. 269, 271). From 1868 onward Sijthoff successfully tapped the market with his *Algemeene bibliotheek* ('General Library') (Van der Meulen 1891, pp. 59-70; Van der Meulen 1876, p. 14; Van Lente & De Wit 1993, p. 190; Simons 1915, p. 21). Prior to 1875 as many as 90 volumes appeared, priced from 15 to 30 cents, in which also some chemistry-related topics were addressed (*e.g.* De Loos 1872).

Apart from these trailblazers in the area of illustrated books and magazines, there were countless other publishers in the period 1850-1865 who issued popular science works.[21] It is hardly relevant to name all of them, but two publishers of chemistry books deserve special mention. Between 1854 and 1861 the Amsterdam publisher Weytingh & Van der Haart published its *Volks-bibliotheek* that "addresses all branches of art and science, crafts and professions", which was designed to comprise as many as 103 booklets ("with woodcuts") of some 25-50 cents. Whether or not all volumes indeed appeared cannot be established with certainty here, but in the area of chemistry and its applications alone at least nine books were published (Van Moorsel 1855b; Van Moorsel 1855c; Jacobson 1859; see also Van der Meulen 1876, pp. 175-6). In 1854 the Sneek-based publisher Van Druten & Bleeker started its *Goedkoope bibliotheek voor alle standen* ('Cheap Library for All Classes'). This series, which would appear until after 1887, contained several fairly successful popularizing works on chemistry. Both J.W. Gunning's translation of J.F.W. Johnston's *Chemistry of Common Life* and Th.A.J. Abeleven's translation of Emil Postel's *Laien-Chemie* were reprinted at least once (Johnston 1855-56, Postel 1864). Contrary to the very practice-oriented *Volks-bibliotheek* of Weytingh & Van der Haart, Van Druten & Bleekers *Goedkope bibliotheek* contained marked physico-theological elements though.[22] It would be the last time that these two styles of popularization

---

[21] For an, incomplete, enumeration, see Simons 1915, pp. 18-23, 34.

[22] The series, for instance, opened with a book by H. Thiele on the history of the Christian church and by H. Burmeister on the history of creation. See also the preface by Gunning in Johnston 1855-56 and that by P. van der Burg in Postel 1864.

of chemistry existed side by side as equal (Homburg 1994, pp. 451, 456-60, 465-6). The new era of professional science was dawning – an era in which the relationships between science practitioners and laypersons, between science and religion, and between scientific knowledge and social utility were substantially revised and redefined.

8. 1845-1865: Period of Flowering and Transition

The 1850s and early 1860s were unmistakably the heyday of the popular science book. Rarely so many different initiatives were undertaken in such a short time span, and various motives and social groups played a role. Precisely because so many dissimilar developments overlapped, the third quarter of the nineteenth century was a decisive and exciting episode in the history of science popularization.

Apart from the role played by publishers, changes in the social position of science practitioners influenced the popularizing of scientific insights and research results. A single class of learned scholars dissolved into numerous discipline-based communities of specialists who earned their living by practicing their discipline. For chemists and other professional scientists the popularization of their field fulfilled an essential role in their striving for social prestige. Publications by Justus Liebig (1803-1873), notably his *Chemische Briefe*, provide a perfect example, but the *Nut der scheikunde voor den industrieel* ('Usefulness of chemistry for the manufacturer'), written by the Amsterdam chemistry professor E.H. von Baumhauer, fits this pattern as well (Liebig 1840; Liebig 1844-46; Bayertz 1985, pp. 214-5; Zott 1993). In addition, the professionalization of science, because of the growing specialization that accompanied it, exerted great influence on the relationship between scientists and laypersons. Everyone who did not belong to the small particular field involved was now a layperson. In this respect it is interesting to observe that around 1850 for the first time a group of authors emerged who became active in the intersecting knowledge domain of the disciplinary specialist and the layperson. Basically these new professional popularizers devoted their life to translating the results of science to a large audience. In France this involved well-known popularizers such as the abbot François Moigno (1804-1884), Victor Meunier (1817-1903), Louis Figuier (1819-

1894), and, later on, Camille Flammarion (1842-1925) and Gaston Tissandier (1843-1899) (Raichvarg & Jacques 1991, pp. 41-4, 59-65, 68-76), while for the Netherlands one might think of W.H. Logeman and Douwe Lubach, two of the editors of the *Album der natuur* and of many other works.

The professionalization of science had major consequences for the nature of science popularization, yet it was not the main driving force behind the new wave of publications at that time. The science popularization of the early 1850s was still too much bound up with the tradition of both the old physico-theology and, in particular, the philanthropist and moralizing approach – aimed at education and enlightening the public – as embraced by the Dutch Society for the Common Good and the English Society for the Diffusion of Useful Knowledge. This is why it is perhaps more correct to view the flourishing of science popularization in the years immediately after 1845 as a final twitching of the late-eighteenth and early-nineteenth-century way of science popularization. Stimulated by the new post-1848 political realities – that brought liberal professionals and industrialist to power – a major publishing offensive was realized one more time, geared toward educating the youth and elevating the workers. When its demands were realized in part, as reflected in the Dutch school acts of 1857 and 1863 and the establishment of technical schools, it dwindled again. Chemistry and the other natural sciences were integrated into the regular school curricula, and normal textbooks took over the function that hitherto had been fulfilled by the popular science books. First, however, the popularization of chemistry would flourish as never before.

Farmers and the rural youth were among the first to receive attention from the 'knowledge diffusers'. Already from the mid-1840s books were published especially for them in which agricultural chemistry was explained in simple terms. These books promulgated the view that chemistry might well be the most useful and interesting subject to learn more about (*e.g.* Johnston 1847, Enklaar 1851, Stöckhardt 1854; see also Snelders 1981 and Layton 1973, pp. 48, 51-3).

Not much later the education of the lower classes in the cities gained attention as well. In more cities and on a much larger scale than in the 1830s, industrial schools, evening courses for workers, and reading cabinets were established. They were initiated not only by the Society for the Common Good and the Society for the Promotion of Industry, but also by many new organizations, several of which were set up – in the wake of the revolutionary events of 1848 – in order to assuage the polarization of capital and labor through the spread of useful knowledge. Science for the people was largely meant to serve political pacification and the stabilization of social relations, as was the case with the British Society for the Diffusion of Useful Knowledge.[23] Specific Dutch examples are the Utrecht Vereeniging ter Bevordering van Nuttige Kennis (Association for Promoting Useful Knowledge [1848]), the Maatschappij ter Bevordering van Wetenschap tot Volksgeluk (Society for the Promotion of Popular Happiness by Means of Science [1849]) established in Amsterdam, and several similar societies founded in the years 1849-1854 (Mulder 1881, vol. 1, pp. 195-8; Goudswaard 1981, pp. 94-5, 100-1, 131-2, 176-85, 198-214; Van Lente 1988, pp. 96-105; Simons 1915, pp. 19-20; De Vries 1963, pp. 11-20; Van Lente & De Wit 1993, pp. 189-90). In addition, several local scientific societies – the Genootschap Physica in Zaandijk, the Natuur- en Scheikundig Genootschap (Society for Natural Knowledge and Chemistry) in Deventer, and the Genootschap Tot Nut en Vergenoegen (Society for Usefulness and Enjoyment) in Arnhem – began to organize popular lectures on physics and chemistry.[24] Although some doubted the usefulness of "making available popular scientific writings at low prices" in addition to these lectures because "those of the lesser classes" often "do neither read such writings nor understand them", a number of accessible chemistry books were still published in this period.[25] These included, besides the books by Girardin and Van Moorsel mentioned above, J.W. Gunning's translation of Stöckhardt's *Schule der Chemie*, which in Germany was one of the most successful self-study chemistry books, and the *Voorlezingen over elementaire scheikunde* ('Lectures on Elementary Chemistry') by E.A. van der Burg. The Utrecht-based educational facility for workers (Inrigting tot Onderwijs

---

[23] For a careful treatment of this subject, see Russell 1983, pp. 165-71; and Anderson 1994, pp. 4-7, 53, 67, 77-79.
[24] Statistisch Jaarboekje, 2 (1852), 166; Statistisch Jaarboekje, 7 (1858), 166-8; Berigten over het Fabrijkwezen in het Jaar 1857 (Haarlem 1859), pp. 1, 5.
[25] Verslag eerste Nederlandsche Nijverheids, Congres, Haarlem, 1857, pp. 15, 83.

voor den Arbeidenden Stand), for instance, used Stöckhardt's textbook in its chemistry teaching (Stöckhardt 1848).[26]

In addition, popularizing works on chemistry appeared that had to serve as 'reading books' for primary schools. These books were part of initiatives aimed at a radical reform of primary education. The reading instruction on the basis of the Bible was meant to be replaced by instruction on the basis of books on topics of which the children of workers and farmers would have direct practical benefit in their later professional life. Physics and, especially, chemistry were supposed to play a prominent role in these new reading books. Their content needed to be presented in such way that the direct connection with the child's daily 'lifeworld' was immediately clear. In England, the cradle of many of these ideas, the "movement for teaching the science of common things" was very successful after 1853 (Layton 1973, pp. 35-54, 95-117). There, within a few years more than 200 different science schoolbooks for primary education were published, including 28 on chemistry alone (Layton 1973, p. 111). Given the large influence of church organizations on primary education some caution was called for, though. At all cost it had to be prevented that people would think that the Bible was replaced by godless, materialist readings. This also explains why precisely in this popular science genre, in the period 1845-1865, books still regularly contained physico-theological formulations, while education reformers argued that "the teaching of science [is] essential for the moral and religious salvation of the children of the poor" (Layton 1973, pp. 96-7, 112-3). Thus these books were unmistakably in the tradition of the children editions of the books by Martinet and Uilkens, but there was one major difference: if in Martinet and Uilkens the divinely created surrounding world was center-stage, now also the objects of the technical-industrial society were considered part and parcel of everyday life. Besides the sky, water, soil, and flora, issues such as human food, housing, clothing, health care, and hygiene were extensively addressed. In much smaller editions than in Eng-

---

[26] Later editions appeared in 1850 and 1855. See also *Verslag aangaande den toestand der Inrigting van Onderwijs voor den Arbeidenden Stand te Utrecht over den cursus van 1853-54*, Utrecht, n.d., p. 4; Van der Burg 1860. The books by Girardin and Van der Burg were quite expensive. The one by Van den Burg did cost 3.90 guilders (Van der Meulen 1876, p. 23).

land such books were also published in the Netherlands, with the main example of Johnston's several times reprinted *Scheikunde in het dagelijks leven* ('The Chemistry of Common Life'), which, in the words of its translator and editor Gunning, might also serve as "a suitable reading book in the higher grades of our public schools" (Johnston 1855-56).[27]

Although books on the 'chemistry of everyday life' outside the context of primary education would continue to be published way into the twentieth century, the heyday of this genre was over after 1865 (*cf.* Wijnand 1918, Bokhorst 1933, Römpp 1944, Schouten 1967). The same holds true for popular chemistry books that catered to workers and farmers. While between 1845 and 1864 about 30 popular chemistry books appeared in the Netherlands (including reprints), in the period 1865-1899 their total was not even ten, of which five were between 1865 and 1869.[28] As indicated above, the inclusion of chemistry in regular school curricula seriously lowered the need for specific lectures and courses aimed at popularization. A striking example of the effects of this are the textbooks used by Gunning in his teaching. After first having lectured for years in evening schools for workers on the basis of Stöckhardt's popular chemistry book, after its third edition he decided to write his own chemistry book. He was meanwhile teaching at a technical school, with a regular curriculum and daily classes, for which he deemed Stöckhardt's book and its "aphoristic form" unsuitable (Gunning 1858, vol. 1, p. vi). After 1863 textbooks similar to the one by Gunning were issued in large quantities to serve advanced secondary schools (*hogere burgerscholen*). But also for basic education – technical schools and general evening schools – regular textbooks appeared that no longer were framed as popularizing books, even though their didactics deviated from the books used in the advanced secondary schools (List 1862-64; Huizinga 1869).[29] This is a reflection of profound changes in the general understanding of

---

[27] See also Meijlink & Jacobson 1863, Augustijn 1851, Duflos 1854-55, Enklaar 1857.

[28] The estimate is based on extensive bibliographical study, using the bibliographies mentioned above (Holtrop, Van der Meulen) and all titles found with the help of the on-line national Dutch library catalogue NCC, when using keywords such as 'scheikunde', 'scheikundig', 'chemie', and 'chemisch'.

[29] Huizinga emphasized in his preface that advanced secondary education (HBS) textbooks moved from the general to the specific, while he himself tried to start from 'everyday ... phenomena'. On Huizinga as popularizer, see Van Berkel 1991.

the nature of popular books. Popularization shifted from an activity geared toward the diffusion of knowledge to women, children, and the lower classes to knowledge transfer between researchers and laypersons.

9. Mulder and Gunning

Between 1860 and 1870, not only a quantitative break in chemistry's popularization took place, as illustrated by the numbers mentioned above, but also, and above all, a qualitative one. Views on the use, function, and content of popularization changed drastically. Thereby a role was played by the professionalization of chemistry and the gradual growing apart – for many reasons – of natural scientists and the common people, as well as by the 'educational struggle' in the Netherlands that caused moral and religious education to be disconnected from the transfer of useful knowledge.[30] The nature of the changing insights in popularization can be demonstrated preeminently on the basis of the views of two major Dutch popularizers of chemistry: Gerrit Jan Mulder (1802-1880) and his student Jan Willem Gunning (1827-1900).

In the history of Dutch chemistry Mulder holds a prominent place, but not just in chemistry.[31] Despite his unmistakable shortcomings, especially on a personal level, he literally and figuratively dwarfed most of his contemporaries. There are few areas in Dutch society with which he did not engage. Medicine and public health care, pharmacy, chemistry, secondary and higher education, national and colonial agriculture, tax politics and trade, technology, and local and national politics – on all these areas he has left his mark. Also in the area of science popularization Mulder played a leading role, which, strangely, has not received the attention from those in the history of science that it deserves.[32] In the late 1840s in the field of chemistry he stood at the heart of the then emerging popularization movement.

---

[30] After the controversial act of 1857, public primary schools first retained their general Christian character, but after more private schools had been founded, public schools grew much more neutral. In private schools religious education was obviously tied to the school's specific denomination (*cf.* Idenburg 1960, pp. 82-119).

[31] On Mulder, see Snelders 1993, pp. 93-108; Wels 1985; Van Raak 2001.

[32] A recent exception is Theunissen 2000, pp. 80-97.

Just like his teacher Gerrit Moll (1785-1838), Mulder had great admiration for English science and its prevailing utilitarian view. Moll was the leading example of a science popularizer for Mulder (Mulder 1881, vol. 1, p. 188). The English influence on Mulder's views is appropriately reflected in the fact that he preferred to use the English term *useful knowledge* where others would simply refer to its Dutch equivalent (Mulder 1881, vol. 1, pp. 182, 195).[33] Not surprisingly, we encounter many of the views promoted by the *Society for the Diffusion of Knowledge* and the *Penny Magazine* also in his writings almost word for word. Mulder considered "thou shall be useful to others" as the highest command citizens had to live by. Scientists, therefore, should not be men of learning but "men of *useful knowledge*". They should gear their research toward socially useful matters and be fully committed to passing on their knowledge to workers, women, boys, and other members of society. Much as in his English examples, this knowledge diffusion served a major moral goal, according to Mulder, because it would make an essential contribution to the "moral and material happiness of the people". Knowledge of nature would encourage young people to admire "the Creator of all things". Our 'knowing', he felt, determined our 'action', which is why all knowledge had direct ethical relevancy (Mulder 1881, vol. 1, pp. 31, 38, 182, 193-8, 294; Mulder 1850, pp. 8, 11, 30-3; Mulder, 'Voorrede', in Stöckhardt, *De scheikunde* (1848), cited after De Vrijer 1946, p. 45; Gunning 1882, pp. 153-7; *cf.* also Anderson 1994, pp. 53-4, 67, 79). For Mulder, therefore, science popularization was hardly a marginal activity; it was to him an essential and integral part of his identity as a scientist. Energetically, he dedicated himself to the popularization of chemistry, notably in the years between 1845 and 1851. He was involved in nearly all the kinds of popularization activities discussed above. For example, in the 1840s he gave popular lectures on chemistry for the Society Physica in Utrecht, he gave evening classes to boys between 12 and 16, he was one of the founders of the technical school in Utrecht, he was an initiator and for years the chairman of the Vereeniging ter Bevordering van Nuttige Kennis, and he was secretary and co-founder of the Maatschappij

---

[33] See also his correspondence with the Ministry of the Colonies (personal information from Margaret Leidelmeijer).

Wetenschap tot Volksgeluk, an organization that set up so-called *consultatiebureaux*, a sort of precursor to the late-twentieth century 'science shops' (Mulder 1881, vol. 1, pp. 188, 193-8; Mulder 1849; Mulder 1850).

In addition, Mulder played a stimulating role in the publication of two popular chemistry books that marked the beginning of the 1850s hype. In 1847 he had his student J.R.E. van Laer translate Johnston's *Catechism for Agricultural Chemistry* and one year later he pushed his student Gunning to translate Stöckhardt's chemistry book. Moreover, it was he who in 1853 convinced King William III to organize public, popular lectures on the agricultural sciences, which resulted in a lecture series published by Kruseman (Mulder 1847; Mulder 1881, vol. 1, p. 261).

Gunning was the most active of Mulder's students in the field of science popularization, with the possible exception of Mulder's own son Louis (1828-1897). Especially at the beginning of his career, he adored his teacher and closely followed in his footsteps. In 1849 he became Mulder's assistant and still before earning his doctorate in 1853 he translated Stöckhardt's chemistry book and *Schoedler's boek der natuur* (with J.J. Altheer). He taught, most likely, at the Inrigting tot Onderwijs voor den Arbeidenden Stand in Utrecht, and from 1854 also at the technical school, co-founded by Mulder. Besides his role as translator of *Scheikunde der dagelijkse dingen* for Van Druten & Bleekers' *Goedkoope bibliotheek* (1855-56) and as author of *Wat men uit zeewater maken kan* ('What can be made from sea water') for Kruseman's *Nijverheidsbibliotheek* (1857), he was active – together with other leaders of the Vereeniging ter Bevordering van Nuttige Kennis as editor of the 25 cents magazine *Pantheon: tijdschrift ter verspreiding van nuttige kennis* (1853-1858) (Gunning & Altheer 1850-52; Simons 1915, p. 18; Mulder 1881, vol. 1, pp. 195-6; De Vrijer 1946, pp. 36-75, 216-64, esp. 37, 43-5, 65-6, 225).[34]

After a personal conflict in 1857, Mulder radically broke with his student. Thereafter Gunning went his own way. The break with his teacher not only meant a watershed in his social career, but also in his thinking

---

[34] See also Verslag Inrigting voor den Arbeidende Stand; 'Otto van Rees', NNBW III, 1046-7.

on science popularization. From about 1860 he developed his views on the social role of science and the relationship between science and religion that sharply deviated from those of Mulder. His marriage to Petronella Adriana Pierson in 1858 not only brought him into contact with circles associated with the orthodox Protestant movement 'Reveil', but also with the movement of emerging Modernist theology, led by his brother-in-law Allard Pierson and the then famous Dutch author Conrad Busken Huet. Without ever subscribing to the Modernist direction, Gunning showed himself to be in the remainder of his life a fierce proponent of a strict dualism between religion and science, which was professed by both Modernists and orthodox (!). This dualism radically broke with more than a century of physico-theology, Enlightenment didactics, and the diffusion of 'useful knowledge'. For Gunning the Bible, and the figure of Christ in particular, was the foundation of religion, while science had to be practiced experimentally and objectively, unrelated to any philosophical-moral or religious ideology. As a child of the professionalizing science of his time he demanded full freedom for scientific research "for its own sake", regardless of whatever social usefulness (Gunning 1865; Gunning 1882; De Vrijer 1946, pp. 38-42, 47-61, 222-3, 251-60). From this perspective, in 1882 Gunning looked back on the work of his teacher and criticized his views with singular sharpness. Mulder, Gunning argued, did not know the "autonomy of science in the modern sense"; he valued "science only [...] to the extent it could elevate humanity morally [and] not for its own sake". Such "fatal" views had troublesome consequences for both science and ethics. "To attribute a morally edifying character to science, by asking it to be subservient to objectives that as such – no matter how lofty and honorable – are foreign to it, is to make it unfree." Which knowledge will become useful could not be determined in advance, according to Gunning, notwithstanding Mulder's self-reliant view on this issue (Gunning 1882, pp. 155-7, 171-2, 185-7). While Mulder saw himself as a transitional figure, in between the traditional scholar and the 'man of useful knowledge', he failed to recognize that, as he grew older, the 'train of chemistry', influenced by Liebig and his followers, had already moved on to the next station: the 'man of useful knowledge' was replaced by the professional chemist who transferred his knowledge to the next generation of professional chemists rather than to the public (Mulder 1881, vol. 1, p. 182, 257-9; *cf.* Homburg 1993a, pp. 287-373). A new generation of chemists opted to give low priority to educating the people and put their knowledge in the service of science itself, the government, and the victors of the liberal revolution of 1848, the industrialists (Homburg 1993c, pp. 266-70; Verbong & Homburg 1994).

This is why Mulder, regardless of his major role in the establishment of Dutch education in chemistry, cannot be characterized as an early professional chemist. He belonged to an earlier phase of the cultivation of science. His entire life he remained faithful to views articulated around 1830 within organizations such as the Society for the Common Good and the Society for the Diffusion of Useful Knowledge – views he first embraced during and right after his college years (*cf.* Homburg 1987; Homburg 1993a, pp. 223-51, 313-28, 341-50).

10. Wonders of Technology

These new views, such as Gunning's, had obvious consequences for the popularization of science. After all, the old justification of spreading social virtues through knowledge of nature was no longer accepted. By 1855 Kruseman, who in Haarlem had intensive contact with Busken Huet, became painfully aware of this. Consequently, he altered the subtitle of *Familie-magazijn* from 'reading-matter for entertainment and the diffusion of useful skills' to 'moral reading-matter for entertainment and also for the diffusion of useful skills'. A subtle change that was meant to express that the moral and the scientific were separate worlds (Enschedé 1898, vol. 1, pp. 320-6). Some time thereafter he gave up nearly all his popular science activities.

In the vacuum that emerged in the area of popularization on account of the rise of regular chemical education and the more limited appeal of the useful knowledge diffusion movement only a small niche remained for the popular chemistry book: showing the wonders of technology. Whereas astronomers, paleontologists, biologists, and other earth scientists in popular, lavishly illustrated works managed to entertain the public at large with the results of their science, the chemist's test-tubes proved to be no attention-grabbers. More promising were spectacular, or mysterious, images of factories, or of mineral, vegetable, and animal materials used and produced by them. It was this road that was taken by the popularizers of chemistry after about 1865.

The *Boek der uitvindingen* ('Book of Inventions'), published by Sijthoff, is the best example of the new popular genre that came into being at that time. Between 1852 and 1893 eight German editions were published, each one revised to such extent that the size of the book gradually expanded from two to nine volumes (Thomas 1852, Reuleaux 1889-93). Between 1857 and 1892 as many as five Dutch adapted versions appeared, the last one in seven volumes. In this series chemistry took up a prominent place. The last edition devoted a full volume, called *Organic chemistry in everyday life*, to organic chemical technology (sugar, vinegar, soap, gaslight, *etc.*) as well as a volume to inorganic chemical technology, entitled *Chemistry and technology* (iron and steel, porcelain, gun powder, paint, *etc.*) (Bosscha 1892ff.). We encounter the same technology-colored vision on chemistry in works such as Figuier's *Wonderen der wetenschap*, and in the six-volume series *De wonderen der techniek*, with one entire volume devoted to chemistry (Figuier 1867-72, Borgerhof van den Berg et al. 1906-10; *cf.* Deherrypon 1872). If popularization before was about the wonders of God's divine creation, the new books that catered to the general public emphatically put mankind's wondrous scientific and technological creations center-stage.

11. Conclusion and Outlook

There are four main reasons, I think, for the dramatic change in the popularization of chemistry after about 1860: (1) first and foremost, the introduction of chemistry as a regular subject at secondary schools, which greatly reduced the need for popular chemistry books for self-instruction; (2) the professionalization of chemistry, which shifted the role of popularization from an emphasis on the great works of the Creator and on the general usefulness of science to roles linked to legitimation and recrutement strategies of the chemical profession; (3) changing views on the relation between science and religion that emphasized the separation of the two; and (4) last but not least the changing nature of the genre of the popular book, which increasingly dictated the use of illustrations. The rise of a visual culture during the second half of the nineteenth century was in my view, next to the expansion of the industry itself, one of the major causes of the increasing role of chemical technology and chemical industry in popular books on chemistry.

In the twentieth century the emphasis on technical chemistry would continue to play a decisive role, not in the last place because of the then emerging direct involvement of chemical corporations in the popularization of chemistry. In contrast to the years 1865-1899, in which in the Netherlands all popular chemistry books had a technological outlook, after 1900 new styles of popular chemistry books would (re)emerge: books completely devoted to simple experiments that boys could perform at home, in order to prepare their minds (and hands) for becoming a chemists; and books on new developments, such as new theories of atoms and molecules, the world of radioactive rays, and the discoveries in biochemistry, which also resulted partly from attempts to enhance the recruitment into chemistry. Yet these books on chemical science and chemical experimentation were outnumbered – at least in the Netherlands, and probably elsewhere as well – by books in which the chemical industry was treated in a popular way. Starting approximately in 1865, the popularization of chemistry and the promotion of the chemical industry became so strongly entwined that one cannot blame the general public for not always being capable of keeping the two apart. In my view, the long lasting emphasis in popular chemistry books on utility, technology, and industry has made the science of chemistry particularly vulnerable with respect to criticism of social, political, and environmental behavior of the chemical industry.

When in August 1965 several worried public relations officers from the Dutch chemical industry gathered in The Hague to consider the deteriorated public image of chemistry, their concern was not without precedent. Perhaps without realizing it, they tackled an issue the historical foundation of which was put in place a full century before. As we all know now, the results of their publicity campaigns have been rather futile, or even counter-productive. In Eibert Bunte's *Leven met chemie* ('Living with Chemistry') of 1968, the old story of the utility and necessity of chemistry was repeated for the umpteenth time. Not much later student numbers in chemistry started to drop dramatically, and they have never really recovered until today (Homburg & Palm 2004, pp. 6-9). It is only recently that communication between chemical science, the chemical industry, the environmental movement, and the public at large has begun to improve. The replacement of popularization and public relations campaigns by dialogue is crucial here. In that respect, perhaps, we are now witnessing the final days of traditional approaches to the popularization of chemistry. How the new approaches will influence the public image of chemistry, can only be known in the future.

References

Anderson, P.J.: 1994, *The Printed Image and the Transformation of Popular Culture*, 2nd edn., Clarendon, Oxford.

Augustijn, J.A.: 1851, *Aanleiding tot de beoefening der natuur - en landhuishoudkundige scheikunde. Een leesboek voor de hoogste klasse der lagere scholen*, Van Nooten, Schoonhoven.

Bayertz, K.: 1985, 'Spreading the Spirit of Science: Social Determinants of the Popularization of Science in Nineteenth-Century Germany', in: T. Shinn & R. Whitley (eds.), *Expository Science: Forms and Functions of Popularisation*, Reidel, Dordrecht, pp. 209-227.

Beets, M.N.: 1815, *Volks-scheikunde, of onderwijzingen en raadgevingen tot nuttig gebruik*, Van der Hey, Amsterdam.

Berzelius, J.J.: 1834-41, *Leerboek der scheikunde*, 6 vols., Van den Heuvell, Rotterdam.

Bokhorst, S.C.: 1933, *Scheikunde in het dagelijksch leven*, Wereldbibliotheek, Amsterdam.

Borgerhof van den Berg, H.J., *et al.* (eds.): 1906-10, *De wonderen der techniek*, 6 vols., Dalmeijer, Amsterdam.

Bosscha, J. (introd.): 1892ff., *Het boek der uitvindingen, ambachten en fabrieken*, 7 vols., Sijthoff, Leiden.

Brougham, H.P.: 1826, *Over eenige hulpmiddelen tot vermeerdering van beroepskunde bij ambachtslieden*, Van Cleef, The Hague/Amsterdam.

Bunte, E.H.: 1968a, *Leven met chemie*, Vereniging van de Nederlandse Chemische Industrie, The Hague.

Bunte, E.H.: 1968b, *Chemie in opmars*, Elsevier, Amsterdam/Brussels.

Buys, J.: 1811, *Volks-natuurkunde, of onderwijs in de natuurkunde voor mingeoefenden; tot wering van wanbegrippen, vooroordeel en bijgeloof*, Van der Hey, Amsterdam.

Coffeng, L.: 1994, 'Het Album der Natuur. Popularisering van de natuurwetenschap in een tijdschrift uit de eerste (*sic*) helft van de negentiende eeuw', *Groniek. Historisch tijdschrift*, no. 123, pp. 52-66.

Curie, E.: 1938, *Madame Curie: haar leven en werk*, 7th edn., Leopold, The Hague.

De Galan, C.: 1965, 'Blijft Nederland bewoonbaar?', *Socialisme en democratie*, **22**, 313-23.

Deherrypon, M.: 1872, *Les merveilles de la chimie*, Hachette, Paris.

De Loos, D.: 1872., *Zetmeel en melk, een paar onderwerpen uit het gebied van scheikunde*, Sijthoff, Leiden.

De Vries, J.: 1963, *Ontsloten poorten. Vijftig jaren Volksuniversiteit in Nederland 1913-1963*, Van Gorcum, Assen.

De Vrijer, M.J.A.: 1946, *Gunning Tragicus. Prof. Dr. J.H. Gunning Jr. in den kring zijner broeders*, Daamen, The Hague.

Duflos, A.: 1854-5, *De scheikunde toegepast op het dagelijks leven en de nijverheid*, 2 vols., Blussé en Van Braam, Dordrecht.

Enklaar, E.C.: 1857, *Gemeenzame gesprekken over onderwerpen uit de schei en volkshuishoudkunde enz. in betrekking tot den landbouw. Een volksleesboek vooral geschikt voor plattelands schoolen*, Van Hulst, Kampen.

Enklaar, F.A.: 1851, *Handleiding bij het onderwijs in de landhuishoudkundige scheikunde, voornamelijk ingerigt ten gebruike der lagere scholen ten platte lande*, Noorduyn & Zoon, Gorinchem.

Enschedé, J.W.: 1898, *A.C. Kruseman*, 2 vols., Van Kampen, Amsterdam.

Erdmann, O.L.: 1836, *Algemeen overzigt der nieuwere scheikunde met bijzondere aanwijzing van derzelver nuttige toepassingen*, 2 vols., Berntrop, Amsterdam.

Figuier, L.: 1867-72, *De wonderen der wetenschap, of de geschiedenis der nieuwste uitvindingen aan het volk verhaald*, 4 vols., Belinfante, Amsterdam.

French, S.J.: 1937, *The Drama of Chemistry. How Man Deals with Atoms*, The University Society, New York.

Gee, B.: 1989, 'Amusement Chests and Portable Laboratories: Practical Alternatives to the Regular Laboratory', in: F.A.J.L. James (ed.), *The Development of the Laboratory*, Macmillan, Basingstoke/London, pp. 37-59.

Girardin, J., *Scheikunde voor den beschaafden stand en het fabriekwezen*, 2nd edn., 2 vols., Van Goor, Gouda.

Golinski, J.: 1992, *Science as Public Culture: Chemistry and Enlightenment in Britain, 1760-1820*, Cambridge UP, Cambridge.

Goudswaard, N.B.: 1981, *Vijfenzestig jaren nijverheidsonderwijs*, Van Gorcum, Assen.

Greiling, W: 1938, *Chemie erobert die Welt*, Wilhelm Limpert, Berlin.

Gunning, J.W.: 1857, *Wat men uit zeewater maken kan*, Kruseman, Haarlem.

Gunning, J.W.: 1858, *Leerboek der scheikunde. Ten gebruike aan inrigtingen van lager en middelbaar onderwijs, en tot zelf-onderrigt*, vol. 1, Van Nooten, Schoonhoven.

Gunning, J.W.: 1865, *De eisch van het natuuronderzoek, toegelicht uit de geschiedenis der scheikunde*, Van der Post, Utrecht.

Gunning, J.W.: 1882, 'G.J. Mulder', in: N.C. Balsem (ed.), *Mannen van beteekenis in onze dagen*, Tjeenk Willink, Haarlem, pp. 139-88.

Gunning, J.W. & J.J. Altheer: 1850-52, *Schoedler's Boek der natuur. Algemeene beginselen der physica, astronomie, chemie, mineralogie, geologie, physiologie, botanie en zoölogie*, W.F. Dannenfelser, Utrecht.

Hemels, J. & R. Vegt: 1993, *Het Geïllustreerde Tijdschrift in Nederland: bron van kennis en vermaakt, lust voor het oog. Bibliografie. Deel 1: 1840-1945*, Cramwinckel, Amsterdam.

Hoefnagels, J.P.: 1993, *Van milieuzorgen naar milieuzorg*, MA thesis, Erasmus University Rotterdam.

Holtrop, L.S.A.: 1842, *Bibliotheca medico-chirurgica et pharmaceutico-chemica*, Fuhri, The Hague.

Homburg, E.: 1987, 'Over het boekenbezit van Gerrit Jan Mulder, aan de hand van een veilingcatalogus', *Tijdschrift voor de Geschiedenis der Geneeskunde, Natuurwetenschap, Wiskunde en Techniek*, 10, 45-56.

Homburg, E.: 1993a, *Van beroep 'Chemiker'. De opkomst van de industriële chemicus en het polytechnische onderwijs in Duitsland (1790-1850)*, Delftse Universitaire Pers, Delft.

Homburg, E.: 1993b, 'Industrie, chemie en milieu (1750-1815)', in: H.W. Lintsen *et al.* (eds.), *Geschiedenis van de techniek in Nederland. De wording van een moderne samenleving (1800-1890)*, vol. 4, Walburg Pers, Zutphen, pp. 158-79.

Homburg, E.: 1993c, 'Een bedrijfstak in verandering', in: H.W. Lintsen *et al.* (eds.), *Geschiedenis van de techniek in Nederland*, vol. 4, Walburg Pers, Zutphen, pp. 258-70.

Homburg, E.: 1994, ' 'Schrikbeelden van scheikundigen aard': chemische industrie, chemische wetenschap en het milieu', *Tijdschrift voor Geschiedenis*, 107, 439-466.

Homburg, E.: 1995, 'Van volksscheikunde tot technologie: popularisering van de chemie in de negentiende eeuw', *Gewina*, 18, 72-101.

Homburg, E.: 1999, 'The Rise of Analytical Chemistry and its Consequences for the Development of the German Chemical Profession', *Ambix*, 46, 1-32.

Homburg, E. & L. Palm: 2004, 'Grenzen aan de groei – groei aan de grenzen: enkele ontwikkelingslijnen van de na-oorlogse chemie', in: E. Homburg & L. Palm (eds.), *De geschiedenis van de scheikunde in Nederland 3. De ontwikkeling van de chemie van 1945 tot het begin van de jaren tachtig*, Delft University Press, Delft, pp. 3-18.

Hufbauer, K.: 1982, *The Formation of the German Chemical Community (1720-1795)*, University of California Press, Berkeley.

Huizinga, D.: 1869, *Handleiding bij het eerste onderwijs in scheikunde aan burgeravondscholen*, Noordhoff, Groningen.

Idenburg, Ph.J.: 1960, *Schets van het Nederlandse schoolwezen*, Wolters, Groningen.

Imhof, M.: 1802, *Anfangsgründe der Chemie*, Lentner, München.

Jacobson ABzn., G.J.: 1859, *De plantaardige verwstoffen*, Amsterdam.

Johnston, J.F.W.: 1846, *Catechismus voor landbouwkundige scheikunde en aardkunde*, Kramers, Rotterdam.

Johnston, J.F.W.: 1855-56, *De scheikunde in het dagelijks leven*, 3 vols., Van Druten & Bleeker, Sneek.

Knight, D.: 1986, 'Accomplishment or Dogma: Chemistry in the Introductory Works of Jane Marcet and Samuel Parkes', *Ambix*, 33, 94-8.

Krätz, O.: 1991, 'Die Chemie im Spiegel der Literatur des 20. Jahrhunderts', *Chemie in unserer Zeit*, 25, 44-50.

Layton, D.: 1973, *Science for the People: The Origins of the School Science Curriculum in England*, Allen & Unwin, London.

Lenders, J.: 1988, *De burger en de volksschool. Culturele en mentale achtergronden van een onderwijshervorming in Nederland 1780-1850*, SUN, Nijmegen.

Liebig, J.: 1840, *Ueber das Studium der Naturwissenschaften und über den Zustand der Chemie in Preussen*, Vieweg, Braunschweig.

Liebig, J.: 1844-46, *Brieven over scheikunde en de betrekkingen waarin deze wetenschap staat tot koophandel, physiologie en landbouw*, 2 pts., Kruseman, Haarlem.

Liebig, J.: 1855, *De grondslagen der landbouw-scheikunde*, Kruseman, Haarlem.

Lindee, M.S.: 1991, 'The American Career of Jane Marcet's 'Conversations on Chemistry', 1806-1853', *Isis*, **82**, 8-23.

List, K.: 1862-64, *Handleiding bij het eerste onderwijs in de scheikunde*, 2 vols., Binger, Amsterdam.

Loschacoff-de Kanter, S.C.J.B.: 1970, 'Het industrie college te Leiden', *Leids Jaarboekje*, 125-146.

Lowood, H.E.: 1987, 'Patriotism, profit and the promotion of science in the German Enlightenment: the economic and scientific societies, 1760-1815,' Phil. Diss. University of California, Berkeley.

MacLean, J.: 1977, 'Het handels- en nijverheidsonderwijs van 1800 tot 1850', *Kleio*, **18**, 3-30.

Marcet, J.: 1810, *Zamenspraken over de scheikunde, waarin de grondbeginselen dezer wetenschap op eene eenvoudige wijze voorgedragen en met proefnemingen opgehelderd worden*, vol. 1, Immerzeel, Amsterdam.

Marcet, J.: 1841, *Conversations on Chemistry, in which the Elements of that Science are Familiarly Explained and Illustrated by Experiments*, 2 vols., 11th edn., Longman, London.

Martin, L.-A.: 1810, *Les lettres à Sophie sur la physique, la chimie et l'histoire naturelle*, 2 vols., Nicolle, Paris.

Meinel, C.: 1983, 'Theory or Practice? The Eighteenth-Century Debate on the Scientific Status of Chemistry', *Ambix*, **30**, 121-32.

Meinel, C.: 1985, 'Reine und angewandte Chemie. Die Entstehung einer neuen Wissenschaftskonzeption in der Chemie der Aufklärung', *Berichte zur Wissenschaftsgeschichte*, **8**, 25-45.

Meijlink, B.: 1836-38, *Allereerste beginselen der scheikunde: eene handleiding voor allen, die eene oppervlakkige kennis dezer wetenschap wenschen te verkrijgen*, 2 pts., Van den Sigtenhorst, Deventer.

Meijlink, B. & G.J. Jacobson ABzn.: 1863, *Beginselen der technologie*, Van Hulst, Kampen.

Mulder, G.J.: 1847, *Een woord bij den catechismus der landbouwkundige scheikunde*, Kramers, Rotterdam.

Mulder, G.J.: 1849, *Wetenschap en volksgeluk: een woord voor Nederland geschreven*, Kramers, Rotterdam.

Mulder, G.J.: 1850, *Reglement en toelichting betreffende de Maatschappij ter bevordering van Wetenschap tot Volksgeluk*, Van de Weijer, Utrecht.

Mulder, G.J.: 1881, *Levensschets van G.J. Mulder, door hem zelven geschreven en door drie zijner vrienden uitgegeven*, 2 vols., Kramers, Rotterdam.

Mijnhardt, W.W.: 1988, *Tot Heil van 't Menschdom. Culturele genootschappen in Nederland, 1750-1815*, Rodopi, Amsterdam.

Paasman, B.: 1971, *J.F. Martinet: een Zutphens filosoof in de achttiende eeuw*, Van Someren, Zutphen.

Parkes, S.: 1830, *Chemical Essays*, 3rd edn., Baldwin and Cradock, London.

Parkes, S.: 1837, *A Catechism of Chemistry*, 13th edn., Scott, Webster and Geary, London.

Parkinson, J.: 1799, *Chemical Pocket Book*, Symonds, London.

Postel, E.: 1864, *Grondbeginselen der anorganische en organische scheikunde, door de eenvoudigste proeven toegelicht, voor beschaafde lezers van allerlei stand*, 2nd edn., Van Druten & Bleeker, Sneek.

Raichvarg, D. & J. Jacques: 1991, *Savants et ignorants. Une histoire de la vulgarisation des sciences*, Seuil, Paris.

Reichen, C.-A.: 1964, *A History of Chemistry*, Leisure Arts, London.

Reuleaux, F. (ed.): 1889-93, *Das Buch der Erfindungen, Gewerben und Industrien*, 8th edn., 9 vols., Spamer, Leipzig.

Roberts, L.: 1993, 'Filling the Space of Possibilities: Eighteenth-Century Chemistry's Transition from Art to Science', *Science in Context*, 6, 511-53.

Römpp, H.: 1944, *Chemie der dagelijkse dingen*, 13th edn., Roskam, Amsterdam.

Russell, C.A.: 1983, *Science and Social Change 1700-1900*, Macmillan, London.

Schenzinger, K.A.: 1937, *Anilin*, Zeitgeschichte-Verlag, Berlin.

Scherer, A.N.: 1795, *Versuch einer populären Chemie*, Danner, Mühlhausen.

Schneider, M. (ed.): 1986, *Justus von Liebig. Briefe an Vieweg*, Vieweg, Braunschweig.

Schouten, H.: 1967, *Eenvoudige scheikunde uit het dagelijks leven: ten dienst van opleidingen met een beperkt scheikundeprogramma*, 4th edn., Haarlem.

Ségur, O.-G.: 1803, *Lettres élémentaires sur la chimie*, 2 vols., de Migneret, Paris.

Ségur, O.: 1811, *Brieven over de grondbeginselen der scheikunde, ingerigt volgens de lessen van Berthollet, Fourcroy, Chaptal, enz.*, 2 vols., Locke, Rotterdam.

Shapin, S. & B. Barnes: 1977, 'Science, Nature and Control: Interpreting Mechanics Institutes', *Social Studies of Science*, 7, 31-74.

Simons, L.: 1915, 'Het goedkoope boek', in: *Gedenkboek der Wereldbibliotheek 1905-1915*, Wereldbibliotheek, Amsterdam, pp. 11-73.

Snelders, H.A.M.: 1981, 'James F.W. Johnston's Influence on Agricultural Chemistry in the Netherlands', *Annals of Science*, **38**, 571-584.

Snelders, H.A.M.: 1992, 'Professors, Amateurs, and Learned Societies: the Organization of the Natural Sciences', in: M.C. Jacob & W.W. Mijnhardt (eds.), *The Dutch Republic in the Eighteenth Century: Decline, Enlightenment, and Revolution*, Cornell UP, Ithaca/London, pp. 308-23.

Snelders, H.A.M.: 1993, *De geschiedenis van de scheikunde in Nederland. Van alchemie tot chemie en chemische industrie rond 1900*, Delftse Universitaire Pers, Delft.

Stöckhardt, J.A.: 1848, *De scheikunde van het onbewerktuigde en bewerktuigde rijk, bevattelijk voorgesteld en met eenvoudige proeven opgehelderd*, Van Nooten, Schoonhoven.

Stöckhardt, J.A.: 1854, *Algemeene landbouw-scheikunde, bevattelijk voorgesteld*, Siddré, Utrecht.

Sturkenboom, D.: 2004, *De elektrieke kus. Over vrouwen, fysica en vriendschap in de 18de en 19de eeuw: het verhaal van het Natuurkundig Genootschap der Dames in Middelburg*, Augustus, Amsterdam.

Theunissen, B.: 2000, *'Nut en nog eens nut.' Wetenschapsbeelden van Nederlandse natuurondrzoekers, 1800-1900*, Verloren, Hilversum.

Thomas, L.: 1852, *Das Buch der wunderbaren Erfindungen. Das illustrirte goldene Kinderbuch*, Spamer, Leipzig.

Van Berkel, K.: 1985, *In het voetspoor van Stevin. Geschiedenis van de natuurwetenschap in Nederland 1580-1940*, Boom, Meppel/Amsterdam.

Van Berkel, K.: 1991, 'Dirk Huizinga als redacteur van Isis (1872-1875). Een Groningse bijdrage aan de popularisering van de natuurwetenschap in negentiende-eeuws Nederland', in: K. van Berkel, H. Boels & W.R.H. Koops (eds.), *Nederland en het Noorden*, Van Gorcum, Assen/Maastricht, pp. 184-207.

Van der Boon Mesch, A.H.: 1831-35, *Leerboek der scheikunde, met toepassing op kunsten en fabrijken*, 3 vols., Sterck, Delft.

Van der Burg, E.A.: 1860, *Voorlezingen over elementaire scheikunde, gehouden op uitnoodiging van het departement Rotterdam der Maatschappij ter bevordering van nijverheid*, Campagne, Tiel.

Van der Meulen, R.: 1876, *Bibliografie der technische kunsten en wetenschappen 1850-1875*, Brinkman, Amsterdam.

Van der Meulen, R.: 1891, *Een veertigjarige uitgeversloopbaan. A.W. Sijthoff te Leiden. 1851 – 1 Januari – 1891*, Van Kampen, Amsterdam.

Van Lente, D.: 1988, *Techniek en ideologie. Opvattingen over de maatschappelijke betekenis van technische vernieuwingen in Nederland, 1850-1920*, Wolters-Noordhoff, Groningen.

Van Lente, D. & O. de Wit: 1993, 'Papier, druk en communicatie', in: H.W. Lintsen et al. (ed.), *Geschiedenis van de techniek in Nederland. De wording van een moderne samenleving*, vol. 2, Walburg Pers, Zutphen, pp. 175-283.

Van Moorsel, F.H.: 1855a, *Kunstlicht*, Kruseman, Haarlem.

Van Moorsel, F.H.: 1855b, *Algemeene scheikunde*, Weytingh & Van der Haart, Amsterdam.

Van Moorsel, F.H.: 1855c, *Toegepaste scheikunde*, Weytingh & Van der Haart, Amsterdam.

Van Raak, R.: 2001, *In naam van het volmaakte. Conservatisme in Nederland in de negentiende eeuw van Gerrit Jan Mulder tot Jan Heemskerk Azn.*, Wereldbibliotheek, Amsterdam.

Verbong, G.P.J.: 1994, 'De uitgangssituatie', in: H.W. Lintsen et al. (ed.), *Geschiedenis van de techniek in Nederland. De wording van een moderne samenleving 1800-1890*, vol. 5, Walburg Pers, Zutphen, pp. 22-49.

Verbong, G.P.J. & E. Homburg: 1994, 'Chemische kennis en de chemische industrie', in: H.W. Lintsen et al. (ed.), *Geschiedenis van de techniek in Nederland. De wording van een moderne samenleving 1800-1890*, vol. 5, Walburg Pers, Zutphen, pp. 242-69.

Vermij, R.H.: 1991, *Secularisering en natuurwetenschap in de zeventiende en achttiende eeuw: Bernard Nieuwentijt*, Rodopi, Amsterdam.

Von Baumhauer, E.H.: 1855, *Over het nut der scheikunde voor den industrieel*, Kruseman, Haarlem.

Watson, J.D.: 1968, *The Double Helix. A Personal Account of the Discovery of the Structure of DNA*, Weidenfeld and Nicholson, New York.

Watson, R.: 1793, *Chemical Essays*, 6th edn., Evans, London.

Weber, J.A.: 1791, *Leichtfassliche Chemie, für Handwerker und deren Lehrlinge*, Heerbrandt, Tübingen.

Wels, C.B.: 1985, 'Mulder, Gerardus Johannis', *Biografisch Woordenboek van Nederland*, vol. 2, Elsevier, Amsterdam, pp. 396-398.

Wurzer, F.: 1806, *Handbuch der populären Chemie*, Barth, Leipzig.

Wurzer, F.: 1809, *Beknopt handboek der scheikunde voor ongeoefenden en voor hen, die alleen een algemeen denkbeeld van deze wetenschap trachtten te krijgen*, Alter, Utrecht.

Wijnand, W.E.: 1918, *Scheikunde in het dagelijksch leven. Leergang Volksuniversiteit Groningen 1918-1919*, Volksuniversiteit, Groningen.

Zott, R.: 1993, 'The Development of Science and Scientific Communication: Justus Liebig's Two Famous Publications of 1840', *Ambix*, **40**, 1-10.

CHAPTER 8

ABRAHAM CRESSY MORRISON IN THE AGORA: BRINGING CHEMISTRY TO THE PUBLIC

Andrew Ede

Department of History, Simon Fraser University, Burnaby, BC, V5A 1S6 Canada; histgo@sfu.ca

This chapter looks at the visual and textual images of chemists in A. Cressy Morrison's *Man in a Chemical World*. It argues that Morrison was attempting to create a public image of an American chemist different from European chemists. Morrison and the illustrator Leon Söderston, working on behalf of the American Chemical Society, attempted to associate chemists and chemical industry with American prosperity by linking the 'man in the white lab coat' to religious and secular themes. This approach is analyzed using the concept of metonyms. Metonyms are a way of encapsulating complex ideas and associations within simple, often iconic, images in text and illustrations.

1. Introduction

When Abraham Cressy Morrison published *Man in a Chemical World* in 1937, it joined a growing tradition of books that tried to make science better known to the public. What makes it different from most of the other popular works was its polemical style and the illustrations, which were some of the most interesting representations of scientists ever presented to the general public. Morrison was attempting to present a new and American image of chemistry. A key component in this effort to present a new public image for the American chemist was to recast the 'man in the white lab coat' as American and linked to beneficial (and even divine) activity. By examining the images and strategies used in Morrison's book, we can gain a better understanding of the complex nature of image creation, especially the way that images encapsulate wider concepts.

All the popularizers of the era had to bring their work to the 'agora' of print media and influence the public through texts and images in magazines and books aimed at a general audience. As a topic, chemistry needed popularization in both the sense of making it better known and making the study of chemistry more attractive. Through the post-war years, American chemists were battered by public antipathy to chemical warfare.[1] The extent of this image problem can be seen in the results of a 1922 *New York Times* poll. When asked if chemical warfare should be abolished by international treaty, 366,795 respondents voted for aboli-tion, while only 19 supported its continued use (Anonymous 1922). The subject was also kept in the public eye by a host of popular books such as Will Irwin's *The Next War* (1921), M. Dalton's *The Black Death* (1934), and most significantly H.G. Wells' *The Shape of Thing to Come* (1935) and its movie version *Things to Come* (1936). Wells' work started with a world ravaged by war and devastated by chemical weapons. The ongoing debate over the existence of the U.S. Chemical Warfare Service also af-fected public perception. This continued into the 1930s particularly be-cause the United States helped to created and then refused to ratify the 1921 Geneva Gas Protocol (Ede 2002, p. 131).

Although the public concern about chemical warfare was significant, the story was not completely negative. The dramatic rise in the number of American-born and educated chemists attested to the increasing ac-ceptance of chemistry as an academic subject and career choice.[2] The appetite among publishers for popular science titles such as Morrison's also reflected a growing public interest in science. *Man in a Chemical World* joined a substantial list of other popular books on chemistry from the era that tried to make clear the importance of chemistry. These in-cluded multiple editions of Floyd L. Darrow's *The Story of Chemistry* (1927, 1930) and Alexander Findlay's *A Hundred Years of Chemistry* (1937, 1948, 1955, 1965). H.E. Howe's two volume *Chemistry in Indus-*

---

[1]   For a brief overview of the history of the public debate about chemical warfare in the U.S., see Ede 2002.
[2]   For details of the rise in chemical education, see Thackray *et al.* 1985.

try (1924-5) was widely distributed, with a print run of 10,000 copies (Howe 1924-5, front apparatus). One of the most prolific popularizers of the period was Williams Haynes, who published many chemical titles, including *Chemical Economics* (1933), *Our Chemical Heritage* (1935), *Men, Money and Molecules* (1936) and *Chemical Pioneers: The Founders of the American Chemical Industry* (1939).

2. The American Context and the Origin of the Text

The issue facing science popularizers was how to make the public understand the importance of a topic that was not recognized as a part of daily life. Although there had been a number of notable Americans such as Benjamin Franklin and Thomas Jefferson interested in science, it was not a subject that had garnered wide public interest. There were several reasons for the lack of interest. Until World War I, science education in America was not very advanced at any level, and the number of scientists in the population was quite small. American competition in international trade was relatively limited, focusing mostly on raw materials, as were the demands to meet or surpass the technical standards of countries like Germany, England, and France. The majority of scientists in the U.S. working before the war were either foreign born or trained for their higher degrees at European universities (Thackray *et al.* 1985). Although the United States was slowly rising in scientific and industrial power before the war, there was an explosion of growth because of the war. While certain aspects of science might be seen a dangerous, after the war it was clear that a strong scientific community was increasingly desirable.

It is against this mixed image of chemistry that Morrison's book must be read. The genesis of *Man in a Chemical World* started with one of the most significant attempts to promote and 'Americanize' chemistry undertaken by the American Chemical Society (ACS). For the 1935 conference, the ACS chose as their theme the tercentenary of chemical industries in America. (Morrison 1937, p. x) This offered an excellent platform to promote chemistry as an important American industry. The official poster (Figure 1) for the tercentenary showed a native in loincloth and feathered headband working with a Pilgrim stirring a giant steaming caldron.

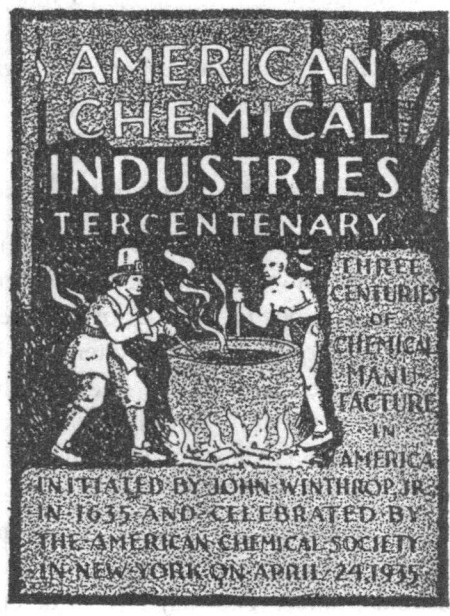

Figure 1. Poster for the American Chemical Industries Tercentenary used by the American Chemical Association 1935 meeting in New York (from Morrison 1937, p. 1).

Although there was chemical activity in the New World in the seventeenth century, the tiny number of European settlers in 1635 made the claim for three hundred years of chemical 'industry' a bit of a historical exaggeration. Regardless of whether the claim was historically justified, the association of chemistry with the founding of America was a direct argument that chemistry was a national enterprise and part of American history from the beginning, not a recent and foreign import. The scientific audience for this message was significant; when the annual meeting opened on 24 April 1935, more than 10,000 delegates from around the world had traveled to New York to attend (Anonymous 1935).

The conference was front-page news in New York and across the country, and all the published reports suggested that the conference was a rousing success. However, the executives of the ACS also wanted to present a more substantial view of the importance of chemistry than could be obtained from brief newspaper articles, even if those reports were positive. During the planning stages of the conference, the ACS had established the Executive Committee of the American Chemical Industries Tercentenary, with Francis P. Garvan as the honorary chairman and Arthur W. Hixson, a chemist at Columbia University, as the general chairman. The Committee in turn asked Morrison to write a companion book about the importance of chemistry and chemical industries (Morrison 1937, 'Acknowledgment').

Morrison's book may have been modeled in part on E.F. Armstrong's *Chemistry in the Twentieth Century* (1924). Armstrong was the chair of the Committee of Scientific Societies and coordinated the participation of British scientific organizations including the Royal Society in the 1924 British Empire Exhibition.[3] His book was "offered as a contribution made by British men of science to the work of building up the Empire" (Armstrong 1924, preface). Just as Armstrong had linked the importance of chemistry to the success of the Empire, so too did Morrison attempt to show how integral the role of chemists and chemistry was to American life.

3. Morrison and the 'Agora' of Popular Writing

Morrison was a good choice to write the companion book. He had a strong interest in popularizing science, having written articles for *Scientific American* and *Science Digest*, as well as *Reader's Digest*. He was also the author/compiler of *The Baking Powder Controversy*, a massive two-volume work that compiled all the important documents and explained the convoluted legal, political, and business history of the fight to control the production of baking powder in the U.S. (Morrison 1904-7). He had been the President of the New York Academy of Sciences, which named a prize in his honor. The A. Cressy Morrison Award for Natural Sciences was conceived to acknowledge not only important scientific work, but also the best communication of that work.

---

[3] For a history of the exhibition, see Knight & Sabey 1984.

What is less clear is the degree to which Morrison's work was directed or overseen by the ACS. It is likely that Morrison worked with Hixson, and the plan for the book originated with the Tercentenary Committee, but beyond that there is no direct evidence of 'writing by committee'.[4] There were numerous sub-committees for the conference (including 'Golf' and 'Plant Visits') but nothing specific about this project. Publishing records do not appear to exist, but the print run may have been as large as 10,000 copies, a substantial number, but in keeping with other books of the period.[5] According to copies bearing company stamps or labels, the book was purchased by at least two chemical companies and given away to libraries, and both Hixson and Morrison gave out copies.[6]

Although *Man in a Chemical World* was Morrison's most significant work of science popularization, his most widely circulated work was an article cum pamphlet entitled 'Seven Reasons Why a Scientist Believes in God'.[7] Morrison further explored the issue of religion and science in his 1944 book *Man Does Not Stand Alone* (Morrison 1944). It is important to see the material in *Man in a Chemical World* as part of Morrison's larger conception of science and religion. Chemistry, and science more generally, was linked to the divine.

It is easy to see Morrison and the other popularizers simply as promoters of science and their books as boosterism, but there is a deeper layer to their work that is about the struggle to create a public voice for a discipline that had grown increasingly private (Shapin 1988). The extent of the concern among the chemical community, particularly among the leadership of the ACS, about public awareness can be seen in Arthur W. Hixson's 'Foreword' to Morrison's book. It is a good example of the en-

---

[4] If readers are aware of any information about the production of *Man in a Chemical World*, the author would be grateful for the assistance. Publishing records are often difficult or impossible to find.

[5] Charles Scribner's Sons is now an imprint of Thomson Gale. They have little exact information on this title (personal discussion with the publisher).

[6] Author's collection includes a form letter from Hixson inserted in a copy and Morrison dedication in another copy.

[7] For an expanded version, see Morrison 1962. The basic article is widely available on the Internet.

thusiasm, verging on hyperbole, common to many of the promotional books of the time.

> This book is intended to be educational, from the cultural as well as the utilitarian point of view. Its object is to impress the man in the street with the fact that the chemical industries of the United States render a service that touches practically every activity in which he engages. In fact, it is the main purpose of the book to awaken him to the realization that he is utterly dependent upon these industries not only for the necessity and luxuries of life, but also for his very existence. [Hixson, in Morrison 1937, p. ix]

That the 'man in the street' owed his life to chemistry was an extravagant claim, but one that Hixson and Morrison felt justified in making, based on the vast number of applications they identified as being within the realm of chemical industries. This covered everything from the pharmaceutical industry to farming and the conduct of war. The extent to which the 'man in the street' was aware of this assessment might be summarized by the brief book review in the *New York Times* (reprinted in the *Times Literary Supplement*). The anonymous reviewer commented that "Mr. Morrison has acceptably pointed out the practical universality of chemistry in or behind the activities of industry and programs of ordinary life".[8] This tepid acknowledgement of Morrison's thesis can be contrasted with the positive comment of C.C. Furnas, writing in *Industrial and Engineering Chemistry*, who said, "An astonishingly good job which the intelligent portion of the public will appreciate", and he encouraged chemical engineers and their "non-technical friends" to read it (Furnas 1937).

Framing Morrison's work in the tradition of the agora offers a useful way of discussing the rhetorical and iconic strategies of *Man in a Chemical World*. In the ancient world, the agora was more than the early version of the supermarket; it was also the public forum, the center of political debate, the source of gossip, and the market place of ideas. Philosophers and physicians, magicians and barbers, adventurers and charlatans

---

[8] Brief book reviews, *New York Times*, 4 July, 1937, p. 67. Other reviews were published in the *Journal of Physical Chemistry*, and the *Minnesota Library Journal*, while the *Times* of London reprinted the *New York Times* review. For a complete list of reviews, see the *Book Review Digest*, New York: H.W. Wilson, 1937.

shared the public space with wine merchants and fruit sellers. The very idea that there is a 'public' comes to us because the agora, or its various equivalents throughout history, existed as meeting place that was not private space. Although natural philosophy and later science has always had a level of public presence, whether it was Socrates in the actual agora or Benjamin Franklin at fashionable French salons (*e.g.* Tucker 2003, Isaacson 2004), the practice of modern science does not lend itself well to the culture of the agora. As science became dominated by experiment, the locus of investigation became increasingly private. For Robert Boyle and his assistant Robert Hooke, the gentlemanly enterprise of experimentation took place in a laboratory that was part of a private residence (Shapin & Schaffer 1985). Admission was by personal invitation or referral by a close associate. Even the 'public' demonstrations of the Royal Society were largely restricted to members. By the twentieth century, the physical place of scientific activity was not just private, but often carefully separated from other activities and hidden behind locked doors. The private world of science was partly a matter of utility, since scientists had to contend with safety issues, such as the control of toxic chemicals, and to protect sensitive and expensive equipment. Equally, science became increasingly private as more scientists began to work on secret military projects.

While the necessity for such security was perfectly reasonable, it was nonetheless the case that the practice of science took place far from the public gaze. The potential problems of the isolation of science was part of the motivation to create the British Association for the Advancement of Science in 1831 and the American Association for the Advancement of Science (AAAS) in 1848.[9] These two organizations have expended a great deal of effort to keep science in the public forum. To reach a wider audience, the AAAS began publishing the journal *Science* (partly financed by Thomas Alva Edison) in 1880. It joined the magazine *Scientific American*, which had first appeared in 1845, as conduits between the scientific community and the American public. Another important venue

---

[9]   See MacLeod & Collins 1981 and www.the-ba.net; for the AAAS, see Kohlstedt 1999 and www.aaas.org.

for public exposure were the natural history museums and the later creation of science museums and interactive science centers.

It is against this background of concern about the place of science in the public domain that we must see Morrison's work. *Man in a Chemical World* employs two strategies to present a positive image of chemistry: polemic and iconography. Morrison's text was frequently polemical, particularly using statistics to demonstrate just how important chemistry was to the individual and the nation. In addition to telling the reader how dependent they were on chemistry, the text was reinforced by the powerful and provocative illustrations done by Leon Söderston. Rather than follow the more common practice of the period of illustrating the book with photographs or diagrams of chemical experiments or apparatus, the majority of the drawings in *Man in a Chemical World* were metaphorical representations of chemistry and the spirit of science more generally.

4. Leon Söderston, the Illustrator

Information about the illustrator is scarce. Only one reference to Leon Söderston of Yonkers, New York appears in standard dictionaries of illustrators and artists (Mallett 1948, p. 412). His name does not appear in the National Archives' searchable database, but it is possible that he worked for the Federal Art Project during the Depression. Although his work likely appeared in magazines or advertising copy, he is known to have illustrated only one other book, *The Congressional Library* (1922) by the poet Amy Lowell. Söderston was mentioned in the author's acknowledgement, but it is not clear what degree of interaction there was between the author and the artist. Typically, illustrators worked from the text, or at least from detailed outlines. Authors would see the illustrations and have some say in approving them, but often the illustrator would only deal directly with the editor. In this case, the images are too closely linked to the text to have been created without access to the text prior to creating the illustrations. We can therefore read the text and the illustrations as a unified whole, while still acknowledging the two hands at work.

Historians and philosophers have frequently attempted to deconstruct the meaning of scientific images ranging from the insects in Robert

Hooke's *Micrographia* to particle trails in cloud chambers (e.g. Adams 1994, Hankins 1995, Lightman 1997). Some images, such as the double helix and the Bohr-Rutherford atom have become so well-known that they are iconic, and even the simplest doodle is all that is needed to call to mind the larger subject matter they represent. More recently, there has been growing interest in images of science and scientists. In particular, LaFollette (1990) explores this topic, looking at the impact of public images of science on science itself.[10]

5. The Use of Metonyms

One of the problems with attempting to decode images is that the interpretation is subjective. Different viewers see different things and can trace different roots. There is also the Derridian problem of endless reinterpretation.[11] In terms of setting images before the public, Norman M. Klein provides a way to interpret the link between image and public perception. According to Klein (2002), powerful images such as the picture of Einstein or the double helix create metonyms. A term borrowed from literature, a metonym is the use of one name (often a short form) for another, often more complex, concept. This kind of coding is very common, such as a reporter saying 'the White House' to represent the president or the executive branch more generally. Morrison and Söderston employed visual metonyms in both a direct and an exoteric manner. To understand what direct and exoteric metonyms are, consider the mass media image of Albert Einstein. Although Einstein was not the only wild-haired eccentric genius from whom this image was drawn – recall Charles Darwin's or Dimtri Mendeleev's magnificent bramble of beard, for example –, his image has really taken over the category. Einstein's picture appears on everything from coffee mugs to boxer shorts. As a direct metonym, a picture of Einstein in a biography of Einstein attempts to capture a small slice of time, placing an image of the man in the mind of the reader in the context of the story of the great scientist. Just as the use of the term 'White House' brings to mind the executive branch of the

---

[10] For various aspects of the origin of images in science, see Shea 2000.
[11] Or as Lodge (1975) put it "every decoding is another encoding".

American government, so is the picture of Einstein a direct visual metonym that when viewed brings to mind the life of Einstein, especially at the time of the image. Put the same picture of Einstein on a T-shirt and it continues to convey the first aspect of the metonym, but it also suggests that the wearer admires Einstein and has a high regard for a certain approach to science and rationalism. The T-shirt image is an exoteric metonym: a public or outward declaration of the worldview of the wearer encapsulated in a picture.

The direct metonyms in *Man in a Chemical World* are relatively mundane; the Söderston images attempt to encapsulate the thematic material of the text. For example, in chapter eight 'Serving Industry', Söderston illustrates the pouring of molten metal (most likely steel) in an industrial plant. While the illustration can evoke the concept of all heavy industry, it does not carry the same complex package of meaning as other images.

The exoteric use of the images, on the other hand, created in the mind of the viewer a link between the image and a larger concept. In particular, Söderston's illustrations become a statement about the place of the scientist in society. Morrison was not looking to promote chemistry as the domain of geniuses, but as a field and industry essential to the prosperity of America. Thus, the textual and visual images of the chemist had to be work-oriented without making the chemist appear as a technician. This was a difficult set of requirements, but the image of the man in the white lab coat fit those requirements. It suggested both hands-on work and a higher calling, since the lab coat was transformed into a uniform with strong religious overtones in Söderston's illustrations.

6. The Evolving Image of the Scientist in the White Lab Coat as Scientific Icon

There is some debate about when scientists were first shown in lab coats. Their appearance in *Man in a Chemical World* does not represent a new image, but rather an important interpretation of the image that contributed to the creation of a powerful visual metonym in the public sphere. The use of the lab-coated scientist as a metonym does not have a single source of origin. In part, it evolved from images of chemists and other scientists at work, where they often wore aprons or light overcoats to protect their suits. As photography improved, candid pictures of scientists at the lab bench became more common by the 1920s, so the wearing of the lab coat came to be associated with a scientist at work. The other source of the image came from physicians, who started wearing white overcoats and aprons in the late nineteenth century and were far more likely in this period to be pictured in their white overcoats than most scientists.[12]

Morrison's iconographic efforts were shaped by the necessity of creating an 'American' scientist. In both the text and the images, *Man in a Chemical World* repeatedly returns to the 'American-ness' of the chemistry. In the chapter 'All the Comforts of Home', chemistry was both American and domestic: "In America, the soft soaps of our ancestors were made in every home by boiling fat with the lye extracted from the wood ashes from the hearth" (Morrison 1937, p. 161). In the second chapter, 'Chemistry in Overalls', Morrison makes clear the distinction between the European intellectual and the New World researcher while pointing out that the industry was run by Americans. "These developments [chemical industry] are characteristically American and fully illustrate the ramifications of chemical industry, both as showing the high type of Yankee ingenuity behind them and as typifying industrial chemical progress." (Ibid., p. 30) Nothing foreign in soap, and the chemical industries were the product of the same Yankee creativity that made heroes of people like Thomas Edison and Alexander Graham Bell.

For Morrison, the American scientist was to be differentiated from his European counterpart in much the same way as Robert Boyle distinguished the gentlemanly chemist from the medieval alchemist. Yet this had to be done without denigrating Europeans or European science, so it was done by emphasizing American work in the text and through the images. The European image of a scientist against which Morrison's portrait was drawn came primarily from the style and fashion of the late nineteenth-century European professorate. A typical European image of a scientist can be seen in the publicity photograph of Sir William Ramsay (Figure 2), taken shortly after he was knighted in 1902.

---

[12] For a brief history of the medical lab coat, see Blumhagen 1979.

Figure 2. Photograph of Sir William Ramsay (1902) showing the formal image of a chemist of the era (from Picture card 1920).

The European scientist was a member of the intellectual class, dressed in a three-piece suit, watch chain across the vest and wearing a carefully trimmed beard or goatee. This style remained popular for professional men in the U.S. until the early 1920s, as can be seen in the formal portraits of chemists in the ACS's *A Half-Century of Chemistry in America, 1876-1926* (Browne 1926). This image, however, was completely absent in Morrison and Söderston's depiction of American chemists.

Morrison's American scientist was a leader, economically as well as scientifically, but he was not an outsider, nor an effete scholar or from an upper class. Söderston shows us this Americanized scientist. The American scientist is dressed practically, either in the lab coat or working man's clothes. His clothes carry with them no hint of social rank, just as the monk's habit abolishes the distinction of class at birth. The new scientist was clean-shaven, with short, slicked down hair. This reflected the new fashion for men of the day, especially in the U.S. and it also made clear that these men were progressive, concerned with the needs of the market, and distinct from the old professors. The new scientist was also pictured, metaphorically and literally, with his sleeves rolled up and getting down to work.[13]

7. The Artistic Style of the Illustrations

Söderston's choice of style was well suited to this new presentation of the scientist. Broadly speaking, the illustrations are in the American realism tradition, which had developed through the 1920s and become popular during the Depression era. Many of the public murals and friezes commissioned by the federal government as part of the Federal Art Project (a division of the larger Works Progress Administration) were in this style. American realism frequently celebrated the struggle of humanity overcoming adversity, but there was also a darker side to the presentation and subject matter. American realist subjects tended to be urban, often focusing on work and industry. Paintings like Victor Arnautoff's 'City Life' (1934) or Thomas Hart Benton's series on different types of dangerous work such 'Coal' and 'Steel' (1930) looked at their eponymous subjects with an eye for detail, but were not romantic. Life was hard and dangerous, and even a stroll on a city street exposed people to potential peril.

These works also represent a strong interest in art as social commentary, and this often meant the juxtaposition of elements such as poverty and wealth. One of the best and most powerful of these juxtapositions can be seen in Lucienne Bloch's 'Land of Plenty' (1935) that shows a poor family fenced out of a lush farm field growing under electrical power pylons.[14] Söderston was also influenced by futurism. In the era when Flash Gordon was playing on movie screens, futurism's interest in machines, fantastic architecture, and motion made it a logical choice to link chemistry to a bright future. This is particularly true of the cityscape in the chapter 'The Crystal Reveals' (Figure 3) which shows fantastic

---

[13] Rolled up sleeves continue to be a symbol of getting down to work. During the 2005 Katrina hurricane disaster, Michael Brown, the head of the Federal Emergency Management Agency, was advised to roll up his sleeves before appearing on camera. For the email exchange, see Anonymous 2006.

[14] These images are available from various sources including Lucie-Smith 1994. The Lucienne Bloch image is available at www.library.georgetown.edu/dept/speccoll/prints/jpg/03.jpg.

flying machines zooming between gigantic towers and over sweeping bridges. (Morrison, p. 279)

Figure 3. Futuristic city, from Morrison 1937, p. 279.

8.   Key Images of Chemistry and Chemists

The first illustration of *Man in a Chemical World* has become one of the best-known images from chemistry in the era. It was the color frontis-piece entitled 'Chemical Industry, Upheld by Pure Science, Sustains the Production of Man's Necessities' (Morrison, frontis).[15] It is a striking image, showing an Atlas figure carrying the modern industrial world above his head. Supporting the elbows of Atlas was a woman (the personification of Pure Science or Athena), clad in a flowing gown. The Athena figure looks directly at the viewer, while the Atlas figure's head is bowed under his load. Behind the figures are arrayed chemical appa-ratus and a halo of bright orange and yellow light surrounds them.

---

[15]   For a color version, see Schlüpmann 1994.

Although the illustration was based on classical motifs, Söderston connected it to the origin of the book by making the Atlas figure a native American, with tawny skin, loin cloth, and head band, linking it to the aboriginal aspect of the 1935 ACS poster (Figure 1).

The image of science that comes from this is of science as the servant of humanity. Athena and Atlas are powerful exoteric metonyms, evoking the entire history of western philosophy and science. Particularly with the inclusion of the native figure, this linked the glory of Athens with the modern power of the American state. Although this was the most directly classical reference, it set the tone for the visual images of the book. Science as the servant of humanity was the connection between man and Nature as 'the great chemist'. In this schema, scientists interceded on behalf of humanity and were called to the noble enterprise of science. Morrison says of this relationship:

> Although Nature, the great chemist, has provided man with the prototypes and methods by which he has attempted, with considerable success, to conquer his environment, her motives and objectives have seldom been man's [...] It is beyond us to fathom the great plan of Creation in which we play at most a very minor role, but obviously the value of natural products to us is wholly fortuitous. [Morrison 1937, p. 13]

Morrison's tone is pious, but this only serves to reinforce the message of the connection between science and the divine. Even more important than reverence for Creation is the idea that the power over nature is granted to those who are capable of using the tools that Nature (or God) has provided for us.

The overt religious symbolism in many of the images reinforces the idea that scientists are a new order of priests. In the chapter 'Feeding Millions' (Figure 4a), the chemist is clad in a lab coat that is distinguishable from priestly raiment only because of the pens in the breast pocket. The lab coat is transformed into a white robe that falls from the shoulder almost to the ground. The mystical aspects of the image are further heightened by having the figure float, spirit-like, above the fields. The chemist makes the land fertile with material falling from one hand while reaping the products of the land with the other. The scientist's head is in the industrial world of trains and factories, but his feet connect him to the earth. The spiritual symbolism can be projected even further, as the scientist replaces the shaman of ancient fertility rites. The difference between the shaman and the scientist was that the shaman was a supplicant before the gods and nature, while the modern, rational scientist controls nature.

There is a temptation to see the illustrations in *Man in a Chemical World* as containing some hint of irony, since the religious references seem so extreme. There was, however, no hint of levity or ironic awareness in Morrison's writing. In Morrison's text, food does literally flow from the work of chemists. It is an actual life and death struggle, and we are reliant upon chemistry for survival:

> numerous agencies are in wait to pounce upon and destroy foodstuffs before they can serve their ultimate purpose. Insect and fungus pests attack growing crops; bacteria and other destructive agencies prey upon the harvested food to render it unsuited or unavailable for human use; and countless other hazards must be avoided or overcome before the farmer's product is set upon the table. In all of these protective measures, the products of chemical industry are potent weapons against the enemies of men. [Ibid., p. 90]

Two other overtly religious images reinforce the exoteric metonym of the man in the white lab coat. The first illustration is in chapter two, 'Chemistry in Overalls' (Figure 4b). The chemist, his back to the viewer, is offering up his chemicals and apparatus as a priest might offer up the host at communion. This offering, made before the work bench/altar, links the chemist/priest to the great power of industrial chemistry represented by the cracking towers in the background (ibid., p. 31). The chemist/priest image is closely replicated in the lead illustration for chapter eleven, 'The Crystal Reveals' (Figure 4c). In this picture, the scientist again appears with his back to the viewer, standing before a work bench/altar, but this time with hands raised in supplication before a glowing globe (ibid., p. 261).

Figure 4. (a) Chemist connecting agriculture and industry in the chapter 'Feeding Millions'; (b) the supplicant chemist from 'Chemistry in Overalls'; (c) the supplicant chemist in 'The Crystal Reveals'; (d) the spirit of chemistry in 'From Papyrus to Television'; (from Morrison 1937, pp. 91, 31, 261, 147).

Since these two images are in no way based on actual activity in the laboratory, they were meant to convey the role of the chemist as intermediary and conduit between the mundane and the powerful and sacred. These images place in the viewer's mind the association between the scientist's appearance and the larger context. Even if viewers reject the idea of the chemist as a religious figure, viewers have added the metonym to their interpretive framework.

Compare the priest image in Figures 4a and 4b with the scientist in chapter six, 'From Papyrus to Television' (Figure 4d). Here is a different application of the metonym, since in this image, the lab coat is worn by the spirit of chemistry, who floats over an inventor, perhaps representing Guglielmo Marconi. The inventor's sleeves are rolled up, indicating work, but clearly he is having some trouble, and is sitting, head on hand, struggling to solve some problem. The spirit of chemistry, chemical apparatus cradled in one arm, appears to be dispensing some material, which presumably will solve the inventor's problem (ibid., p. 147).

Figure 5. (a) A chemist and family from 'All the Comforts of Home'; (b) Chemist protecting society in 'Security'; (from Morrison 1937, pp. 159, 231).

Although industry was the primary focus of Morrison's argument, he also introduced a more domestic connection between the chemist and the average person in the chapter 'All the Comforts of Home' (Figure 5a). The chemist is presented in his priestly garb, but rather than commanding nature or celebrating a chemical Mass, he is working to make a home for an American family. The beautiful home appears in a burst of radiance and a cloud of smoke that are thrown out by the chemical equipment. The four other figures, father, mother, son, and daughter, hold hands with the chemist, and look up at the house. The large suburban home was presented as the ideal dwelling for the modern, middle class American family. In this case, Söderston was using an existing motif of the middle class home, but the illustration inserts a twist on the structure of the family. Rather than the father being shown as the patriarchal provider for the family, Söderston makes the chemist the source of family comfort. In the context of the Great Depression such a house could only be a dream for many Americans. The book's view of the future was a promise of material wealth for everyone through modern chemistry.

Morrison's text in 'All the Comforts of Home' was primarily didactic, consisting of a long list of consumer goods such as rayon ('better than silk') or aniline dyes ('better than natural dyestuffs') that were the product of chemical industry. Morrison tells the reader that Americans use the most soap in the world, at 27 pounds per person annually. This beats out other 'clean' countries such as Holland, Germany, and England. The Chinese were the least clean people, using only six ounces of soap each per year (ibid., pp. 165-6). This brief passage establishes a clear hierarchy of nationalism, with the United States at the top (clean and industrial) and China at the bottom (dirty and unindustrialized).

Although *Man in a Chemical World* was unrelentingly positive about chemistry, Morrison could not completely ignore the military aspects of chemistry. He included chapter nine, 'Security', to cover the topic of chemicals and warfare (ibid., p. 230-41). Public concern about chemical warfare had been heightened by the rise of fascism in Europe, particularly as Germany rose in power. As late as January 1927, the *New York Times* reported that the Germans were operating a secret phosgene plant called the "Rusko-Germanskaya Fabrika Bersol" in Russia (Anonymous 1927a). This was followed by a report that all the European powers were continuing to manufacture war gasses and train their military forces to use them (Anonymous 1927b). In the same year that *Man in a Chemical*

World came out, Augustin Prentiss' *Chemical in War* (1937) appeared. Although it was not aimed at a popular market, it was the most comprehensive evaluation of chemical warfare available in English (Prentiss 1937).

'Security' was quite different from all the other chapters in the book. It was very brief at 12 pages, tied as shortest with the introductory chapter 'Nature Points the Way'. The chapter was also very vague compared to the lists and descriptions that accompanied the other sections. There was no mention of the U.S. Chemical Warfare Service, the main source of chemical weapons for the American forces in World War I. In fact, no specific war chemicals were referred to by name and Morrison did not name a single chemist, unlike the other chapters that list materials and note the work of famous scientists. About a third of the chapter is devoted to fire fighting, police work, and safety at sea rather than warfare. Morrison deals with actual gas warfare in a mere two paragraphs, comparing it to perfume.

> The most important characteristic of effective "poison gases" (using the term with reservation) is that they must penetrate and distribute themselves quickly toward their objective. In this respect, they resemble perfumes. The reservoir of knowledge on which any nation must draw in the event of war is its industries of synthetic perfume. Few "poison gases" are actually lethal poisons. [Ibid., p. 237]

Rather than seeing chemical weapons as the scourge of modern war, Morrison portrayed them as a relatively minor innovation, and went on to argue that other forms of chemistry were responsible for improvements in the lives of soldiers in battle because of better sanitation and medicine. Although Morrison did not go as far as some supporters of chemical warfare in claiming them to be more humane than traditional weapons, he did say that chemical weapons were here to stay.

> Regardless of either the effectiveness or the disastrous consequences of using "poison gases", they will continue to be employed whenever a nation at war feels that its interests will be served by such use. This is a situation which has become an acknowledged fact and can never be controlled by international agreement. [Ibid., p. 235]

In addition, according to Morrison, most of the war work was really just a by-product of peaceful chemistry, forced on the nation by the necessities of war.

> Chemical industry thus stands as a great bulwark of strength for the maintenance of peace, for its beneficent and peaceful activities can, in case of absolute necessity, be quickly turned into the manufacture of materials without which no successful defense of our country could be maintained and no army could withstand attack in modern warfare. [Ibid., p. 232]

The chapter head illustration for 'Security' portrayed the chemist not as a soldier but as a civilian guardian (Figure 5b). The chemist had no weapons, only a collection of instruments, but stood like a colossus between civilization (represented by the factory/city in the background) and barbarism (represented by devices of war in the foreground). Science protected society by intellectual and moral superiority, not by force.

9. Conclusion

There was no doubt in Morrison's work that the U.S. was the greatest nation, and that a large part of its greatness rested on the work of chemists. Morrison concluded his book by saying:

> Many occupations in this world, while profitable, make no contribution to human advancement. Employment in such occupations may be satisfactory to the unthinking, but whoever realizes that employment in the chemical industries is an opportunity to serve in a fundamental occupation, upon which all others rest, without which our country would become a backward nation, and out of which grows civilization itself, glows with justifiable pride in the fact that his life has purpose and that he is serving humanity well. He, individually, feels that he is making a contribution to the industrial and intellectual development of all people everywhere, and especially to our country, the greatest nation in the world. [Ibid., p. 283]

As an argument brought to the agora of American public discourse, *Man in a Chemical World* was extremely bold. Its nationalism fit well with the concerns of many scientists, particularly the leadership of the ACS, that the U.S. needed to establish strong industries and train American scientists and workers for those industries, and potentially for future wars. While it would be difficult to establish the degree to which Morrison's book independently influenced people, and even more difficult to isolate the effect of Söderston's illustrations on the image of the chemist, their work was part of the establishment of a powerful metonym. The exoteric visual metonym of the scientist as a man in a white lab coat has been established so strongly that it has moved beyond metonym to stereotype and even the object of humor. For example, F.E. Warburton (1960) playfully suggested that characteristic stains on a lab coat should be used to identify the field of science of the wearer – blackish-brown (mud) for a geologist or greenish yellow and scarlet (sulphuric acid and bichromate) for chemists, and so on.

Although it would be impossible to prove that *Man in a Chemical World* by itself changed the public conception of chemistry or chemists, Morrison and Söderston's work, produced at the behest of the ACS (a large and increasingly powerful organization) represents a significant effort to influence public perception. It attempted to link the image of the chemist to the divine, promote the utility of science, and to redraw chemistry as an American endeavor. To the extent that we continue to associate the white lab coat with the practice and utility of science, this aspect of the project was successful.[16] Morrison's more specific attempt to link chemistry to nationalism and to a solely positive image of science was less successful. The white lab coat is now as likely to be associated with mad scientists in the Hollywood tradition of Frankenstein as it is with Morrison's benevolent defender of humanity. Further, the lab coat was too widely used to be taken over as a solely American uniform. Even in 1937, the lab coat was international.

Metonyms (both visual and textual) are an innate part of human communication and have been used to attempt to influence public thinking throughout history, ranging from medieval heraldry and corporate logos to campaign slogans. The metonyms in *Man in a Chemical World* represent one of the more overt attempts to construct a public image of science. Morrison's aim may have been to convince the American public

---

[16] For examples of modern investigations of the image of scientists, see Barman 2004 and Dalgety & Coll 2004.

that chemistry and chemical industries were vitally important, but in taking his book to the *agora* he also contributed to the formation of a larger image of science and scientists. Looking at the origins and use of these metonyms offers us a way to understand and discuss the relationship between the public and private spheres in science, both historically and in the present.

References

Adams, A.E.: 1994, *Reproducing the Womb: Images of Childbirth in Science, Feminist History and Literature*, Cornell UP, Ithaca.

Anonymous: 1922, 'Preventing a Chemists' War', *New York Times*, Mar. 31, 16.

Anonymous: 1927a, 'Tell of Poison Gas Made for Germans', *New York Times*, Jan. 10, 2.

Anonymous: 1927b, 'All Europe Turns to Gas Warfare', *New York Times*, Jan. 31, 1, 3.

Anonymous: 1935, 'Chemists Meet', *New York Times*, April 25, 1.

Anonymous: 2006, 'Fashion Disaster', *Harper's Magazine*, **312** (no. 1869), 18-9.

Armstrong, E.F. (ed.): 1924, *Chemistry in the Twentieth Century*, Macmillan, New York.

Barman, C.R. *et. al.*: 2004, 'Fifth Grade Students' Perceptions about Scientists and How They Study and Use Science' [available online: www.physics.ucsb.edu/~scipub/f2004/StudentPerceptions.pdf]

Blumhagen, D.W.: 1979, 'The Doctor's White Coat. The Image of the Physician in Modern America', *Annals of Internal Medicine*, **91** (1), 111-6.

Browne, C.A. (ed.): 1926, *A Half-Century of Chemistry in America, 1876-1926*, American Chemical Society, Easton, PA.

Dalgety, J. & Coll, R.K.: 2004, 'The influence of normative beliefs on students' enrolment choices', *Research in Science and Technological Education*, **22** (1), 59-80.

Darrow, F.L.: 1930, *The Story of Chemistry*, Blue Ribbon Books, New York.

Ede, A.: 2002, 'The Natural Defense of a Scientific People: The Public Debate Over Chemical Warfare in Post-WWI America', *Bulletin for the History of Chemistry*, **27** (2), 128-35.

Findlay, A.: 1965, *A Hundred Years of Chemistry*, Duckworth, London.

Furnas, C.C.: 1937, 'Book review', *Industrial and Engineering Chemistry News*, **15**, 301.

Hankins, T.L.: 1995, *Instruments and the Imagination*, Princeton UP, Princeton, NJ.

Howe, H.E. (ed.): 1924-5, *Chemistry in Industry*, Chemical Foundation, New York.

Isaacson, W.: 2004, *Benjamin Franklin: An American Life*, Simon & Schuster, New York.

Klein, N.M.: 2002, 'Instruments of Power: Notes on the Future of Media', in: B. Latour (ed.), *Iconoclash: Beyond the Image Wars in Science, Religion, and Art*, ZKM, Karlsruhe, pp. 490-7.

Knight D.R. & Sabey, A.D.: 1984, *The Lion Roared at Wimbley*, Barnard & Westwood, London.

Kohlstedt, S.G.: 1999, *The Establishment of Science in America: 150 Years of the American Association for the Advancement of Science*, Rutgers UP, New Brunswick.

LaFollette, M.C.: 1990, *Making Science Our Own: Public Images of Science, 1910–1955*, Univ. of Chicago Pr., Chicago.

Lightman, B.V.: 1997, *Victorian Science in Context*, Univ. of Chicago Pr., Chicago.

Lodge, D.: 1975, *Changing Places*, Secker & Warburg, London.

MacLeod, R. & Collins, P. (eds.): 1981, *The Parliament of Science: The British Association for the Advancement of Science, 1831-1981*, Science Reviews, Northwood.

Mallett, D.T.: 1948, *Mallet's Index of Artists*, P. Smith, New York.

Morrison, A.C.: 1904-7, *The Baking Powder Controversy*, American Baking Powder Association, New York.

Morrison, A.C.: 1937, *Man in a Chemical World: The Service of Chemical Industry*, Scribner's Sons, New York.

Morrison, A.C.: 1944, *Man Does Not Stand Alone*, Flemming H. Revell, New York.

Morrison, A.C.: 1962, *Seven Reasons Why a Scientist Believes in God*, Fleming H. Revell, Westwood, NJ.

Picture card: 1920, 'Sir William Ramsay and the Rare Gases', *The Mentor*, **8** (7).

Prentiss, A.: 1937, *Chemical in War*, McGraw-Hill, New York.

Schlüpmann, K.: 1994, 'Un kaleidoscope de la vulgarisation à l'époque de l'autotypie, 1880 – 1939', *Etudes des sciences – Science Studies* [available online at www.aleph99.org/etusci/ks/avat.html].

Shapin, S. & Schaffer, S.: 1985, *Leviathan and the Air-Pump*, Princeton UP, Princeton.

Shapin, S. 1988, 'House of Experiment in Seventeenth-Century England', *Isis*, **79**, 373-404.

Shea, W.R. (ed.): 2000, *Science and the Visual Image in the Enlightenment*, Science History Publications, Canton, MA.

Thackray, A. *et al.*: 1985, *Chemistry in America, 1872-1976: Historical Indicators*, Reidel, Dordrecht.

Tucker, T.: 2003, *Bolt of Fate. Benjamin Franklin and His Electric Kite Hoax*, Public Affairs, New York.

Warburton, F.E.: 1960, 'The Lab Coat as a Status Symbol', Science, **131** (3404), 895-944.

Wells, H.G.: 1935, *The Shape of Things to Come*, Hutchinson, London.

CHAPTER 9

THE VISUAL IMAGE OF CHEMISTRY: PERSPECTIVES FROM THE HISTORY OF ART AND SCIENCE

Joachim Schummer* and Tami I. Spector**

*Department of Philosophy, University of Darmstadt,
Schloss, 64283 Darmstadt, Germany; js@hyle.org
**Department of Chemistry, University of San Francisco,
2130 Fulton St., San Francisco, CA 94117-1080, USA; spector@usfca.edu

In this chapter we investigate the most important visual stereotypes of chemistry as they occur in current portraits of chemists, depictions of chemical plants, and images of chemical glassware and apparatus. By studying the historical origin and development of these stereotypes within the broader context of the history of art and science, and by applying aesthetic and cultural theories, we explore what these images implicitly communicate about the chemical profession to the public. We conclude that chemists, along with commercial artists, have unknowingly created a visual image of chemistry that frequently conveys negative historical associations, ranging from imposture to kitsch. Other elements of this image, however, aestheticize chemistry in a positive manner by referring to classical ideals of beauty and borrowing from revered motifs of modern art.

1. Introduction

When chemists complain about their bad public image they frequently forget that this image has been shaped over many centuries, and that chemists themselves have played an active part in its creation. PR managers know well that the public image of science is created at the interface between science and the public and results from the interaction between scientists and non-scientists. They also appear to understand that visual images are extremely important for carrying a message to the public, otherwise they would not produce such a wealth of picture-laden glossy brochures. Like their clients from chemistry or chemical industry, however, they are less versed in the historically based cultural implications of the visual elements they employ to portray chemistry, in part because scholarly studies on this topic are virtually nonexistent. Although chemistry is routinely portrayed by visual stereotypes, no effort has been made thus far to understand what implicit sociocultural messages they convey. The use of such images without knowledge of their historical contexts, no matter how highly polished, can be embarrassing if, as we show, the stereotypes carry with them negative associations.

In an earlier quantitative study we have analyzed the popular image of science and the visual self-representation of scientists (Schummer & Spector 2007). Unlike other disciplines, chemistry not only dominates the popular image of science overall, it also stands out for its extremely conservative visual self-representation. Chemists, rather than correcting the popular clichés that they frequently complain about, reinforce these clichés in their own self-representation. In this chapter we use the visual material from our earlier study for a complementary qualitative analysis of the most important visual stereotypes of chemistry as they occur in portraits of chemists (Section 2), depictions of chemical plants (Sections 3&4), and images of chemical glassware and apparatus (Section 4). In order to explore their meaning and visual associations, we delve deeply into our visual culture, which includes the history of science, the history of art, and aesthetics. We investigate the historical origins of these stereotypes, their predecessors, and the cultural contexts in which they emerged and how they have changed over time to assume their current meaning. A historical approach not only has the advantage of tracking the development of these stereotypes, and thus the dynamics of our visual culture, it also reveals their earlier sociocultural associations and connotations which, even if they no longer prevail, are still contained by the images. In addition, examining these visual chemical stereotypes within the broader visual culture allows us to interpret them in the context of past and present aesthetic and cultural frameworks.

2. The Chemical Portrait: Its Origin and Meaning

Whenever today's chemists want to be portrayed in such a way that anybody can recognize their professional identity, they usually hold up in their hand a flask filled with some liquid that they visually inspect.[1] This posture has become the stereotypical visual icon of chemistry in self-portraits, professional photographs, and clip-art cartoons (Figure 1a/b). Some chemists might feel uncomfortable with this pose because it does not accurately embody their daily professional work. They might wonder about the visual conventions that forces them to assume this strange pose or about the historical origin and implications. In this section we investigate the historical origin and development of this motif. We argue that before chemists assumed it as their professional icon, the motif, originally representing uroscopy, was first an icon of medicine and then became a symbol of quackery and imposture.

2.1 Uroscopy becomes an emblem of medicine

Along with pulse feeling,[2] uroscopy (the examination of the patients' urine) was the major means of medical diagnosis in late ancient, medieval, and early modern medicine. Color, smell, taste, and precipitate in fresh urine were supposed to reveal to the learned physician the specific disease and temperament of his patient. Briefly mentioned in the Hippocratic Corpus and extensively dealt with by Galen, the doctrine of uroscopy later became part of the medical core curricula of the newly established Christian universities in Western Europe. This shift of uroscopy into the core curricula of Christian universities was facilitated by the translation of Islamic medical texts from Arabic into Latin and the establishment of the school of Salerno, the first medical school in Europe.

Before this time medicine had been considered a mechanical art or craft, such as carpentry and forging, and excluded from Church school

---

[1]   Although chemists are photographed and sketched in some other poses, that pose is by far the most dominating public image of chemistry on the Internet and in cliparts according to our previous work (Schummer & Spector 2007).

[2]   Pulse feeling was not the same as pulse taking in today's meaning, as long as transportable clocks were unavailable. Instead it consisted of feeling the pressure and rhythm of the pulse.

curricula, which had focused on the seven liberal arts and the study of the Bible. Despite this, when medicine did become part of the university curricula, it was quickly accepted as a highly revered discipline. In this setting 'academic physicians' had to distinguish themselves from 'lay' medical practitioners, who continued to provide major medical care for people well into the eighteenth century. In particular, they distinguished themselves through their knowledge of the nature and causes of diseases and health – hence the English term 'physicke' for medicine up to the eighteenth century. This knowledge was largely based on Galen's theory of humors, from which the diagnostic capacities of urine as an indicator of humoral imbalance derived. Thus, when it came to the academic physicians choosing an emblematic representation for their field – each of the seven liberal arts had a long established emblem or visual symbol (Lindgren 1992) – they chose the symbol of uroscopy: a man holding up and examining a glass flask filled with urine, a so-called 'matula'.

Although we still know little about medieval visual culture, there is some evidence for the early development and use of this emblem. Since late antiquity, outside of the Islamic world, illustrations were frequently used in medical texts for entertainment rather than for demonstration (Grape-Albers 1977, Zotter 1980). Typically, written medical recipes and treatments were illustrated by a physician handing over a vessel of medicine to his patient. Because that image strongly resembles the later depictions of uroscopy, where a patient hands over a matula to the physician, it is very likely that this motif is the iconographical origin of the symbol of uroscopy. Moreover, there was a well-developed medieval Christian art of decorating the Bible with colorful miniatures of Bible stories in the margin or within the enlarged first letters of each chapter. That art was also applied to the earliest Latin translations of Arabic and Greek medical texts such as Avicenna's *Canon medicinae*, the *Articella* (a digest of Galen), and what was known as the *Aphorisms of Hippocrates*. In all of these early Latin manuscript translations we find miniatures representing the practice of uroscopy in prominent places (see Figures 2a and b).[3]

---

[3]   According to Zglinicki (1982, pp. 23-24), the oldest known uroscopy image is in the twelfth-century manuscript *Regulae urinarum* by Maurus and Urso of Salerno.

Figure 2 shows three depictions of uroscopy from the thirteenth and fourteenth centuries that later, with some modifications, became common motifs: the study of uroscopy with matula and book, the teaching of uroscopy to a pupil, and the medical practice of uroscopy, with patients lining up with their boxed matulae in front of a physician. However, in the first two manuscript based images the physician holds the bottom of the matula, which is still reminiscent of the late antique motif of the medicine vessel described above. Only the third one (Figure 2c) presents the posture that later became stereotypical for medicine and much later for chemistry: the flask held at the neck and raised high in front of the eyes. Unlike the two medical manuscript illustrations (Figures 2a and b) this relief, which was publicly placed among Giotto's and Pisano's famous emblematic representations of the liberal arts at the Campanile of the Cathedral of Florence, was clearly intended to be a popular emblematic representation of medicine.[4]

Prior to the establishment of European universities a debate had begun about the order of knowledge and thus about the ranking and order of the arts and crafts. This debate continued for centuries and employed emblematic depictions of the various disciplines, which are another useful source for medieval visual studies. In these illustrations medicine was routinely portrayed through uroscopy (Figures 3a and b). By the late fourteenth century uroscopy was a fully established public emblem of medicine throughout Europe. The image was probably even used as a trademark of medicine and put on signboards at the doors of practicing physicians.[5] By the early fifteenth century this symbol was so highly venerated that the twin saints Cosmas and Damian, who had become the Christian patrons of medicine due to a 'miraculous' surgery in the third or fourth century, were often portrayed in the pose of urine inspection in churches and other religious contexts (Figure 3c).[6]

---

[4] Relief variations of the motif soon appeared on other public places, like the Notre-Dame cathedrals in both Rouen (Zglinicki 1982, p. 133) and Paris (http://education. umn.edu/EdPA/iconics/wander/tour7la.htm, Figure 1-023).

[5] Connor 2001, referring to Garrison 1917, pp. 165-6.

[6] For a collection of examples, see Zglinicki 1982, pp. 135-146.

2.2 Uroscopy becomes a symbol of quackery and fraud

Medicine has never been without its critics. A widespread early Christian critique involved an argument based on how useless and powerless medicine was compared to the Almighty. In late medieval caricatures, which widely used animals to mock their subjects, the 'physician as ape' or the 'ape as physician' became a popular motif (Janson 1952) (Figure 4a). In the late fifteenth century, along with the devastating pests in Europe, the skeleton (a symbol of death) began to replace the ape in popularity, resulting in images that portrayed powerless urine inspecting doctors confronted with naked death. A typical example is Holbein's *Dance of the Death* (Figure 4b).[7]

Apart from the religious criticisms of medicine, more specific critiques of medical practice with a particular focus on uroscopy grew during the sixteenth century. People began to mock the increasingly fantastic claims about the diagnostic potential of uroscopy, which by this time had expanded to include Paracelsian methods of urine distillation and quasi-chemical tests. In particular, the notion that the urine-filled matula would somehow map the body of the patient and thus allow localizing diseases, which culminated in Leonhardt Thurneisser's urine distillation apparatus in the shape of a man (Figure 4c), became subject to satire. For instance, Pieter Brueghel the Elder produced a satirical drawing of a doctor and his dog discovering a fanciful humunculus in a matula (Figure 4d). Despite these criticisms the business of uroscopy flourished during this time period and its practitioners were quite well-paid, which further encouraged satirists like Thomas Murner to attack both physicians for their greed and uselessness and uroscopy patients for their foolishness (Figure 4e).

Because vernacular textbooks on uroscopy began to be printed in large numbers in the sixteenth century, the art of urine inspection and 'pisse prophecy' (uromancy) became extremely popular among patients, inducing a rapid growth of self-educated uroscopists. As a result the medical establishment was challenged to defend their academic prestige by clearly distinguishing themselves from these practitioners. By 1601

---

[7] On uroscopy in the Dance-of-the-Death tradition, see Zglinicki 1982, pp. 77-96.

the statutes of the College of Physicians of London declared, "It is ridiculous and stupid to attempt to interpret anything definite and certain merely from inspection of the urine and by inference there from, whether about the type and nature of the illness, or the state and condition of the sufferer," to which was later added "for that reason we desire and decree that neither any Collegiate nor any candidate should, like the sly imposter, use mere inspection of the urine in his consultation" (Connor 2001). Physicians all over Europe published pamphlets and books, such as Thomas Brian's *Pisse-Prophet* (London, 1637) and Johan Van Dueren's *De Ontdekking der Bedriegeryen Vande gemeene Pis-Besienders* (Amsterdam, 1688) (see Figure 4f) to denounce the quackery and fraud of uroscopy practitioners. Of course, physicians continued to practice urine inspection, but, as they were quick to point out, their analysis was based on the knowledge of causes ('physicke') while their competitors relied on the unlearned practice of 'empirical medicine'. By the seventeenth century the medical establishment had deliberately destroyed the medieval emblem of medicine. Uroscopy was no longer a symbol of learned medicine. The image of a man gazing at a flask in his hand was now a symbol of quackery, imposture, and fraud, and medicine was left without a professional icon. To fill the gap, the medical establishment of that time rediscovered the ancient Greco-Roman symbol of medicine, the Rod of Asclepius, which had been virtually absent in the previous Christian era, and claimed it as their new symbol (Figure 4g).[8]

2.3 From quack medicine to alchemy

Among generations of seventeenth-century Flemish and Dutch genre painters, who frequently derived from the schools of Rubens and Rembrandt, medical quackery became a favorite topic. Apart from brutal tooth-pullers and stupid surgeons, urine inspection was their most important motif. Since their paintings sold well, Flemish and Dutch genre painters produced an enormous flood of urine inspecting doctors

---

[8] For a review, see Wilcox & Whitham 2003; on the related Caduceus symbol (two snake twisted around a rod), which was occasionally used by pharmacists, see Friedlander 1992.

obviously copying each other and themselves hundreds of times. Dozens of paintings of this motif are known, including those of David Teniers the Elder (1582-1649), Adriaen Brouwer (1605-1638), Joos van Craesbeck (1605-1661), Adriaen van Ostade (1610-1685), David Teniers the Younger (1610-1690), Jan Olis (1610-1676), David Ryckaert the Younger (1612-1661), Gerard Dou (1613-1675), Thomas Wyck (c.1616-1677), Gerard (II) Ter Borch (1617-1681), Matheus Van Helmont (1623-1679), Jan Steen (1626-1679), Samuel van Hoogstraten (1627-1678), Gabriel Metsu (1629-1667), Abraham van Dyck (1635-1672), Gilles van Tilborgh (c.1635-c.1678), Frans van Mieris (1635-1681), Jacob van Toorenvliet (c.1635-1719), Godfried Schalcken (1643-1706), Gerard Thomas (1663-1720), and Balthasar van den Bossche (1681-1715).[9]

Neither uroscopy nor the general image of a man gazing at a flask in his hand was part of the otherwise rich iconology of alchemical text illustrations. However, in the works of the Flemish and Dutch genre painters this motif became closely associated with alchemy. Indeed, many of the artists cited above also produced paintings of alchemists. The association of the uroscopy icon with alchemy was fostered for several reasons. First, alchemists or chymists had long used glass flasks that were similar in shape to the classical matula. Second, Paracelsian iatrochemistry had given a boost to uroscopy through the distillation and quasi-chemical analysis of urine. Third, both classical alchemists and Paracelsian iatrochemists, like uroscopists, were the subject of numerous satires and biting pamphlets accusing them of imposture and fraud.

A selection of paintings from David Teniers the Younger illustrates how uroscopy and alchemy became visually melded. In many of his alchemist paintings Teniers employed one of the two classical satirical motifs in the foreground: the reading alchemist (Figure 5a) or the puffer alchemist (Figure 5c). To show that the first motif is not a symbol of esteemed scholarship, it is useful to compare it with the Italian painting *Jesus and the doctors of the Faith* (Figure 5b) which Teniers took as the model for his reading alchemist.[10] During the Renaissance the image of

---

[9] This list is compiled from various sources, notably from Holländer 1903, Read 1947, Zglinicki 1982, and Principe & DeWitt 2002.

[10] Teniers knew this painting at least since 1651 when it became part of the collection in Brussels that he supervised (Klinge & Lüdke 2005, p. 278).

the twelve-year old Jesus among the doctors (from *Luke*, 2, 41ff.) was commonly used to demonstrate the inferiority of human scholarship compared to divine inspiration. In this painting (Figure 5b) the artist accentuated the expression of the inferiority of human endeavors by giving the figure in the foreground a particularly stubborn and book-wormish demeanor, which Teniers meticulously copied in his reading alchemist (Figure 5a). Teniers' puffer alchemist (Figure 5c) is a variation of an older motif, the Antichrist/Satan who teaches gold-making to the people, illustrations of which became popular in fifteenth-century Germany. Both Hans Weiditz (Figure 5f) and Albrecht Dürer (Figure 5e) employed that motif in their woodcut illustrations of the written satires of alchemy by Petrarch and Sebastian Brant, respectively, who had made alchemy the epitome of forgery, fraud, greed, and moral corruption (Schummer 2006). Pieter Brueghel the Elder further developed this motif into a pictorial drama with an obsessed alchemist ruining his family (Figure 5d).

Teniers and his colleagues employed these two classical alchemy motifs but combined them with the classical uroscopy/imposture motif. Note that Figures 5a and 5c each show an alchemist in the foreground and a group of men in the background with one holding a flask in his hand like a uroscopist. In the next 'alchemist' image (Figure 5g), the composition of Figure 5c is almost inverted: the 'puffer' has moved to the background, while the reading alchemist now holds a flask in his hand. The pose of the alchemist in Figure 5g is virtually identical to the classical pose of the urine inspecting quack doctor in Figure 5h. Thus, quack doctors and alchemists became exchangeable and merged towards one and the same motif in the works of Teniers and his colleagues.

2.4 Satire continues

Flemish and Dutch genre paintings of quack doctors/alchemists were extremely popular throughout Europe well into the nineteenth century. Many of them were reproduced in etchings and widely disseminated during the eighteenth and early nineteenth centuries. In addition, painters from other countries employed or copied the motifs, such as Trophîme Bigot (1579-1650) in France, Pietro Longhi (1702-1785) in Italy, Franz

Christoph Janneck (1707-1761) in Austria, James Northcote (1746-1831) in England, Carl Spitzweg (1802-1885) in Germany, William Fettes Douglas (1822-1891) in Scotland, and Newell Convers Wyeth (1882-1945) in the USA, but only few artists made original modifications (*e.g.* Figures 6a/b).

Once established as a symbol of quackery and fraud this motif was used for all kinds of satire. For example, Figure 7a shows a political satire by Temple West (c. 1739-1783) mocking King George III's misjudgement of Napoleon by depicting 'the little emperor' as a small figure in a large glass retort. Throughout the nineteenth century, images based on this motif frequently included such nationalistic overtones, but the primary satirical attacks continued to be aimed at medicine (Figures 7b/c).

2.5 Portraits of nineteenth-century chemists and their twentieth-century transformation

In general the image of a man holding up and gazing at a flask – the archetypical pose of twentieth-century chemists – was carefully avoided by nineteenth-century chemists. Nobody wanted to be portrayed as an imposter or swindler. Based on our analysis of hundreds of painted and photographed portraits in various collections, nineteenth-century chemists preferred four types of portraits:[11] (1) Most chemists, particularly in the German and English traditions, are depicted sitting on a chair with some glassware or chemical apparatus in the background and books or notes in the foreground (Figure 8a). (2) In some portraits the only accessories are books, indicating the scientist's strong theoretical orientation (Figure 8b). (3) A third group of particularly English chemists are presented with their inventions, which suggests their ambition for technological applications of chemistry (Figure 8c). (4) Finally, a fourth

---

[11]   Useful internet image sources include the Science & Society Picture Library and the Ingenious database at the Science Museum London <http://www.scienceandsociety. co.uk> <http://www.ingenious.org.uk/>, the Smith Collection at the University of Pennsylvania <http://dewey.library.upenn.edu/sceti/smith/>, the Wellcome Library <http://medphoto.wellcome.ac.uk>, Wikipedia Commons <http://commons.wiki-media.org>, and Google Images <http://images.google. com>.

group, consisting particularly of French chemists, are depicted working in the laboratory, and it is only here that some slight association with the quack/imposture motif sometimes appears (Figure 8d).

How then did this pose become so popular among twentieth-century chemists? We suspect that commercial artists and photographers, whether consciously or not, gradually manoeuvred chemists into that pose and that chemists were increasingly uninformed about its negative symbolism. Eventually, without a clear understanding of its cultural and historical implications, they unwittingly embraced as the icon of their professional identity a symbol of imposture and fraud that had been firmly established for centuries.

To support our thesis we analyze three series of portraits of eminent nineteenth-century chemists in which the classical uroscopy/imposture motif gradually moves from satirical caricature to serious portraiture. Figure 9a shows John Dalton (1766-1844) in typical portrait type 1, *i.e.* with some chemical apparatus in the background and books or notes (here, his atomic formulae) in the foreground. This painting by Joseph Allen (1770-1839) was definitely made during Dalton's life and certainly with his agreement. In contrast, Figure 9b shows a later caricature (probably from 1882) by James Stephenson (1808-1886) of Dalton as President of the Literary and Philosophical Society of Manchester, which illustrates that the uroscopy/imposter motif was deliberately applied to chemists in nineteenth-century satire. Although the vessel he gazes at is somewhat unusual, it is clearly a version of the uroscopy/imposter motif. Because Dalton was famously color blind – he published the first account on what in England is still called Daltonism (Dalton 1798) – and because classical urine inspection was focused on color, we may assume an additional irony in the caricature. Moreover, Dalton gazes at the vessel as if he was reading a book, which one would expect from the president of a literary society. Thus, the caricaturist employed the uroscopy/ imposter motif and adjusted it with subtlety to the case of Dalton: The president of the literary society cannot read books and instead prefers reading liquids (urine), but he is even unable to do that because of his color blindness. While the satirical content of this image was certainly clear for contemporaries of Stephenson, later viewers might have misunderstood it as a caricature of a scientists engaging in overly pedantic empirical work in chemistry; if only he would lower the vessel a bit and look more relaxed, he might be viewed as the perfect experimental chemist.

Our second example is a series of portraits of Marcelin Berthelot (1827-1907) in which, unlike in the case of Dalton, the uroscopy/imposture pose already appears in what seems to be a serious painting, before it was actually transformed into a proper satirical caricature. Figure 10a is a well-known photograph of Berthelot at work in a laboratory from the late nineteenth century. He is looking down at his work-bench where in his left hand he holds a test tube as if he is preparing to run a reaction. Figure 10b is an oil painting of Berthelot by Harry Herman Salomon (1860-1936) based on a photograph taken in the late nineteenth or early twentieth century and perhaps painted after Bertholet's death. If you compare both images (the setting, equipment, and dress), it is obvious that the painting was made either directly after the photograph in Figure 10a or from a photograph taken on the same occasion. Thus, Salomon either modified the pose of the photograph or chose another one from the set to present Berthelot in a pose that almost exactly matches the classical uroscopy motif, except that the flask is replaced with a test tube. Since the painting otherwise fits the classical genre of portraiture, we may assume that the reference to the uroscopy motif was meant only as a mild satirical allusion. One might suspect that at the turn of the century many viewers no longer understood the allusion and its symbolic meaning. However, even if the symbolic knowledge was beginning to fade, it was still present, as a further transformation of Berthelot's portrait illustrates. To leave no doubt of the connection to uroscopy, a later unknown caricaturist lifted Berthelot' arm a bit higher and replaced the test tube with a urinal, now the modern version that is still used in hospitals today (Figure 10c).

The famous 1885 painting of Louis Pasteur (1822-1895) by Albert Edelfelt (1854-1905) is probably the first authorized portrait of a nineteenth-century chemist that appropriates the classical uroscopy/imposter motif without being a satire or bearing deliberate satirical allusions (Figure 11a). Given Pasteur's fame, particularly in the early twentieth century, and the significance of the painting, it is likely that this image considerably contributed to making this pose the icon of the chemical profession. Nevertheless? There are still differences between it and the classical motif which a superficial viewer of the portrait might ignore. Pasteur holds a bottle rather than a flask, the bottle is filled with a solid instead of a liquid, and he looks down at the bottle in his right hand and a paper note in his left hand as if he were comparing them. In Robert Thom's portrait of Pasteur from the mid-twentieth century (Figure 11b), these differences are corrected: Pasteur gazes at the liquid-filled flask at eye level. In addition, since Thom painted this portrait as part of his extensive series of paintings of "historical moments in science and pharmacy" (Metzl & Howell 2004), he was certainly aware of the historical iconology and symbolism of his image. The image was intended to capture Pasteur's experiments disproving the spontaneous generation of life. Anyone familiar with the history of these experiments would know that it is not the flasks but the connection between the flasks that was crucial to Pasteur's experiments. The connection is visible in Thom's painting, but the emphasis is clearly on the flask, so as to repeat with slight modification the classical uroscopy/imposter motif. A clear reiteration of the motif appears in the bronze statue of Pasteur in Figure 11c, which is probably from the early twentieth century when many such statues were created to commemorate Pasteur's fame. It is unfortunate that, although today's chemists might consider this statue a tribute to Pasteur's greatness as a scientist, it is actually fraught with unsavory historical allusions.

Misunderstandings of cultural symbolism can be particularly problematic if one deliberately strives to create a professional identity. A chemist with such an ambition was Charles F. Chandler (1836-1925). He was co-founder of the American Chemical Society, and its president in 1881 and 1889, and co-founder of the *Journal of the American Chemical Society* and its predecessor, the *American Chemist* (1870-7), which he co-edited with his brother. He was also "an organizer and first president (1898-1900) of The Chemist's Club, a club whose goal was to foster a social and professional identity in the chemical community" (Bowden 1997, p. 155). It must have been during these years that the photograph shown in Figure 12 was taken: Chandler in front of his porch under a tree with suit, tie, and hat, holding a flat-bottom flask in his right hand. Although it is a variation of the classical uroscopy/imposter motif (*e.g.* Figure 4b), its strong resemblance to the classical image suggests that he had seen such images before but was probably unaware of its negative historical legacy. By all indications this is an amateur photograph, so we can assume that artists or professional photographers did not influence his choice of pose. Rather like a self-portrait, it shows how Chandler himself – and thousands of chemists since then – chose to portray the visual identity of their profession.

The pose of a man holding up and gazing at a flask has changed in meaning over the past nine centuries. Originally it was a professional icon of the newly established academic medicine, which combined empirical diagnostics with causal knowledge. As the validity of the diagnostic tool was debunked, it came to represent 'merely empirical medicine' without deeper knowledge and ultimately became a symbol of quackery and imposture, first in medicine and alchemy and then as a general satirical motif for close to four centuries. When chemists, assisted by commercial artists, made this motif their professional icon at the turn to the twentieth century, its satirical associations were still alive. Since this pose now represents chemistry, and more generally experimental laboratory science, it might be easy to conclude that its debased associations have disappeared. However, we would argue that such a ready dismissal would be inappropriate. As with all powerful iconic imagery that possess a long, and predominately distasteful, historical lineage, the negative implications of that image can never be completely suppressed in the public consciousness. Even if present day viewers of such images are no longer overtly aware of their negative cultural connotations, the choice of early twentieth-century chemists and artists to make this pose *the* visual icon of chemistry has indirectly influenced the public perception of the chemical profession. Ultimately, that choice confirmed and reinforced the negative attitudes of those who were already critical of chemistry before, and it is this historical legacy that lives on in the non-visual public images of chemistry today.

3. Chemical Plants: The Panoramic View

Like the stereotypical chemical portrait that emerged out of a long history of science portraiture, depictions of chemical plants developed from the broader history of industrial landscape paintings and drawings. In this section we analyze typical early twenty-first-century photographs of chemical plants against this art historical background. We argue that the stereotypical features of these photographs break with the important art historical traditions most often used to depict industry and instead rely on art historical traditions that were not typically used to depict industrial scenes. In doing so, we suggest that today's photographs of chemical plants employ a visual strategy that sanitizes the negative cultural associations of chemistry while simultaneously embracing a demeaning kitsch aesthetic.

3.1 Industrial landscape: historical traditions

Since the eighteenth-century period of industrialization, artists' renderings of industry began to express a conflicted reaction to industry in the larger culture, a response that is at once celebratory and admiring and a site of distain and distrust.[12] During the British romantic period these responses were expressed through renderings of the industry within the tradition of the picturesque or sublime landscape painting. A proto-typically sublime rendition of industry is famously captured in Philippe Jacques de Loutherbourg's 1801 painting *Coalbrookdale by Night* (Figure 13a). Coalbrookdale, the center of early English iron works and therefore an engine of English prosperity during this time period, was itself a conflicted site where the quintessential English countryside was, as expressed by the renowned agriculturist Arthur Young, "too beautiful to be much in union with the variety of horrors spread at the bottom; the noises of forges, mill *etc.*, with their vast machinery, the flames bursting from the furnaces with the burning of coal and the smoke of the lime kilns" (Briggs 1979, p.13). This painting and an aquatint of Coalbrookdale from 1805 by William Pickett for Loutherbourg's book on *The Romantic and Picturesque Scenery of England and Wales* (Figure 13b)[13]

---

[12] For a documentation of industry in art, see the exhibition catalogue Beneke & Ottomeier 2002 as well as Frese 2000 and Türk 1997; for early industrial landscape paintings in England, see Klingender 1968, Wagner 1979, and Briggs 1979.
[13] Loutherbourg, P. J. de: 1805, *The romantic and picturesque scenery of England and Wales*, Bowyer, London Plate II.

together encapsulate the complexities of the attitude toward industry in England at that time. While Loutherbourg's painting stands as an emblem of the fear and mystery articulated by the Burkian sublime (see Section 3.3), the later aquatint transforms Coalbrookdale into a relatively benign picturesque landscape for English tourists. Later in the nineteenth century artists in various traditions, including the impressionists, sometimes placed industrial sites harmoniously into natural landscapes or towns.[14] In early twentieth century North America, images of the industrial landscape were usurped by powerful industrialists such as Herbert Dow (Frese 2000) and Henry Ford (Troyan & Hirshler 1987, pp. 17-21), who commissioned artists to celebrate their economic prowess and enhance their public relations. Naturally these paintings provided a positive, and suitably unthreatening, image of the industries they depicted. For these, unlike earlier images of industry such as *Coalbrookdale at Night*, therefore, we can unambiguously read the smoke coming out of the chimneys as a symbol of economic productivity and wealth rather than as a noxious indicator of industrial pollution (Figure 14).

A varied representation of industry can also be found in images of workers in industrial settings (Figure 15). In many paintings of this genre the workers are rendered as heroic and hard-working and it is the representation of their surroundings that expresses the artists' attitude toward industry itself. A typical early example is Joseph Wright's *An Iron Forge* (Figure 15a). Using his trademark chiaroscuro technique, this middle-class artist painted the iron workers in a picturesque setting being observed by affluent tourists and their curious children apparently seeking, in one critic's words, a "thoughtful balance [...] between sense and sensibility, between the prosaic, necessary task efficiently performed which is going to benefit mankind, and the fear or amazement that its accomplishment inspires" (Nicoldon 1968, p. 50). It also, however, reveals the darker side of the picturesque in which the working classes were aestheticized for the consumption of the affluent. In nineteenth-century real-

---

[14] For example see Camille Pissarro's *Factory near Pointoise* (1873) (Frese, p. 5) and Vincent van Gogh's *The Huth Factories at Clichy* (1887) (Hughes 1981, p. 326). On impressionist industrial landscapes, see Diers & Hedinger 2002; on the German Biedermeier tradition of frequently commissioned industrial landscape paintings, see Vorsteher 2002.

ist paintings, such as Adolf von Menzel's *Iron Rolling Mill*, this idealized view of industrial work is superseded by interiors of industrial plants that are overcrowded with workers, replete with machinery, and overheated by steam and fire (Figure 15b). In the early twentieth century depictions of industrial workers became more overtly politicized emblems of the socialist (and national-socialist) movements in many countries. As seen in the soviet era propaganda poster *Let's consolidate the victory of socialism in the USSR!* (Figure 16) such images accorded the workers with even more blatant heroic status than those of the eighteenth and nineteenth centuries.

3.2 Chemical plants as architectural photographs

In current photographs of chemical industry,[15] the classical art historical motifs of industry, such as plants harmoniously embedded in natural landscapes, smoking chimneys as a symbol for prosperity, and heroic workers are virtually absent. Instead, the typical modern image, like those shown in Figure 17, is remarkably reiterative and self-reflexive. The most important pictorial elements of chemical plant photographs are smokestacks, towers, storage tanks, piping, and conduits, with towers or smokestacks typically growing (by perspectival correction) straight out of the bulk of the plant into the sky, taking up two thirds or more of the image (Figures 17a-b). Most of the images employ special lighting effects: industrial plants are imaged shortly before or after sunset to ensure vibrant skies that recall the colorful pictorial liquids filling glassware in most stereotypical representations of the laboratory equipment (see below), while some photos, taken at night, foreground buildings with spectacular interior illumination (Figures 17c-d).

In addition, modern images of chemical plants are typically static rather than dynamic. They are most often portrayed without smoke coming out of their smokestacks and without people working near or with the equipment. These images, in addition to the curious fact that the plants

---

[15] The following qualitative analyses are based large sets of images that we retrieved from the internet for a quantitative study of the self-image of science (Schummer & Spector 2007).

appear to be neither in operation nor in ruin or decay (in fact, are in pristine condition), disconnects them from the picturesque industrial landscapes of the eighteenth and nineteenth centuries. Furthermore, in the absence of people, modern photographers of chemical industry belie their debt to more overtly propagandistic images of industrial workers and industrial sites, *e.g.* in Soviet social realism and American WPA murals, and to their historical progenitors in the artistic tradition of genre paintings. Finally, the fact that the photographs are situated away from towns or cities and have no smoke emerging from their smokestacks divorces them from a variety of conflicting pictorial traditions: the meliorative nature of 'man's' interaction with nature, the contrasting blight of industrialization in the landscape, and the economic prowess of a particular nation. By choosing to photograph them as static structures free of humanity in a background featureless except for the atmospheric essence of the sky, photographers of chemical plants would seem, in fact, to forcefully sever their connection to earlier artistic traditions. Indeed, the very contextlessness of the chemical plants shifts them from early twentieth century industrial images that reflected nationalist pride to the postnationalist identity of the globalized corporation.

To what do these images owe their historical debts if not the industrial landscapes of art history? Because of their focus on smokestacks, tanks, and other equipment essential to industrial-scale chemistry, and because of their lack of context, one might be tempted to interpret them as representationally realistic and therefore to fit, perhaps, within the tradition exemplified by Bernd and Hilla Becher's bleak industrial landscape photographs taken from 1959 forward (Becher & Becher 2002). It might also be easy to dismiss these repetitive photographs as simply the products of commercial photographers commissioned by chemical industry, and thus being of little visual interest. Some would say that they simply become boring; yet others would point out that these are precisely the qualities that make them interesting: their stance of disinterestedness, their visual isolation, their juxtaposition of an industrial, unnatural subject against an atmospheric sky, and the very fact that they are reiterative. Indeed, in this latter reading, if instead of being produced in a commercial context, the photographs had been created as 'high' art, a critic might comment that they fit within the construct of ironic banality explored by many of today's most influential visual artists.

Furthermore, when we focus less on the subject materials of the photographs and more on their composition, especially the use of perspective and atmospheric effects, we find that the formal aspects of these images borrow from various traditions. First, the isolation of the plants, which contrasts so markedly with most early representations of industry, impresses upon the viewer their lack of context. Framed by the edge of the photographs, chemical plants are portrayed without reference to the land or people that their presence might affect, either positively or negatively. This cropped frame removes them from all external reference points allowing the photograph to symbolically eliminate the chemical plants potential for contamination. The static, unpeopled content of the photographs, in collusion with the reiterative character of the images, thus simultaneously produces and reinforces a sense of containment and safety. Important to this effect is the photographic perspective, which aligns the plants with early architectural photographs of castles and cathedrals that contain similar formal features such as towers and conical elements (Figure 18) (Robinson & Herschman 1987, pp. 2-55). Like those images, these are often frontal shots from ground level viewpoints, which emphasize the vastness of the structure. Although less frequently, some chemical landscape photographs are shot from an elevated position, a perspective also common in early architectural photographs of cathedrals and castles. Ironically, like the genre of landscape painting itself, which marked an artistic shift from Classic to Romantic and Christian to secular (Mitchell 2002, p. 13), images of chemical plants transpose the art historical perspective used primarily to image cathedrals (Christian) and castles (classical) into the ultimate site of secularization – industry. By a unique legerdemain, however, the simple fact that these photographs participate in this tradition has the simultaneous effect of hallowing the industrial site and placing it under the symbolic aegis that cathedrals and castles historically sustained. In effect, these photographs invite a symbolic exchange in which the industrial site can stand in for the signs of governance and social order historically signified by castle and church.

3.3 Chemical plants as sublime landscape

Even with these traditions in mind, however, photographs of the chemical landscape may not initially impress the viewer with an experiential sensibility beyond that associated with the magnitude of the plant. From an art historically informed perspective, however, it is clear that the composition of such photographs introduces an emotive element which links their lineage to the sublime landscape images of the eighteenth and nineteenth centuries. Borrowing from the atmospheric effects of J.M.W. Turner and the grandiosity of Casper David Friedrich (Figure 19), they are expansive in scope, employ the sky as "the key note, the standard of scale, and the chief organ of sentiment" (Constable 1998, pp. 50f.), and operate on a vertical rather than horizontal axis. In addition to displaying the proportional conventions of sublime landscape painting, the use of special lighting effects in chemical landscapes has a clear allegiance to the atmospheric effects found in Romantic era industrial landscape paintings. As epitomized by Loutherbourg's *Coalbrookdale by Night* (Figure 13a), this subgenre of paintings represents some of the most dramatic atmospheric effects from the sublime landscape tradition.

Previous studies of landscape have shown that artists' representations of 'natural' landscapes are not naïve, realistic representations of nature, but are undergirded with cultural narratives (*e.g.* Mitchell 2002). Thus, for many art historians and literary critics even the most 'natural' landscape paintings and photographs express social hierarchies, labor relations, and imperialism in such a way that they effectively contain class conflict, labor unrest, and concerns about national identity – in the same way that modern chemical landscape photography contains fears concerning labor practices, industrial safety, and environmental contamination. Within the paradigm of landscape painting, nature itself is a human construct laden with conventions that make it comprehensible as 'landscape', and artistic representations of the landscape overtly articulate these conventions. Similar conventions are smuggled into the decidedly unnatural vistas of the chemical landscape.

By acknowledging the constructed nature of landscape and the articulation of its visual conventions in landscape painting, we can understand visual representations of the industrial landscape as an extension of traditional landscape painting. The landscape conventions of the picturesque and sublime, which are readily visible in nineteenth century paintings of industry (Figure 13), are cloaked in the images of chemical plants with which we are concerned. When we consider contemporary images of chemical industry within the larger landscape tradition, rather than simply as photographs of chemical plants, we secure the connection of these images to sublime landscape painting. As noted by Snyder (2002), nineteenth-century commercial landscape photographers "did not escape landscape conventions; they adopted and reformulated them". Thus, like Carleton Watkins who took industrial photographs for the California State Geological Society in the nineteenth century, early twenty-first century photographers of chemical plants have adopted and reformulated a formal and philosophical link to the sublime tradition. Formally, their photographs are composed along the same physical scale, with the same vertical forms, and with the same attention to atmospheric effects; philosophically, they are framed by Edmund Burke's and Immanuel Kant's aesthetic theories of the sublime.

In his *Philosophical Enquiry into the Origins of Our Ideas of the Sublime and Beautiful* (1757, pt. II), Burke distinguished beauty as a form of pleasure, from the sensation of the sublime, which is caused by imagined threats to our existence that, if compared to real threats, are accompanied by delightful relief. For instance, an image of the devastating power and grandeur of nature can cause us to experience the emotion of the sublime if we are simultaneously aware that the threat is only imagined. In the chemical landscape this view of nature is transmogrified into an industrial site and the trigger for the sublime experience is reconstituted as a fear of chemicals and the power of the chemical industry.[16] In Kant's *Critique of Judgment* (1790, §§ 23-9), the delight of the sublime results from a self-reflection of the human mind, which further helps us to understand today's photographs of chemical plants. From this perspective when nature through her grandeur and power intimidates our sense of self as physical beings and makes us look and feel small and powerless, we can resort to the capacities of human reason that is ultimately power-

---

[16] See the American Chemical Society National Benchmark Survey, July 2000 for a summary of the public's attitudes towards chemistry, chemicals, and chemists.

ful. Thus, according to Kant, the original fear and intimidation produced by nature is turned into the delight of the sublime once we recognize our capacity to comprehend and ultimately control its seemingly overwhelming might. By a clever displacement, when industry, such as the Coalbrookdale industrial site, is placed into natural landscape or replaces nature all together, as in today's chemical landscapes, the Kantian sublime assumes a new dimension: industry becomes the object by means of which the human mind can recognize its own greatness.

3.4 Chemical plants as kitsch

Kitsch has been a topic of debate among art/cultural critics and scholars for more than a century (Kulka 1996, pp. 13-22). The most influential critics on the subject include Clement Greenberg (1909-1994) and Hermann Broch (1886-1951). Greenberg (1939) defined kitsch as "popular, commercial art and literature" (as opposed to avant-garde art and literature) that "is a product of the industrial revolution which urbanized the masses of Western Europe and America" and "is mechanical and operates by formulas [... and] vicarious experience and faked sensations". Similarly, Broch (1969) considered kitsch a "system of imitation" that corrupts real art (in his case the art of Romanticism) serving as an "element of evil in the value system of art" (Broch 1969). More recently scholars have attempted to recuperate kitsch from these harsh critiques by reframing it as a distinct aesthetic without regard to class-based tastes. These include Robert C. Solomon's (1991) defense of sentimentality in art, Sam Binkley's (2000) argument "for a uniquely kitsch aesthetic that employs the thematics of repetition, imitation and emulation as a distinct aesthetic style" and Kulka (1996, pp. 1-12) who conservatively attempts to reduce kitsch to an aesthetic category (like the grotesque or the beautiful) that is objectively deficient as an art form rather than subjectively a matter of taste. In sum, despite the complexities and inconsistencies between the arguments articulated by these critics and others, kitsch can be understood as a sociocultural phenomenon (normally connected to the development of the middle-class in the nineteenth century) and a debased artistic sensibility with roots in the Romantic era.

Broch made clear how the aesthetic ideals of Romanticism became the progenitor of what we now know of as kitsch: although not kitsch, Romantic art is "the mother of kitsch and that there are moments when the child becomes so like its mother that one cannot distinguish between them" (Broch 1969, p. 62). From this perspective Romantic era paintings like Friedrich's *Wanderer Above the Sea of Fog* (1818), Schinkel's *Medieval City on a River* (1815) and even Loutherbourg's *Coalbrookdale by Night* (Figure 13a) cross into the realm of kitsch because they contain "a range of references to high or legitimate culture" (Ross 1989, p. 145), but in doing so rely on the use of formal clichés and an overwrought sentimentality that undermines their artistic intentions. This slippage between Romanticism, and in particular the Romantic sublime, and kitsch is also found in modern chemical landscapes. The expressive note of these images manifests itself in the expanse of richly atmospheric sky juxtaposed against the chemical plant. That the sky is the intended site of emotionality in these images is made clear when viewed in contrast to the typical images of academic chemistry buildings, which do not include such skies and thus strike one as mundane and visually uninteresting. The sky in photographs of chemical plants, on the other hand, adds an element of over-sentimentality to the image that potentially links it to a disingenuously emotive stance and threatens to topple the images from sublimity into kitsch. Viewed in this way, these ornate skies imitate those found in sublime landscape paintings and the images themselves are therefore merely draped in the most overt trapping of this tradition. Through this lens, these images like the classic visual clichés of kitsch (*e.g.*, exaggeratedly round eyed children and puppy dogs (Solomon 1991) provide a falsely benign image of the world – where chemical plants are only associated with the production of goods that yield 'better living through chemistry' and never with the realities of chemical pollution and toxicity.

Kitsch developed as a consequence of the mechanization of mass-production along with the simultaneous growth of the middle-class in the nineteenth century (Kulka 1996, pp. 13-22). The ability to cheaply reproduce art (as posters, postcards, *etc.*) gave the middle-class access to a simulacrum of images that were previously available only to the privileged. Cheap reproduction yielded a new aesthetic based on the imitative rather than the authentic. (In an ironic twist to this history, kitsch has since been hijacked by the elites of the world of art). Chemical land-scapes are therefore doubly endowed with the mechanized qualities of kitsch. They imitate the art of the sublime tradition and they have a reit-erative impulse – so that each image mirrors the content and structure of the others – yielding a mass-produced quality. Through sheer repetition images of chemical plants become commonplace inuring the viewer to their potential hazards and ultimately rendering them as culturally neu-tral, even inert, objects. Thus, although kitsch might be viewed as the poor, uneducated cousin of the sublime, it, like the sublime, has the power to subdue the dangerous power of chemical plants for the viewer of such images.

Whether viewed through a sociocultural, art historical, or aesthetic lens, chemical plant landscapes at once revere and deflate the actualities of chemical industry. When viewed in the context of architectural pho-tography chemical plants literally and metaphorically stand in for the castles and cathedrals of earlier photographs, replacing these iconic sym-bols of power (monarchy and church) with a later day equivalent – indus-try. Like architectural images of castles and cathedrals, and unlike early depictions of industry, current images of chemical industry decontextual-ize and sanitize their presence in the larger landscape, visually minimiz-ing their potential for hazards. This dichotomy is recast by a reading of these images within the framework of the sublime and kitsch. In this aes-thetic context, chemical plants become symbolic of the sublime power of the human mind to both create and control chemical industry and its products, while kitsch, when viewed as an overwrought visual extension of the romantic sublime, diminishes their cultural power through cliché and reiteration.

4. Abstraction

4.1 Chemical plants: close-up view

An alternative but also common image of the chemical plant provides a close-up perspective of the tubes and towers discussed as primary ele-ments in the previous section. Even more than those of the panoramic chemical plant, however, these cropped images decontexualize the plants from their sociocultural implications – formally obscuring their relationship to any past or present landscape, industrial or otherwise. As shown in Figure 20 they are sometimes photographed from above, but, more commonly from below, a 'worms-eye' perspective that can make the viewer of the photograph feel slightly off-kilter and reverentially endows the plants with a beauty not found in the chemical plant landscapes we have just discussed.[17]

With these changes in perspective also comes an alteration in the art historical associations of the images, albeit one with a more positive valence. Thus, instead of being aligned with the fakery of uroscopy or the kitschyness of the overwrought sublime landscape, these images participate in the 'high-art' aesthetics of early twentieth-century modernism. In particular, the myriad of ordered yet entangled tubes in these images recall the art of the Machine Age, which exalted the rise of industrial culture as a symbol of rationality and hope after World War I. A proto-Machine Art had emerged in the years just prior to World War I when the epic-cubists, futurists, and constructivists (Herbert 1997) embraced the machine as a subject material for serious abstract art.[18] By the 1920s a 'machine aesthetic' had developed that employed the geometric forms of abstract art but was essentially representational. Early in this time period the shift towards the representational is perhaps best exemplified by Fernand Léger, whose paintings often situated cartoonishly rendered people within backgrounds composed of mechanized and industrial elements (Figure 21a). By the 1930's many Weimar artists had assumed a philosophy of Neue Sachlichkeit that was reflected in a style of detached realism compared to the high emotionality of classic German expressionism (Guenther 1995, pp. 35-36). Most notable among these for our purposes is Carl Grossberg who painted colorful, often whimsical images of industrial sites including *Kessel in Einer Raffinerie* and *Der Gelbe Kessel*

---

[17] In the introduction to *High Techne* Rutsky writes that "The aesthetic impulse in modernism continually returns to romantic notions of the aesthetic – or of beauty, at least – as an eternal or spiritual realm, unchanging and whole [...] To this end, it often connects the spiritual and the technological, attempting to impart a sense of wholeness and the eternal to technological forms" (Rutsky 1999, p. 9).

[18] For example see Luigi Russolo's *Dynamism of an Automobile* (1913), Musée National d'Art Moderne, Paris (www.futurism.org.uk/russolo/rus_im20.htm)

(Figure 21b).[19] Ultimately the machine as the subject of art was realized in the aesthetic of 'machine purity' by the precisionist artist Charles Sheeler and others (Figure 21c). These American artists revered the inherent beauty of machines rendering them in a pristine fashion akin to those found in mechanical drawings. Although historians of machine-age art often tend to focus on an artist's fascination with the mechanical aspects of the machines they portrayed, as shown in Figure 21 the relationship of such art to chemical processes is just as, if not more, important. These artists not only employed tubular shapes as principle geometric forms in many of their compositions, which implicitly links their work, and much of the abstract art of that time, to the conduits and smokestacks associated with industrial chemistry, they often *explicitly* represented chemistry. This is clearly shown in Léger's *Le Mécanicien* which portrays a man holding a cigarette backgrounded by a small industrial plant with a smokestack which presumable indicates his status as a 'mechanic' (Figure 21a); Grossberg's *Der Gelbe Kessel* where a chemical tank is the primary subject of the painting (Figure 21b); and Sheeler's *Ballet Mechanique* which depicts a network of conduits carrying "compressed air and excess gases between the power house and the blast furnaces" (Troyen 1987, p. 124) of Ford's River Rouge Plant. As demonstrated by these images there is a direct visual connection between the work of the machine-age artists and the abstracted images of chemical plants created by today's commercial photographers (see Figure 20).

The precisionists also rendered machines as pristinely devoid of grime and human interaction. As machine purists they, unlike the Dadaists of this same time period (who employed a machine aesthetic as social critique), embraced an aesthetic of the machine endowed with an optimism representative of the rise and promise of American industry, including chemical industry (Lugon 2003). In fact, for American precisionists in particular, the line between their art and the utopian promise of American industry was porous, enabling them to work as both fine artists and commercial artists without hesitancy and to employ the same

---

[19]   Although recognized as an Neue Sachlichkeit artist Grossberg's images of industrial plants have also been considered to be aligned with surrealism and magical realism (see Hughes 2004, pp. 123-125 and Guenther 1995, pp. 46-48.

visual tropes in both artistic spheres.[20] These visual tropes were eventually subsumed by many commercial photographers and, as illustrated in Figure 20, are still employed today.

Like the work of the machine purists, close-up images of chemical plants appear representational but in fact rely heavily on the formal canon of abstract art, including an emphasis on primary geometric forms juxtaposed into complex arrays akin to the work of the cubists. In theory, the geometric nature of these images reflects the order and rationality of the machines they depict, but, as Rutsky (1999, pp. 73-101) has argued, their relationship to abstract modernism ultimately separates their technological function from their form shifting them into a purely aesthetic realm. In their close-cropped askew perspective these images, like Machine Age photographs themselves, also reveal their connection to the abstract movement of avant-garde photography made popular by the Bauhaus photographer László Moholy-Nagy and others in the 1920s and 1930s who "strove to separate objects from their natural settings" by employing "disorienting viewpoints, radical cropping, strong figure-ground relationships, [and] compositions oriented on the diagonal" (Light 1995, p. 97).

4.2 Glassware: the chemical still life

Like the close-up images of chemical plants, many contemporary images of chemical apparatus play on the abstract tradition. Initially they appear simply representational, but closer inspection shows that they are not. As in Figure 22 the prototypical contemporary chemical 'still life' photograph is composed of a collection of various flasks and test-tubes containing colored liquids sitting on an indeterminate surface (*i.e.* not clearly a table or lab bench) or, more often, shot from an odd angle and/or so closely cropped that there is no recognizable surface. Their focus on decontextualized glassware provides little clue to how the equipment is manipulated by people in a laboratory environment. Instead, these images are intended to represent the discipline of chemistry. In fact, as we

---

[20] Sheeler, in particular, made this connection between his art and American industry explicit with his commissioned paintings of the Ford Motor Company.

have shown in a previous paper, in popular visual culture images of prototypical chemical glassware such as flasks and test-tubes are emblematic icons of chemistry, and indeed of all of science (Schummer & Spector 2007).

Unlike chemical plant abstractions, however, the formal aspects of many of these images have a strong allegiance to a particularly spare mode of still life painting rather than to Machine Age precisionism. This style, as exemplified by Giorgio Morandi in the mid twentieth century and later by William Bailey, express the neoclassical ideal of beauty through their simplicity, balance, and harmony (Figure 23a/b). Both of these painters worked within the still life tradition through their choice of subject material (bottles, plates, cups, and so forth sitting on tables) but at the same time altered the tradition by stripping it down to its bare essentials, leaving behind the elaborately crowded still lifes of earlier periods that admit decay and death as a marker of time in the form of animal carcasses, dying flowers, and insect infested fruit.[21]

Tony Cragg makes explicit this connection between images of chemical apparatuses and still lifes in his series *Laboratory Still Life No. 1-4* (Figure 23c). Like Morandi and Bailey he strips the still life down to its bare essentials (in his case objects without even a table), but unlike these artists he employs chemical flasks as his subject material imparting a sense of irony into his still lifes. Like these artists' still lifes, chemical 'still lifes' are generally simple and well balanced compositions (see Figure 22). Unlike Cragg's paintings, however, chemical 'still lifes' extract self-conscious irony through their institutional intentions. Instead, like the chemicals and chemical industry that substitute for nature in their manifestation of the sublime, an unintended irony emerges from the tension between beauty and danger in the chemical 'still lifes'. Renaissance still lifes sometimes seductively depict idealized fruits and vegetables, which on closer inspection actually show signs of decomposition and insect infestation. Similarly chemical 'still lifes' work on two levels – those of the beautiful and the grotesque. Unlike the explicit (and whimsical) grotesque aesthetic of Renaissance still lifes, however, the associa-

---

[21] For example see Renaissance and Baroque period still lifes in Ebert-Schifferer 1999, pp. 115-223.

tion of chemical 'still lifes' with the grotesque is expressed only implicitly through the negative associations that chemicals often elicit from the public.[18]

Tony Cragg was schooled as a chemical laboratory technician and we can assume that he was exposed to illustrations of chemical apparatuses in chemistry textbooks. It comes as no surprise, therefore, that his work reveals an intimate conceptual parallel to the long historical tradition of scientific textbook illustrations. Nevertheless, although Cragg's paintings are representational in so far as they depict actual chemical glassware, they are also unmistakably symbolic rather than didactic. Taken as scientific illustrations, his paintings would provide no guidance for performing an actual experiment. His images emblematize chemistry itself rather than depicting its processes.

Such depictions of chemical glassware, both in contemporary photographs and fine art, assume their emblematic and symbolic function through their historical lineage. From ancient Alexandrian manuscripts to medieval alchemical treatises, images of chemical apparatus were frequently interspersed with the text to illustrate the specific shape or construction required for an experiment (Obrist 2003). In Renaissance textbooks of distillation and metallurgy, such illustrations sometimes consumed larger parts of the volume, as in Biringuccio's *Pirotechnia* (1540). During the eighteenth century such drawings gained in popularity, culminating in the inclusion of numerous detailed illustrations of distillation apparatus in one of the grand symbols of the Enlightenment, Diderot's *Dictionary of Science, Arts, and Trades* (Greenburg 2003, pp. 150-4) – ostensibly providing information to the educated reader on instrumental details. Starting with Lavoiser and continuing into the nineteenth century, illustrations of apparatus became more accurate and gradually included some drawings that attempted to depict dynamic chemical processes, in alliance with the drive to legitimize and popularize chemistry (Golinski 1992). Illustrations in chemical textbooks and manuals sometimes showed apparatus with disembodied hands manipulating the glassware, which in theory could be used as guides for performing an actual experiment (Knight 2003). These drawings live on in chemistry laboratory textbooks today and effectively communicate how to set up or manually manipulate a particular piece of glassware (*e.g.*, Williamson 2003).

Apart from their specific didactic purpose, however, images of chemical apparatus assumed a life of their own in the broader visual culture. Starting in the late eighteenth century, they drew visual associations between chemistry, experiment, and Lavoisien empiricism (Stafford 1996, pp. 91-110), even though, as Beretta (2000) notes, the illustrations sometimes represented anachronistic chemical apparatus. They helped chemistry to assume the epistemological status of a respected science, to establish a professional identity, and to popularize itself to a broader public. In the late nineteenth century the iconography for representing chemistry as a scientific discipline was fully developed, employing the same elements we find today. These included static and decontextualized drawings of flasks and test-tubes without any indication of how to use them (Knight 1996). Like the subjects of the Machine Age, the depicted apparatus became symbolically abstract and dissociated from its actual function.

Today's photographs of chemical glassware have largely replaced the woodcuts and etchings of earlier centuries, but still operate on two semantic levels. On the one hand, like Cragg's still lifes, they retain the representational content and associations of nineteenth-century chemistry. On the other, they symbolically represent contemporary chemistry. Thus, images of glassware filled with colored liquids are such potent indicators of chemistry that they are used as *the* icons of science, although the chemistry they represent is generally outmoded.[22] Moreover, once abstracted from their representational meaning, the images could become subject to graphical analysis and rearrangement both in photographic self-representations of chemistry and in fine art. Indeed, we contend that these images' conservative, backward-looking, symbolism has ironically led to their thoroughly modern rendition, allowing them to be loosed from any representational context and brought into the realm of pure aesthetics.

---

[22] Of course chemists still use flasks (and sometimes even test-tubes), but like all sciences at this point in the history, chemistry would presumably be much more accurately represented by complex instrumentation.

5. Conclusion

Like any other profession, chemists have been involved in shaping their public image through the production and dissemination of visual material that they believe best depicts their profession. Because these images are often created by commercial artists they are also consciously or, what appears more likely, unconsciously embedded within specific cultural traditions and conventions. Thus, unlike fine art representations of chemistry,[23] chemists and commercial artists presumably do not seek originality (in a broad sense) but rather visual conventions that create immediate associations between the image and chemistry. It can be assumed that in these cases, chemists intend to show their science in a positive light but at the same time need commercial artists to produce images that 'excite' the eye. Therefore, within the highly delineated subject material and conventions that these images demand, they seek to create interesting and original images. Although perhaps less overtly articulated than their formalist qualities, these images also expose conceptual and psycho-social aspects of the chemistry they seek to represent. Visual images of chemistry are situated and perceived within the larger cultural context of chemistry – a science with a dual (some would say split) personality, at once academic and industry-serving, conceptual and applied – so that they express the multiple layers of the science itself. As a result they provide insights into how chemistry seeks to aesthetisize its representation in the larger culture while simultaneously exposing how the larger culture comes to understand chemistry through its visual representation.

A qualitative examination of the visual self-representation of chemistry reveals that three specific motifs prevail so strongly that they have assumed a stereotypical character: the image of a scientist holding up a piece of glassware and gazing at its contents as the key pose of chemical portraiture, chemical landscapes of smokestacks and conduits in atmospherically illuminated skies, and chemical still lifes of various flasks filled with colored liquids. In this chapter we have examined these motifs within the broader cultural-historical context. Not surprisingly, all three 'chemical' motifs can be traced back to longer traditions of the fine arts

---

[23] See the virtual art exhibition 'Chemistry in Art' <www.hyle.org/art/cia/> and Spector & Schummer 2003.

and popular visual culture, which have shaped both the visual conventions and the cultural meanings of today's chemical stereotypes. It turns out that, like the split identity of chemistry itself, these images represent a conflicted public identity for the discipline. All too often, as the chemical portraiture section of this chapter demonstrates, commercial artists, who are likely not apprised of the artistic tradition in which they work, and the chemists who naïvely disseminate their self-representations, unintentionally promulgate an image of chemistry based in a satirically debasing tradition. Or, as in the case of chemical landscapes, these images dabble in a tradition that begins in the high art conventions of the sublime landscape but, like those conventions, has the potential to cross the line into the naïve and unironic aesthetics of kitsch. On the other hand, as is evident in the section on abstraction where we analyzed the chemical still life, chemistry and its apparatus can inspire commercial artists to reach outside of the representational into artistic traditions that have commanded respect throughout the twentieth century.

References

Abramowicz, J.: 2004, *Giorgio Morandi: The Art of Silence*, Yale University Press, New Haven.

Becher, H. & Becher, B: 2002, *Industrial landscapes*, MIT Press, Cambridge, MA.

Beneke, S. & Ottomeier, H. (eds.): 2002, *Die Zweite Schöpfung: Bilder der industriellen Welt vom 18. Jahrhundert bis in die Gegenwart*, Edition Minerva, Wolfratshausen.

Beretta, M.: 2000, 'Chemical Imagery and the Enlightenment of Matter', in: W.R. Shea (ed.), *Science and the Visual Image in the Enlightenment*, Science History Publications, Canton, MA, pp. 57-88.

Binkley, S.: 2000, 'Kitsch as a Repetitive System: A Problem for the Theory of Taste Hierarchy', *Journal of Material Culture*, 5, p. 131-152.

Bowden, M.E.: 1997, *Chemical Archiever: The Human Face of the Chemical Sciences*, Chemical Heritage Foundation, Philadelphia.

Briganti, G. & Hollander, J.: 1991, *William Bailey*, Rizzoli, New York.

Briggs, A.: 1979, *Iron Bridge to Crystal Palace: Impact and Images of the Industrial Revolution*, Thames & Hudson, London.

Broch, H.: 1969 [1950], 'Notes on the Problem of Kitsch', in: G. Dorfles (ed.), *Kitsch: The World of Bad Taste*, Universe Books, New York, pp. 49-76.

Brown, K.: 1996, *Ink, Paper, Metal, Wood*, Chronicle Books, San Francisco.

Burke, E.: 1757, *A Philosophical Inquiry into the Origin of Our Ideas of the Sublime and Beautiful*, Dodsley, London.

Connor, H.: 2001, 'Medieval uroscopy and its representation on misericords. Part 1: Uroscopy', *Clinical Medicine*, 1 (6), 507-9.

Constable, J.: 1998 [1821], 'Letter to his friend Archdeacon Fischer', in: M. Gayford & K. Wright (eds.), *The Grove Book of Art Writing*, Grove Press, New York, pp. 50-1.

Dalton, J.: 1798, 'Extraordinary facts relating to the vision of colours, with observation', *Memoirs of the Literary and Philosophical Society of Manchester*, 5, 28-45.

Daniels, S.: 1999, *Joseph Wright*, Princeton University Press, Princeton.

Diers, M. & Hedinger, B.: 2002, 'Z.B. (Dampf-)Wolken – Von der Natur der Industrie in Bildern des Impressionismus nebst einer Allegorie', in: Beneke, S. & Ottomeier, H. (eds.): *Die Zweite Schöpfung: Bilder der industriellen Welt vom 18. Jahrhundert bis in die Gegenwart*, Edition Minerva, Wolfratshausen, pp. 72-79.

Downs, L. B.: 1999, *Diego Rivera: The Detroit Industry Murals*, W. W. Norton, New York.

Ebert-Schifferer, S: 1999, *Still Life: A History*, Harry N. Abrams, New York.

Frese, G.: 2000, *Dow Chemical Portrayed*, Chemical Heritage Foundation, Philadelphia.

Fried, M.: 2002, *Menzel's Realism: Art and Embodiment in Nineteenth-Century Berlin*, Yale University Press, New Haven.

Friedlander, W.J.: 1992, *The Golden Wand of Medicine: A History of the Caduceus Symbol in Medicine*, Greenwood, New York.

Garrison F.H.: 1917, *An introduction to the history of medicine*, 2nd edn., Saunders, Philadelphia & London.

Golinksi, J.: 1992, *Science as Public Culture: Chemistry and Enlightenment in Britain, 1760-1820*, Cambridge University Press, Cambridge.

Grape-Albers, H.: 1977, *Spätantike Bilder aus der Welt des Arztes: medizinische Bilderhandschriften der Spätantike und ihre mittelalterliche Überlieferung*, Pressler, Wiesbaden.

Greenberg, C.: 1939, 'Avant-Garde and Kitsch', *Partisan Review*, 6 (5), pp. 34-49.

Greenburg, A.: 2003, *The Art of Chemistry*, Wiley, Hoboken, NJ.

Guenther, I: 1995, 'Magical Realism, New Objectivity, and the Arts During the Weimar Republic', in: L. P. Zamora & W. B. Faris (eds.), *Magical Realism: Theory, Histroy, Community*, Duke University Press, Durham, N.C., pp. 33-74.

Herbert, R.L.: 1997, 'The Arrival of the Machine: Modernist Art in Europe 1910-25', *Social Research*, 64, 1273-1305.

Holländer, E.: 1903, *Die Medizin in der klassischen Malerei*, Enke, Stuttgart (4th edn. 1950).

Holländer, E.: 1905, *Die Karikatur und Satire in der Medizin*, Enke, Stuttgart (2nd edn. 1921).

Holländer, E.: 1912, *Plastik und Medizin*, Enke, Stuttgart.

Hughes, T. P.: *Human Built World*, University of Chicago Press, Chicago.

Janson, H.W.: 1952, *Apes and Ape Lore in the Middle Ages and Renaissance*, Warburg Institute, London (Studies of the Warburg Institute, no. 20).

Kant, I.: 1790, *Kritik der Urteilskraft*, Lagarde, Berlin.

Klinge, M. & Lüdke, D. (eds.): 2005, *David Teniers der Jüngere, 1610-1690: Alltag und Vergnügen in Flandern*, Staatliche Kunsthalle, Karlsruhe.

Klingender, F. D.: 1968, *Art and the Industrial Revolution*, Augustus M. Kelley, New York.

Knight, D.: 1996, 'Illustrating Chemistry', in: B.S. Baigrie (ed.), *Picturing Knowledge: Historical and Philosophical Problems Concerning the Use of Art and Science*, Univ. of Toronto Press, Toronto.

Knight, D.: 2003, 'Exalting Understanding without Depressing Imagination: Depicting Chemical Process', *Hyle: International Journal for Philosophy of Chemistry*, **9**, 171-89.

Koerner, J. L.: 1990, *Casper David Friedrich and the Subject of Landscape*, Yale University Press, Hartford, CT.

Kulka, T.: 1996, *Kitsch and Art*, Pennsylvania State UP, University Park.

Lanchner, C: 1998, *Fernand Léger*, The Museum of Modern Art, New York, NY.

Light, E.M.: 1995, *Picturing Modernism: Maholy-Nagy and Photography in Weimar Germany*, MIT Press, Cambridge, MA.

Linden, S.J.: 1996, *Darke hierogliphicks. Alchemy in English Literature from Chaucer to the Restoration*, University Press of Kentucky, Lexington.

Lindgren, U.: 1992, *Die Artes liberales in Antike und Mittelalter: bildungs- und wissenschaftsgeschichtliche Entwicklungslinien*, Institut für Geschichte der Naturwissenschaften, München.

Lugon, O.: 2003, 'The Machine Between Cult Object and Merchandise', in: E. de Chassey (ed.), *American Art: 1908-1947 from Winslow Homer to Jackson Pollock*, Abrams, New York.

MacKinney, Loren C.: 1965, *Medical illustrations in medieval manuscripts*, Univ. of California Press, Berkeley.

Metzl, J.M. & Howell, J.D.: 2004, 'Making History: Lessons from the *Great Moments* Series of Pharmaceutical Advertisements', *Academic Medicine*, **79** (11), 1027-32.

Michalski, S.: 2003, *New Objectivity: Painting, Graphic Art and Photography in Weimar Germany 1919-1933*, Taschen, Kohn.

Mitchell, W.J.T. (ed.): 2002, *Landscape and Power*, 2nd edn., Univ. of Chicago Press, Chicago.

Nicoldon, B.: 1968, *Joseph Wright of Derby*, Routledge, London.

Obrist, B.: 2003, 'Visualization in Medieval Alchemy', *Hyle: International Journal for Philosophy of Chemistry*, **9**, 131-70.

Principe, L.M. & DeWitt, L.: 2002, *Transmutations: Alchemy in Art*, Chemical Heritage Foundation, Philadelphia.

Read, J.: 1947: *The Alchemist: In Life, Literature and Art*, Thomas Nelson, London.

Robinson, C. & Herschman, J.: 1987, *Architecture Transformed: A History of the Photography of Buildings from 1839 to the Present*, MIT Press, Cambridge.

Rodner, W.S.: 1997, *J.M.W. Turner: Romantic Painter of the Industrial Revolution*, University of California Press, Berkeley.

Ross, A.: 1989, *No Respect: Intellectuals and Popular Culture*, Routledge, New York.

Rutsky, R.L.: 1999, *High Techne: Art and Technology from the Machine Aesthetic to the Posthuman*, Univ. of Minnesota Press, Minneapolis.

Schadewaldt, H.; Binet, L.; Maillant, C. & Veith, I.: 1967, *Kunst und Medizin*, DuMont Schauberg, Köln.

Schummer. J.: 2006, 'Historical Roots of the Mad Scientist: Chemists in Nineteenth-century Literature', *Ambix*, **53**, 99-127.

Schummer, J. & Spector, T.I.: 2007, 'Popular Images versus Self-Images of Science: Visual Representations of Science in Clipart Cartoons and Internet Photographs', in: B. Hüppauf & P. Weingart (eds.), *Science Images and Popular Images of Science*, London-New York: Routledge, 2007, pp. 69-95 (in print).

Snyder, J.: 2002, 'Territorial Photography', in: W.J.T. Mitchell (ed.): 2002, *Landscape and Power*, 2nd edn., Univ. of Chicago Press, Chicago, pp. 175-201.

Solomon, R.C.: 1991, 'On Kitsch and Sentimentality', *The Journal of Aesthetics and Art Criticism*, 49, 1-14.

Spector, T.I. & Schummer, J.: 2003, 'Chemistry in Art: Introduction to the Virtual Art Exhibition', *Hyle: International Journal for Philosophy of Chemistry*, **9**, 225-232.

Stafford, B.M.: 1996, *Good Looking*, MIT Press, Cambridge, MA.

Troyan, C. & Hirshler, E.E.: 1987, *Charles Sheeler: Paintings and Drawings*, Little & Brown, Boston.

Türk, K. (ed.): 1997, *Arbeit und Industrie in der bildenden Kunst*, Steiner, Stuttgart.

Vorsteher, D.: 2002, 'Das Industriebild als Auftrag zwischen Vormärz und Gründerzeit', in: Beneke, S. & Ottomeier, H. (eds.): *Die Zweite Schöpfung: Bilder der industriellen Welt vom 18. Jahrhundert bis in die Gegenwart*, Edition Minerva, Wolfratshausen, pp. 66-71.

Wagner, M.: 1979, *Die Industrielandschaft in der englischen Malerei und Graphik, 1770-1830*, Lang, Frankfurt.

White, W.I.: 1991, 'A New Look at the Role of Urinalysis in the History of Diagnostic Medicine', *Clinical Chemistry*, **37** (1), 119-125.

Wilcox, R.A. & Whitham, E.M.: 2003, 'The Symbol of Modern Medicine: Why One Snake Is More Than Two', *Annals of Internal Medicine*, **138**, 673-677.

Williamson, K.L.: 2003, *Macroscale and Microscale Organic Experiments*, 4th edn., Houghton Mifflin, Boston.

Zglinicki, F.v.: 1982, *Die Uroskopie in der bildenden Kunst: eine kunst- und medizinhistorische Untersuchung über die Harnschau*, GIT-Verlag, Darmstadt.

Zotter, H.: 1980, *Antike Medizin: die medizinische Sammelhandschrift Cod. Vindobonensis 93 in lateinischer und deutscher Sprache*, Akadademische Druck- u. Verlagsanstalt, Graz.

Images

Figure 1. The typical chemical portrait in (a) photographs and (b) clip-art cartoons (from clipart.com).

Figure 2. (a) Illustration from Hunayn ibn Ishaq al-'Ibadi (Joannitius): *Isagoge Johannitii in Tegni Galeni* (called *Articella*), Oxford, 13th century ms (DeRicci NLM [78], Fol. 42v, National Library of Medicine). (b) Illustration from Avicenna, *Canon medicinae*, trans. from Arab by Gerard of Cremona) France, 1283; decoration added c. 1350-1400 (The Hague, MMW, 10 B 24, fol. 8r, National Library of the Netherlands). (c) Relief of medicine by Andrea Pisano (1295-1348) from 1334-6, after a drawing by Giotto; lower part, close to the allegorical depictions of the seven liberal arts, of Giotto's Campanile at the Cathedral of Florence (repr. from Schadewaldt 1967, p. 105).

Figure 3a. Emblematic depiction of the seven mechanical arts after Hugo de St. Viktor; from Rodericus Zamorensis, *Spiegel des menschlichen Lebens*, Augsburg 1475 (note medicine no. 6) (repr. from Lindgren 1992, p. 71) (b) Emblematic depiction of the 14 arts, from Bartholomeus Chasseuneux: *Catalogus gloriae mundi*, Lugdunum 1529 (note medicine in the middle of second row) (repr. from Lindgren 1992, p. 67). (c) Cosmas and Damian, the twin saints and Christian patrons of medicine; miniature from "Heures d'Anne de Bretagne", early sixteenth century (Bibliothèque Nationale, Paris, Richelieu Manuscripts Latin 9474, Fol. 173v).

Figure 4. (a) Jacob van Maerlant: *Der Naturen Bloeme*, Flanders c.1350 (KB, KA 16, Folio 69r, National Library of the Netherlands). b. Hans Holbein: *The Dance of Death*, Lyons 1538, XXVI. "The Physician" (woodcut) (repr. from Holländer, 1903, p. 283). (c) Urine distillation apparatus from Leonardt Thurneisser (*Aurora Thesaurusque Philosophorum Paracelsi*, Basel 1577). (d) Pieter Brueghel the Elder (c.1525-1569), detail from a satirical drawing of medicine (repr. from Holländer 1905, p. 52. (e) Thomas Murner: *Narrenbeschwörung* (1512), "Der Kälberarzt" (The calf doctor) (repr. from Holländer 1905, p. 89). (f) Frontispiece of Johan Van Dueren: *De Ontdekking der Bedriegeryen Vande gemeene Pis-Besienders*, Amsterdam 1688. (g) Peter Candid: "Allegory of Medicine", 1619-22, fresco in the town hall of Augsburg.

Figure 5. (a) David Teniers: "The Alchemist", oil on wood, 27,5 x 38,5 cm, ca. 1656-60 (Kunsthistorisches Museum Wien). (b) "Jesus and the doctors of the Faith" by the entourage of Giuseppe Ribera (1591-1652), ca. 1630 (Kunsthistorisches Museum Wien). (c) David Teniers: "The Alchemist", oil on wood, 47 x 36 cm, ca. 1670 (Madrid, Museo del Prado). (d) Pieter Brueghel the Elder (ca. 1525-69): "The Alchemist" (detail); engraving by Philipp Galle, 1558 (Germanisches Nationalmuseum). (e) Hans Weiditz the Younger (ca. 1485-1536) Woodcut (detail), printed in the German trans. of Petrarch's *De remediis*, Augsburg 1519/20, chapter on alchemy. (f) Albrecht Dürer (1471-1528): woodcut of an alchemist, printed in Sebastian Brant's *Das Narrenschiff* (1494), chapter on forgery and fraud.(g) David Teniers (the Younger or Elder?): "The Alchemist", oil on canvas (Palazzo Pitti, Galleria Palatina, Florence). (h) David Teniers: "The Village Doctor", c. 1650, (Palais des Beaux-Arts, Brussels).

Figure 6. (a) Pietro Longhi (1702-1785): "The Alchemists", c. 1757, oil on canvas, 61 × 50 cm (Galery Ca' Rezzonico Venice). (6) Carl Spitzweg (1802-1885): "Der Alchimist", c. 1860, oil on canvas, 36 × 38 cm (Staatsgalerie Stuttgart).

Figure 7. (a) "A British Chymist analizing a Corsican earth worm!!" Coloured aquatint by Temple West (c 1739-1783), published: London 1803 (Wellcome Library). (b) "Le médecin aux urines: Oh! mon bon Dieu, quelle fièvre..." Lithograph after Charles Émile Wattier (1800-1868) (National Library of Medicine). (c) "Nineteenth Century Doctor – still water gazing", Wood engraving after Adam Adolf Oberländer (1845-1923), c. 1890 (National Library of Medicine).

Figure 8. From left to reight: Justus von Liebig; August Kekulé (original painting from 1892); William Henry Perkin with a skein dyed mauve (original painting from 1892); Marcelin Berthelot (all images Edgar Fahs Smith Collection).

Figure 9. (a) Portrait of John Dalton; engraving by William Henry Worthington after a 1814 painting by Joseph Allen. (b) Caricature of Dalton by James Stephenson (1808-1886), probably from 1882 (both Edgar Fahs Smith Collection).

Figure 10a. Photograph of Marcelin Berthelot, probably late 19th century (Edgar Fahs Smith Collection). (b) Oil painting of Berthelot by Harry Herman Salomon (1860-1936) after a photograph, early 20th century. (c) Caricature (mirror image) of Berthelot by unknown artist, probably early 20th century, pencil on paper (both Wellcome Library).

Figure 11. (a) Painting of Pasteur by Albert Edelfelt (1854-1905), 1885 (Musee d'Orsay, Paris). (b) Painting of Pasteur by Robert Thom (1915-1979), 1950s (repr. from Metzl & Howell 2004). (c) Bronze statue of Pasteur, prob. early 20th century (Science Museum).

Figure 12. Photograph of Charles F. Chandler (1836-1925), late 19th/early 20th century (repr. from Bowden 1997, p. 154)

Figure 13. (a) Philippe Jacques de Loutherbourg: "Coalbrookdale at Night" (1801) (repr. from Frese 2000, p. 3). (b) William Picket for Philippe Jacques de Loutherbourg: "Iron Works, Colebrook Dale" (1805) (repr. from Klingender 1968, p. 111).

Figure 14. Arthur Henry Knighton-Hammond: "Looking Down the Tittabawassee River at the Dow Chemical Plant" (1920) (repr. from Frese 2000, p. vi, permission of The Hebert H. and Grace A. Dow Foundation).

a b

Figure 15. (a) Joseph Wright of Derby: "An Iron Forge" (1772) (repr. from Daniels 1999, p. 52). (b) Adolf von Menzel: "Iron Rolling Mill", detail (1875) (repr. from Fried 2002, p. iii)

Figure 16. Konstantin Vyalov: "Let's consolidate the victory of socialism in the USSR!" (1932), permission of the Internationaal Instituut voor Sociale Geschiedenis.

c

a b d

Figure 17. Stereotypical contemporary photographs of chemical plants (from (a) www. liquiteck.com/fs/chemical.htm, (b) www.cwc.gov, c) www.matcon-cone.com/chemical. htm, (d) www.mottcorp.com/industry/process/applications.htm).

Figure 18. Examples of early architectural photographs of castle and cathedral: (a) Anonymous: "Boston Trinity Church" (1876) (repr. from Robinson 1987, p. 5); (b) A. A. Turner, Font Hill Castle (1860) (repr. from Robinson 1987, p. 22).

Figure 19. (a) C.D. Friedrich: "Morning" (1821) (repr. from Koerner 1990, p. 202). (b) J.M.W. Turner: "Staffa, Fingal's Cave" (1832) (repr. from Rodner 1997, plate 4).

Figure 20. Typical close-up images of chemical plants, from left to right: www.umsys-asia.com, www.uyseg.org/industryanimated/photoindex/chemical_plant.htm, www.flost-eer.com.

Figure 21. (a) Fernand Léger: "Le Mecanicien" (1920) (repr. from Lanchner 1998, p. 193), © 2007 ARS, New York/ADAGP, Paris. (b) Carl Grossberg: "Der Gelbe Kessel" (1933) (repr. from Michalski 2003, p. 168), permission of Galerie Michael Hasenclever, München. (c) Charles Sheeler, *Ballet Mechanique* (1931) (Troyen 1987, p. 125), permission of Memorial Art Gallery, University of Rochester.

Figure 22. Prototypical Chemical Still lifes: a) www.philexport.ph/tops/tops2002/3q/, (b) www.education.bham.ac.uk/programmes/pgrad/pgce/secondary/science/chem.htm, c) www. energywipe.com/WhatOurCustomersSay.htm.

Figure 23. (a) Giorgio Morandi: "Still Life" (1941) (repr. from Abramowisz 2004, plate 10.6), © 2007 ARS, New York/SIAE, Rome. (b) William Bailey: "Strada Bianca" (1990) (repr. from Briganiti 1991, p.120), © William Bailey, Courtesy Betty Cuningham Gallery, New York. (c) Tony Cragg, "Laboratory Still Life No. 1, State 2" (1988) (repr. from Brown 1996, p. 67), courtesy the artist and Lisson Gallery, London.

CHAPTER 10

TAKING SCIENCE TO THE MARKETPLACE: EXAMPLES OF SCIENCE SERVICE'S PRESENTATION OF CHEMISTRY DURING THE 1930s

Marcel C. LaFollette

338 Eighth Street, S.E., Washington, DC 20003-2109, U.S.A.
scicompol@aol.com

During the 1930s, Science Service, a not-for-profit independent news organization, promulgated an approach to popularizing science which favored audience preferences over scientific agendas and attended to industry as well as academic research interests. Stories about chemistry and chemists harmonized well with Science Service's emphasis on research utility and relevance. This chapter describes examples from syndicated news reports, radio broadcasts, a newspaper series called 'Fabrics of the Future', and a department store exhibit on chemistry that traveled through the United States in 1939-40.

1. Introduction

In 1936, science journalist Frank Thone declared to members of the American Association for Adult Education that their fellow citizens were "as eager as St. Paul's Athenians to hear some new thing" about science but they preferred flexibility to pontification.[1] His explication foreshadowed today's world of ubiquitous, portable communications devices:

> Their Agora is the daily newspaper. It may be a less sociable institution than the Athenian market-place or the Victorian lecture-hall, but it is a

---

[1] Frank Thone, 'The Press as an Agency for the Diffusion of Science', text of a speech to the American Association for Adult Education, May 21, 1936, p. 2; Smithsonian Institution Archives, Record Unit 7091 (hereafter cited as 'SIA RU7091'), Box 4, Folder 2.

much more flexible one. You can roll up a whole company of heralds, messengers, and gossips, stick them in your pocket, select the ones you want to listen to, and hear their stories whenever you please. [Ibid.]

Thone's employer, a not-for-profit news organization called Science Service, had been delivering just such 'company' since 1921. Through newspaper articles, books, and radio programs, it sought to promote discussion of science in ways that were acceptable to scientists yet profitable to publishers. By the mid-1930s, Science Service had helped to increase news coverage of science, enlarged the worldwide network of science communicators, and whetted the public's interest in knowing what scientists were accomplishing. As an organization, it had achieved respectability and modest financial stability, even if its embrace of the values of popular culture occasionally unnerved otherwise loyal supporters within the research community.

With one foot in the scientific establishment and the other in a commercially driven media marketplace, Science Service played a cautious game. Organized as a sanctioned intermediary between the scientists and the rest of the press, yet compelled to sell its news products in order to survive financially, the group became skilled at occupying the middle ground. Scientists complained about inaccuracy and sensationalism. Editors shouted, 'give me something my subscribers will like!' Science Service reacted by constantly assessing the quality of its news stories and responding to all reasonable criticism, while continually adjusting its products to fit the newspapers' demands.

The challenges that Science Service faced during its early years are, in fact, representative of larger debates at the time about whose interests popularization should serve. When the first director, chemist E.E. Slosson, died in 1929, the organization experienced a wrenching fight for control which emphasized the competing ideals for popularization. Following three years of interim management, the appointment of Watson Davis, an engineer and journalist who had been working for the organization since its beginning, signaled a compromise that placed public interest and marketplace appeal first among the criteria for topic selection, increased attention to applied science and technological innovation, yet attended to scientists' concerns about accuracy and the timing of research announcements. The organization became skilled in the art of compromise, at straddling the middle ground. The images and ideas chosen by its writers during the 1930s thus reflect well what the marketplace – Thone's 'Agora' – was buying.

This chapter summarizes conclusions from my on-going research on the news values promoted and adopted by Science Service from the 1920s through the 1940s, and how negotiation of those values influenced print and broadcast images of science.[2] After a brief summary of the organization's founding, I discuss its initial approach to how (and by whom) science news should be constructed. With emphasis on images of chemistry, I then describe three representative examples of content from the 1930s – *Daily Mail Report* news stories, 'Adventures in Science' radio programs, and a 1939-40 project called 'Fabrics for the Future' in which a traveling department store window display was coordinated with local newspaper publication of articles about synthetic textiles.

Research on the history of Science Service has, to some extent, confirmed my previous conclusions about popular science, although the editorial files have also revealed new aspects of the cultural negotiations affecting it. The news stories and radio broadcasts of Science Service during the 1930s echoed patterns of assimilation, celebration, and pragmatic appraisal found in other popularization venues (LaFollette 1990). Science Service defined 'science news' broadly to include medicine, engineering, economics, and invention, an inclusiveness typical of the time. The messages promoted science's practicality and usefulness, or outlined how research was contributing to economic recovery during the Great Depression; the writers promised a brighter future through research and then borrowed images of alchemy and magic from popular fiction and motion pictures. Stories focused more on conveying factual information, with little attention to controversy or conflict among scientists. Toward the decade's end, Science Service gave increased attention to textile and pharmaceutical products and to chemistry's contributions to national self-sufficiency, and the editorial staff cooperated with the chemical in-

---

[2] Based on the author's research in Smithsonian Institution Archives manuscript collections, especially Record Units 45, 46, 83, 7183, and 7091 and Accession 90-105; materials housed in collections of the Smithsonian's National Museum of American History; 'Cavalcade of America' Collection at the Hagley Library; and Papers of James McKeen Cattell (MSS15412) at the Library of Congress.

dustry to portray chemistry as an essential and positive contributor to American life. By agreeing to broadcasters' demands for increased attention to scientists' personalities, the radio series also helped to extend to science the 'cult of celebrity' emerging during the 1930s.

Science Service should not, however, be assumed to have been either a tool of the scientific elite or a public relations outfit for science and industry or a science education organization.[3] During its first two decades, Science Service acted foremost as a news broker that sought to generate a demand for science among mainstream newspapers, to facilitate scientists' cooperation in the popularization process, and to provide *useful* scientific information to 'the masses, not the classes'. The organization played this role at a critical moment in history, when both science and the mass media were changing dramatically. By the late 1930s, the scientific community was evolving into the complex and large-scale international research system existing today; science had earned front-page attention and would soon grab even more. Advertisers and publishers were transforming consumer expectations for communication style and content. Radio was becoming overwhelmingly commercialized and dominated by drama and entertainment; the telegraphic, visual approaches of Hollywood and magazines like *Time*, *Life*, and *Readers' Digest* were pushing the old style of 'literary' popular science to the margins of public desire. Science Service adjusted its own products to the changing context, and gradually convinced its scientific supporters to participate in this new marketplace for popular science.

2. Origins: A New Institution for a Changing Market

Science Service's financial structure as a not-for-profit business corporation consistently influenced its content selections. Its limited endowment helped to cushion tough economic times and occasional project failures, but it was compelled to sell its news products in order to survive. Established by a wealthy newspaper publisher, and with advisors drawn

---

[3] This latter emphasis on science education and 'science talent searches' arose in earnest only in the 1940s, a topic being explored by such historians as John Rudolph and Sevan Terzian.

from the nation's scientific elite, Science Service derived a substantial portion of its income from syndicating news stories to newspapers and periodical publishers. Organizational sustainability depended upon positive audience reaction and thus continually shaped the decision-making.

This section outlines aspects of the organization's naissance and original direction which are relevant to understanding how it operated during the 1930s. No comprehensive history of Science Service yet exists; this discussion relies therefore on new archival research as well as on work by David Rhees and other historians whose research has focused on the group's early years.[4]

The idea for the organization developed during an era when the scientific establishment had considerable concern about its public image but few practical ideas for how to polish it. The plans of various eminent scientists for establishing popular magazines had been hindered by their lack of real-world experience in the publishing business (see Burnham 1987, Kevles 1978, Tobey 1971). In 1903, millionaire newspaper publisher E.W. Scripps (1854-1926) became intrigued with the holistic and humanistic approach to science embraced by a University of California zoologist, William E. Ritter (1856-1944). With his sister Ellen, Scripps endowed a new oceanographic institute, and Ritter became its first director and a close friend of Scripps (Thone & Bailey 1927). By 1919, the two men had begun to imagine a new entity to foster public communica-

---

[4] The absence of a comprehensive history of Science Service relates both to the complexity and size of its records and to an earlier failure by historians to recognize the importance of these records and how they might illuminate the history of science as well as its public presentation. The organization's multiple parallel filing systems intermingled editorial, business, and personal correspondence with drafts, notes, photographs, and other ephemera for hundreds of projects and activities. Records generated between 1921 and the early 1970s were donated to the Smithsonian Institution in several phases, but not all records were transferred, not all those were housed in the same location, and not all remained intact. The surviving records, located in the Smithsonian Institution Archives and in curatorial collections throughout the Smithsonian museums, comprise many hundreds of cubic feet of papers and photographs, much of it still without comprehensive finding aids and some still incompletely processed. For decades, only a small portion of the early records had been processed. In 2005, the author wrote a brief historical summary of Science Service's first forty years for a Smithsonian Institution Archives finding aid to Record Unit 7091, available online at <http://siarchives.si.edu/findingaids/FARU7091.htm>. Documents relating to the history of the collection are preserved at the Smithsonian Institution Archives, as part of the control files for Record Unit 7091.

tion of science, discussing it with scientists around the United States. Within a year, they were actively designing what would eventually be called 'Science Service'.

A paramount consideration in these discussions was whose interests the organization should serve – science or society? Scripps and Ritter took a liberal democratic approach that differed from the patrician, elitist attitudes of most senior scientists. Scripps saw that science had extraordinary power to affect modern life and therefore citizens deserved better information about it. As his son Robert P. Scripps later explained, the millionaire knew that "for the masses as well as the classes, knowledge is power" (Scripps 1932, p. 156). The elder Scripps had, after all, made his fortune by delivering news and entertainment to those very masses. First consideration in the new group's decision-making should be given, he believed, to the potential audience's practical needs and interests rather than the scientific establishment's agendas.

To implement this approach, Science Service was incorporated independent from any single scientific organization or discipline. To gain respect from skeptical newspaper editors, Scripps argued, the organization must be perceived as an objective and reliable presenter of facts. It should not be a publicity machine for science or engage in advocacy or 'propaganda'.[5] It should "tell the millions outside the laboratories and the lecture halls what was going on inside" (Scripps 1932, p. 156) and do so accurately. Both Scripps and Ritter were convinced that mediocre presentation fed public 'indifference' to science. The new organization's products must be readable, accessible, and interesting as well as accurate and timely. Ritter reinforced this message when he wrote to Scripps in 1921: "Unquestionably there are aspects of science that appeal strongly to popular interest; there is much that is curiosity-satisfying, much that is practically useful, much that is dramatic; and were Science Service to 'play up' these aspects to the extent that it might, [then] it could soon reach a self-supporting basis, and could go on and largely increase its funds."[6] Ritter served as first president of the board of trustees and re-

---

[5]   'Document A - The American Society for the Dissemination of Science', dictated by E.W. Scripps on March 5, 1919; SIA RU7091, Box 1, Folder 1.

[6]   Carbon copy of William E. Ritter to E.W. Scripps, May 13, 1921, mailed to E.E. Slosson; SIA RU7091, Box 1, Folder 3.

mained 'honorary president' and an influential advisor until his death in 1944.

Partial self-sufficiency – in both content and finances – became a key to success. This model of popularization differs from that advocated by many scientists, then and now, for it emphasizes reactivity to audience preferences. Although incorporated as a not-for-profit entity, the organization was never wholly funded by Scripps. He espoused a liberal vision of the free flow of ideas but his philanthropy was rooted firmly in capitalism. If Science Service charged a fair price for its products, then the clients would value its news more; and if forced to sell those products, the organization would be more sensitive to the clients' needs and professional standards. If no newspaper or magazine wanted to buy the stories, then the organization should not survive. Science Service, its first director explained, "is sufficiently endowed to be independent and yet it is intended to be self-supporting although prohibited by its charter from making profits."[7] Or, as one trustee wrote:

> It is a non-profit-making institution, and if it charges enough for the production of its service to keep going, *then assuredly the fact is patent that it is not subsidized; and, moreover, enjoying a real income, it can afford to actually produce not only well-written copy, but copy that has first been verified–that is authentic and UP-TO-DATE.* Constant improvement – or death – is assured by the necessity to charge rates commensurate with the service rendered.[8]

Only the news products ever really met these financial goals during the first decades; most other projects were subsidized by the news sales or endowment income.

Scripps donated $30,000 per year (supplemented by other occasional gifts) from 1921 until his death in 1926. His family trust continued the same annual payment for the next thirty years. By late 1924, endowment income and product sales contributed about equally to support operations, and the managing editor predicted that they might "eventually increase the income from the sale of the product to such an extent that the

---

[7] E.E. Slosson to R.S. McBride, McGraw-Hill Book Co., Inc., April 5, 1921; SIA RU7091, Box 9, Folder 6.

[8] Underlining in original. H.L. Smithton to W.E. Ritter, January 2, 1924; SIA RU7091, Box 23, Folder 6.

endowment income can be used to exploit possibilities which are not on the face of them commercially attractive."[9] Within a relatively short time, such risks were indeed possible, enabling them to experiment with popular radio broadcasting, for example.

The board of trustees included ex officio such prestigious scientists as the presidents of the National Academy of Sciences and American Association for the Advancement of Science and the head of the Smithsonian Institution. Prominent trustees during the 1920s and 1930s included psychologist James McKeen Cattell (editor of *Science* and *Scientific Monthly*), astronomer Harlow Shapley, and such notables as A.A. Noyes, Vernon Kellogg, and John C. Merriam. Science Service advertised the location of its editorial offices within the new National Academy of Sciences building to imply legitimacy and status (Figure 1), even though the staff operated independent of it or any other scientific association.

Figure 1. Cover of Science Service promotion brochure, 1924, showing the National Academy of Sciences building in Washington, D.C. (Smithsonian Institution Archives, Accession 90-105, Box 20, Folder 19). Courtesy of Smithsonian Institution Archives.

Trustees also included executives in the Scripps-Howard newspaper empire and such well-known editors as William Allen White and Marlen Pew, and the historian Mark Sullivan. These latter advisors shared invaluable practical advice on how to compete in the news business, and they proved to be the critical element in the fight over appointment of a new director and in preserving what Scripps and Ritter had envisioned.

---

[9]   W. Davis to S.S. Seward, Jr., October 20, 1924; SIA RU7091, Box 74, Folder 6.

3. Staffing, Credentials, and a Fight for Control

During Science Service's first forty years, two men in particular – one trained as a chemist, the other as an engineer – implemented the Scripps-Ritter vision of an all-inclusive, market-oriented popular science. They shared many common perspectives, not the least being a broad definition of 'science news' which included attention to medicine, engineering and mining technologies, transportation, and parapsychology, as well as such predictable topics as relativity and evolution. The differences in the men reflected the twin impulses of popularization in the twentieth century. The chemist advocated an approach that was more academic and literary, that emphasized science's theoretical foundations and romanticized its practical implementation. The engineer advocated journalistic techniques and values, favored content tied to invention and innovation, courted friendly relations with advertising and public relations representatives, and frequently adopted the language and images of stage and screen rather than the literary *salon*.

The first director, Edwin Emery Slosson (1865-1929), possessed an unusual combination of skills and experience, and had been handpicked by Scripps, Ritter, and their advisors (Rhees 1979).[10] A native of Kansas with sturdy liberal values and a distinctive flair to his writing, Slosson had completed a Ph.D. in chemistry at the University of Chicago in 1902 while teaching at the University of Wyoming. The next year, he moved to New York to become literary editor of *The Independent*, where he worked until moving to Washington, D.C., in January 1921 to head Science Service. With three degrees in chemistry, Slosson had respectable credentials as a scientist, but, as he confessed to another chemist, he much preferred writing to laboratory work:

> I too like you am classed as a 'renegade from natural science' since I have never done any research work in chemistry after having taken my doctorate at the University of Chicago in that science. But I have like

---

[10] Rhees 1979 remains the definitive analysis of Slosson. Like many other historians, I have used it as a guide in interpreting correspondence in SIA RU7091, on which this section draws.

you retained my interest in science and have done what I could to spread a knowledge of scientific achievements among the reading public.[11]

In New York, Slosson built a reputation as one of the premier science popularizers, combining a reverence for technical accuracy with literary flourishes. He regarded dramatization as essential in attracting readers, and so he immediately began 'hunting' for writers who could 'sense the dramatic elements' in basic scientific principles. "Dehydrated potatoes are convenient for conveyance but they have to be soaked up before they are palatable," he wrote (Slosson 1922, p. 482).

Slosson's interests and expertise lay more in the creative than managerial side of the news business. His first employees were a managing editor and a part-time news writer. When the managing editor quit, Slosson took the title of Director, promoted the part-time writer to full-time manager, and returned to making money by writing books and articles and delivering lectures around the country.[12]

That first writer hired by Slosson in 1921, Watson Davis (1896-1967), effectively ran the organization for the next 45 years. A native of Washington, D.C., Davis had earned a civil engineering degree at George Washington University and worked on the research staff at the National Bureau of Standards from 1917-21. He also began contributing science articles to a local newspaper. Although his literary skills paled in comparison to Slosson's, Davis had the instincts of a journalist and an engineer's ability to organize tasks. He could ferret out news and glean the essence from dull research reports, and proved to be a skilled manager.

When Slosson died in October 1929, he was not replaced for over three and one-half years, even though Davis was the logical successor. The struggle over that appointment emphasized differences in how scientists and journalists were still perceiving popularization. To scientists, the best popularizer was always another scientist; no journalist or other pro-

---

[11] E.E. Slosson to Thomas T. Coke, February 7, 1921; SIA RU7091, Box 7, Folder 1. Coke had taken a degree in chemistry from Cornell University but had decided to shift careers and was then studying law at Yale University.

[12] Slosson had originally been hired as 'Editor' of Science Service. He delivered hundreds of paid lectures every year. Income from those lectures was essential to Science Service. As a result, Slosson spent considerable time traveling and appears to have left the management of day-to-day operations (and therefore most news decisions) to Watson Davis.

fessional could ever be an adequate substitute. To those who embraced a vision of scientific popularization as free expression in a free society, it was the quality of the product that mattered rather than the writer's academic training. Was a story accurate? Did it serve the audience's needs and satisfy their curiosity? Was the information useful? Davis had been running the organization since Slosson's illness in January, had earned the trustees' respect, and had many powerful supporters. He lobbied hard for the position. His allegiances had always leaned toward the journalists, however. As chemist W.H. Howell, chairman of the trustees' executive committee, wrote to Davis, "In spite of your protests I reckon you as a newspaper person, because invariably you take that point of view when debatable matters come up".[13] To the scientist-trustees, selection of an eminent researcher to replace Slosson would enhance the organization's reputation among the scientific community. To the newspaper executives, a director who understood the marketplace would assure survival.

Davis pointed out that being a scientist did not guarantee access to newspaper offices. What mattered was whether "editors are confident of the authoritativeness and the reliability of our product."[14] Nevertheless, the executive committee offered the position to a well-known zoologist who had little experience in publishing or popularization. When that scientist refused the job, Davis was kept in limbo for another eleven months, while trustees (led primarily by James McKeen Cattell) attempted to reorient the organization away from the Scripps's vision of democratic expression and toward becoming a publicity machine for science.[15] Finally, in 1933, in the depths of the Great Depression, Davis was appointed director.

Davis was an energetic and ambitious man, described as "exceptionally capable [...] enthusiastic, vigorous and very likeable."[16] He pos-

---

[13] W.H. Howell to W. Davis, June 24, 1936; SIA RU7091, Box 4, Folder 3.

[14] W. Davis to David White, February 10, 1931; SIA RU7091, Box 131, Folder 9.

[15] According to Davis, James McKeen Cattell and physicist Robert A. Millikan wanted to abolish the policy "that we do not operate as a publicity organization, that we charge for everything we send out and pay for everything we get." Davis stated that "there will be a stiff fight on this score, so far as I am concerned." W. Davis to J.W. Foster, Scripps-Howard Newspapers, February 12, 1931; SIA RU7091, Box 124, Folder 10.

[16] H.L. Smithton to W.E. Ritter, January 2, 1924; SIA RU7091, Box 23, Folder 6.

sessed a keen understanding of the dynamics of the relationship between scientists and popularization, tracing much of scientists' uneasiness to their discomfort with popular formats: "It is a distrust of 'sensational presentation', so called; because of the form rather than the quality of the presentation that lies behind the indefinite criticisms that are sometimes directed to our work."[17]

Avoiding the "careless and unintelligent simplification" that can distort meaning is the first line of defense against such criticism, Davis wrote, and so he routinely conducted internal assessments of the organization's performance, emphasizing accuracy as the foremost news value.[18] All external complaints by either readers or sources were "conscientiously recorded upon the filed copy of the [news] report."[19] The conclusion of one survey of Science Service's daily news reports in 1929-30 reflects pride in such vigilance: "in only 36 instances out of 1707 stories issued were any criticisms recorded. Over half of these were what might be called typographical errors and many of them were caught by our own staff rather than outsiders."[20]

During the 1920s, Davis had begun to shape the organization toward a more relaxed relationship with industry, corporate public relations sources, and advertising firms. As an engineer, he was comfortable, perhaps even enamored, with the new industrialists of science; he established cordial working relationships with corporate executives at Du Pont, General Electric, and similar companies. He became friends with public relations guru Edward L. Bernays and advertising executive Ivy Lee. Once director, Davis thus continued on a path he had already begun to blaze, accommodating popularization to the social, cultural, and economic realities of the time. This approach is evident in the content published in the 1930s. Cooperation with publicists and corporate interests seemed the right thing to do. After all, Davis and the rest of the staff perceived themselves as engaged in their own public relations campaign – to

---

[17] W. Davis to F.J. Schlink, American Standards Association, May 12, 1930; SIA RU7091, Box 119, Folder 3.

[18] Ibid.

[19] Ibid.; the records of the *Daily Mail Report* often contain correspondence discussing published errors or scientists' complaints.

[20] Ibid.; Davis's raw notes and data for this analysis are located in SIA RU7091, Box 129, Folder 11.

persuade both press and scientific community to join in a campaign to educate the masses about what was happening inside the laboratories.

That staff included many pioneers in science journalism, including some of the first female science journalists in the United States.[21] Many were among the founders of the National Association of Science Writers in 1934. Almost all Science Service writers had some type of technical training; a few, like Thone, had graduate training but had abandoned full-time research and teaching for a career in journalism.[22] These intermediaries were familiar with scientific organizations, universities, and science-based industries. They understood scientists' culture, respected the authority of their expertise, and were alert to concerns about accuracy and credit. They were also convinced that scientific knowledge was a social asset to be shared and that science's fortunes were irrevocably entwined with those of the 'masses'.

4. Constructing the Daily News about Chemistry

If large numbers of readers (and the newspapers serving them) did not express consistent interest in a particular scientific topic, then Science Service gave it less attention. Coverage of the disciplines was therefore quite uneven, reflecting shifting public interest rather than necessarily the intellectual vigor of a research area. Mathematicians complained constantly about the lack of attention to their work, for example, but theorems or proofs could rarely compete with the glamour of archeology or physics. Special features and syndicated columns during the 1920s concentrated more on astronomy (weekly 'Star Maps'), meteorology ('Why the Weather'), or natural history and botany ('Nature's Notebook'); news articles followed similar patterns. During the 1930s, chemistry attracted more attention, thanks in part to consumer interest in the development of new pharmaceuticals, fabrics, materials, fertilizers, and insecticides. In

---

[21] Mary Tressida has created a web exhibit ('Women of Science Service') that describes some of the staff and contributing writers. See <http://siarchives.si.edu/research/sci-servwomen.html>.

[22] Frank Ernest Aloysius Thone (1891-1949) majored in botany at the University of Iowa, and earned a Ph.D. from the University of Chicago in 1922. His work in California as assistant to William E. Ritter led to the contact with Slosson. After a few years of teaching and research, he became the Science Service biology editor in 1924.

effect, the public became more interested in what chemists were producing, and journalists responded.

Between 1935 and 1939, coverage of chemistry in Science Service's
main product – the 40-50 stories sold every week through a syndicated
service called *Daily Mail Report* – increased steadily from approximately
2% of stories during sampled weeks in September 1935 to 7% in March
1936, 11% in December 1938, 11% in May 1939, and 17% in October
1939.[23] Attention probably increased because of the achievements of interdisciplinary research with obvious relevance to consumers, such as
work on sulfanilamide, plant hormones, fabrics, and insecticides. In
1936, stories discussed rayon and chemical production at Tennessee Val-
ley Authority plants; in 1939, they paid attention to liquid helium and nylon parachutes. It was a view of chemistry as integrated smoothly into –
and essential contributor to – the scientific whole.

Analysis of content provides only one historical indicator. It is also
important to look behind the scenes at how, why, and by whom content
was constructed. Such analysis shows that during the organization's first
decade, the challenge had been to gain attention to *any* science, to convince newspaper editors that the work of botanists, astronomers, and
chemists had sufficient relevance to compete on the front page with elec-
tion campaigns, business decisions, or murders. To do this, it was necessary to create a 'demand' for science news. Scripps had advised Slosson:
"Anything that you could do in the way of attracting the attention of
journalists to the subject of science will naturally create a demand for
your product – and what is even more desirable, will create a demand by
editors for scientific matter generally."[24] Slosson responded that Scripps
was, as usual, correct: "The indirect effects of Science Service are as you

---

[23] These estimates are based on the author's analysis of 202 news stories from a sample
of *Daily Mail Report* for weeks in September 1935, March 1936, December 1938,
May 1939, and October 1939 located in SIA RU7091, Box 374. Newspapers subscribing to the *Daily Mail Report* received about 8 to 10 short news stories a day (40
to 50 each week). Science Service had retained the backup and drafts for each story at
least through the 1960s. During the 1970s, when those records were transferred to the
Smithsonian Institution, Smithsonian archivists unfortunately saved only a sample of
the complete *Daily Mail Report* files, randomly selecting a few weeks out of each
year. The remaining files are located in SIA RU7091, Series 8 (Boxes 373-381).

[24] E.W. Scripps to E.E. Slosson, August 1, 1921; SIA RU7091, Box 12, Folder 2.

surmise, proving to be as important as the direct action. In many cases newspapers have gone after articles for themselves, after having seen some of ours in print".[25] And as Slosson explained to a fellow scientist:

> We are concentrating our efforts largely upon the newspapers, since in this way we can reach the largest possible public. The newspapers, however, demand 'news', that is, something which has a definite event on which to hang the general information and necessary explanation.[26]

Once persuaded of science's potential for news value, editors then had to be convinced that science would sell. In one of his first promotional letters to advertise what became the *Daily Mail Report*, Davis promised that Science Service offered news of importance, news their competitors were getting, and news that was reasonably priced:

> Off the beaten tracks real news is breaking. What scientists and engineers are doing today will affect the world tomorrow. Are you getting this news?
>
> Science Service is covering this important field for over forty newspapers from Bermuda to San Francisco. A news report [...] formerly mailed weekly but beginning today to be mailed daily, brings them interesting, readable copy, scientifically accurate, yet understandable by the non-technical person. It costs them only the fraction of the pay of an office boy.[27]

Such efforts soon had a noticeable impact. By January 1924, Scripps executive H.L. Smithton wrote to Ritter about the publicity received by a recent meeting of the American Association for the Advancement of Science:

> The leading headlines of the [local] papers were given to the subjects of the convention and to interviews with the scientists. Collisions of the atoms displaced automobile and railroad collisions; slaying of bacteria and undesirable insects completely overshadowed similar 'activities' among humankind; pictures of scientists ornamented the pages hitherto deco-

---

[25] E.E. Slosson to E.W. Scripps, September 2, 1921; SIA RU7091, Box 12, Folder 2.
[26] E.E. Slosson to W.A. Cannon, Carnegie Institution of Washington's Coastal Laboratory, February 23, 1923; SIA RU7091, Box 16, Folder 1.
[27] Science Service form letter sent to editors of newspapers from 'Watson Davis, News Editor', September 11, 1922; SIA RU7091, Box 60, Folder 2.

rated by pictures of statesmen and criminals. Believe me: the scientist
had his 'day' in the way of publicity this time.[28]

Journalists also had to convince scientists to share information about
their research, which sometimes meant persuading them to release results
before formal publication. Given the competition in the news business,
timeliness was essential. Editors liked to know that results were 'just
announced' or that a story might 'scoop' rival papers. Science Service
could not wait for scientists to release results according to their own
timetable (which might give the appearance of staleness). In science,
rushing into print had not yet become the norm. Davis tried to explain
this situation to one newspaper editor in 1936: "News of science does not
develop like news of war, politics, crime and sport. Practically all scientific news is the result of months or even years of patient research, and it
is produced by men who would rather remain silent than make an
announcement that was not thoroughly authentic."[29] To secure researchers' cooperation in the news process, Science Service had to build their
trust, had to convince them that while it valued accuracy over haste, there
were deadlines to be met.

The most persistent conflicts centered on who should determine the
quality of science news. Should scientists alone be the judges of what
was accurate and important? Many newspaper editors thought that scientists gave little indication of understanding that communicating successfully beyond their circle of experts required some compromise. A.H.
Kirchhofer, managing editor of the *Buffalo Evening News*, complained in
1932 that scientists gave "little or no credit to the newspapers" for recent
progress in science reporting and that their unwarranted criticism actually contributed to "misunderstanding" between the two groups. Scientists need to "come out of their shells" and take a "human as well as scientific view-point" if they want more attention to their work, he argued
(Kirchhofer 1932, pp. 154-155). Another editor observed that the articles

---

[28] H.L. Smithton to W.E. Ritter, January 2, 1924; SIA RU7091, Box 23, Folder 6.
[29] W. Davis to J.N. Heiskell, Editor, *The Arkansas Gazette*, October 22, 1936; SIA RU7091, Box 424, Folder 14.

"which sell best are those which get down closest to the field of the ordinary, unlettered Sunday newspaper readers."[30]

Science Service's solution to both increasing the flow of news from the laboratories and insuring its accuracy developed by accident. In his first year, with a limited budget and tiny staff, Slosson wrote to several colleagues asking for suggestions of graduate students or other young scientists who might submit short reports about research on their campus. He placed notices in *The Scientific Monthly* and similar publications. Applications began to arrive and these part-time correspondents (or 'stringers') soon became the organization's extra eyes and ears, alerting staff to ongoing projects as well as to impending announcements.[31] Frank Thone had first interacted with Slosson that way in 1921.

By the 1930s, the staff had become quite skilled at identifying potential stringers (met at scientific meetings or recommended by trustees and other prominent scientists). Every year, they sifted through dozens of applications from graduate students, young professors, underemployed writers, and various technically trained people interested in trying popularization. No promises were ever made for payment in advance; disbursements for accepted articles or photographs ranged from $2.00 to $10.00. Because a stringer's name was rarely attached to the published story, popularization by these young scientists (many of them women) did not attract unwanted criticism from colleagues for 'publicity-seeking'.

The existence and vitality of this worldwide network of sources demonstrates that the flow of popular science information may have been more complex than historians have previously assumed. Only about one-tenth of *Daily Mail Report* stories in the 1930s, regardless of discipline, appear to have been based on interviews conducted by Science Service's full-time staff. Instead, they transformed other material into 'news' — editing stringers' reports or sifting through page proofs for journals

---

[30] Bruce Catton, Editor of *EveryWeek*, to Frank Thone, October 3, 1938; SIA RU7091, Box 199, Folder 11.

[31] Many records of transactions with these stringers – job applications, correspondence, payment slips, and drafts – are preserved in Smithsonian Institution Archives Record Unit 7091, and represent an important resource for study. Especially notable are the 1930s applications from women with some science training who sought writing assignments to supplement their incomes.

like *Science* and the *Journal of the American Medical Association* (sometimes writing scientists for additional material before writing a summary).

Through the years, the staff also became adept at exploiting access to the research community. They routinely covered the meetings of major scientific, medical, and engineering associations, persuading organizers to send advance copies of programs, and speakers to send copies of papers. Science Service did its part by voluntarily embargoing news articles until after a researcher's presentation had been delivered, thereby adjusting the newspapers' demand for timeliness to the scientists' desire for credit. To speakers reluctant to provide advance texts, Science Service explained that having a written paper helped to insure accuracy and "intelligent reporting" even if a journalist could be present at a session.[32] As one staff writer explained, science reporting required attention to detail: "All science stuff at meetings is written from the papers; it is impossible to sit down at a convention session and take notes for a story in the same fashion as you do anything else on that order."[33]

Sometimes local stringers were dispatched to interview prominent scientists or obtain exclusive information. In 1938, Davis attended the annual British Association for the Advancement of Science meeting in London and, like all good journalists, paid attention to the scientific gossip. On September 6, he wired his Washington office the news that: "EO LAWRENCE BUILDING TWO NEW MAGNETS FOR FURTHER WORK RADIOSODIUM."[34] Physics and chemistry editor Robert D. Potter then telegraphed a stringer in Berkeley, California (where physicist Ernest O. Lawrence had his laboratory), asking "CAN YOU RUSH COLLECT WIRE DESCRIBING SETUP AND ITS SIGNIFICANCE. TELL LAWRENCE THAT GUSTAV HERTZ BERLIN JUST ANNOUNCED 59 PERCENT PURE NEON MASS 22 BY DIFFUSION

---

[32] For example, W. Davis to Arthur F. Coca, April 26, 1938; SIA RU7091, Box 194, Folder 3.

[33] Leonard H. Engel to Roger E. Chase, June 17, 1938; SIA RU7091, Box 194, Folder 1.

[34] Potter, former science editor of the *New York Herald-Tribune*, joined the staff in 1934 and had responsibility for physics, engineering, and chemistry. Along with others on the Science Service staff, he was one of the founders of the National Association of Science Writers.

METHOD AND IS SENDING HIM SAMPLE." The stringer, George Pettitt, responded immediately; Potter folded the text into a *Daily Mail Report* datelined September 7 ("California Cyclotron Apparatus Being Enlarged and Improved to Make Possible Medical and Biological Research"); and the bookkeeper was instructed to pay Pettitt $5.00. Such rapid-fire exchanges became commonplace in the 1930s as physicists, chemists, and biologists raced to the frontiers of knowledge, and journalists competed to make the first dispatches from those intellectual front lines.

5. Chemistry on the Airwaves

In developing such stories, Science Service perceived itself as facilitating the flow of ideas in society rather than engaging in public education. Especially in radio, pedagogical motives would have been suspect. Broadcasts that centered on intelligent conversations about science with (and for) fellow citizens fit radio's entertainment focus in the 1930s; education did not. Through a one-on-one interview preceded by the latest 'science news of the week', listeners could share a science 'adventure' and Science Service could accommodate the agendas of the networks that controlled access to the airwaves.

Science Service became involved in radio quite early in the development of commercial broadcasting. Soon after Washington, D.C., station WCAP began operation in 1924, its manager asked the National Research Council (NRC) to arrange weekly talks by scientists. Lectures by such experts provided convenient, free content that stations could schedule between musical concerts. NRC's scientists knew little about radio, so they turned to Science Service, appointed Slosson to a Committee on Radio Talks, and the two groups arranged their first 10-minute talk for June 6, 1924.

The talks sought to inspire rather than educate, and were aimed at a broad audience. Slosson, for example, admonished H.E. Howe, editor of *Journal of Industrial and Engineering Chemistry*, not to make a discussion of modern glassmaking "too highbrow."[35] Speakers emphasized the

---

[35] E.E. Slosson to H.E. Howe, June 17, 1924; SIA RU7091, Box 22, Folder 6.

adventure and excitement of research as they described helium, radium, explosives, coal, synthetic rubber, or the spinning of 'artificial silk'. "The progress of science is a continual excursion into the mysteries of the sphere; the impossible is continually being accomplished," one program began.

Popularity was measured by the number of listener requests for scripts or free bulletins. In the late 1920s, listeners consistently preferred either the annual forecasts of 'science to come' or information about poison ivy treatments; by the early 1930s, listeners were asking for scripts and bulletins on the same topics being emphasized in the *Daily Mail Report* stories – medicine, psychology, and engineering. [36] By September 1929, Science Service's 15-minute news and interview program (called either 'Radio Talks' or 'Science Service Series' in the schedules) had proved to be so successful that it was broadcast from the CBS station in New York City and over thirty network affiliates.[37]

Radio in the United States was changing, however. Advertiser-supported entertainment began to dominate the commercial networks (see Douglas 1999, Hilmes 1997, Smulyan 1994), and science programming was soon forced to compete with comedians, jazz singers, soap operas, detective dramas, sports, and live broadcasts of political events (LaFollette 2002). CBS began to pressure Davis to alter his program format – to 'work closer' to the news and to accent scientific 'personalities'. This shift in emphasis echoed changes in how science was being presented elsewhere in the media. Newspaper editors routinely accepted science as newsworthy and important, but remained biased toward 'breaking news' and celebrities. One NBC employee, attempting to persuade Davis to develop a new program for their network, explained that her bosses were:

> very anxious to have scientific material put before the public but only when and if it would be news. [...] with your knowledge of forthcoming events you can get it on the air before it breaks in the papers. They do

---

[36] Author's analysis of data in 'Survey of Requests Received for Science Service Radio Talks, 'Science News of the Week', June, 1926 – November, 1929', sent by W. Davis to the U.S. Advisory Committee on Education by Radio; SIA RU7091, Box 118, Folder 5. Data on the 1930s from a letter by W. Davis to Robert F. Elder, November 2, 1934; SIA RU7091, Box 154, Folder 2.

[37] W. Davis, September 20, 1929; SIA RU7091, Box 102, Folder 8.

want the personality himself or herself – you of course bring the person
to the microphone, introducing them and framing the picture for them.[38]

Davis attempted to explain that science news is more "deliberate": it
"does not break in the way that a murder or shipwreck or other news of
that character happens."[39] He was fighting a losing battle, however, and
he eventually remodeled his CBS series toward more scripted interviews
with guest scientists and engineers and gave more attention to scientists
as celebrities (or, more often, potential celebrities). His broadcasts also
increasingly emphasized pragmatic accomplishments designed to appeal
to Americans clawing through an economic depression – proven winners
like 'That Perennial Public Enemy, Poison Ivy' and practical topics like
highway transportation and household heating. Chemistry became an
integral part of many interviews, from pharmaceutical research to discussion of road-building materials, crime detection, and oil exploration.

The process of developing scripts with scientists required considerable diplomacy and patience. Here, the correspondence between Davis
and his potential guests or their representatives provides a valuable
glimpse of the construction of popular science. When Du Pont Company
scientist Henry J. Wing proposed the title "Application of Research in
the Protective Coating Industry" for his radio talk, for example, Davis
suggested that "Vanishing Varnishes" would be better "bait" to lure listeners.[40] Wing called that suggestion "snappy" but offered "Changing
Varnishes" as "just as suitable and perhaps more accurate" and Davis ac-
quiesced to Wing and the Du Pont representatives who had brokered the
chemist's appearance.[41]

Davis also knew how to play the broadcasters' game. He injected
humor, attempted to humanize scientists, and declared that "Effective
methods of presentation include dialogue, dramatic programs with music,
as well as other types of programs written for the ear instead of the
eye."[42] When he interviewed Charles C. Concannon, chief of the Chemical Division of the U.S. Department of Commerce, in November 1937

---

[38] M. Cuthbert to W. Davis, November 30, 1934; SIA RU7091, Box 167, Folder 11.
[39] W. Davis to M. Cuthbert, December 4, 1934; SIA RU7091, Box 167, Folder 11.
[40] Henry J. Wing to W. Davis, September 10, 1935; SIA RU7091, Box 403, Folder 13.
[41] Henry J. Wing to W. Davis, October 4, 1935; SIA RU7091, Box 403, Folder 13.
[42] W. Davis to H. Bonnet, February 8, 1938; SIA RU7091, Box 193, Folder 3.

about the generally uninspiring topic of tung oil manufacturing and use in waterproofing, Davis opened with the chipper observation that "There are a lot of C's in that name of yours, Mr. Concannon." To which the chemist replied, per the script, "Yes, and in chemicals and commerce. But there aren't any C's at all in tung oil, and perhaps I'd better start by spelling it."[43]

In May 1938, just as the series name was changed to 'Adventures in Science', CBS took over all production and added dramatization and new on-air personalities. The surviving correspondence reveals Davis' frustration at the abrupt changes. His exchanges with the network personnel reflect ever more tension. He struggled to articulate scientists' concerns about inaccuracy, sensationalism, and trivialization, but the radio executives remained convinced that dramatizing or fictionalizing science would attract huge audiences.

The CBS decision had probably been influenced by two educational programs that *were* attracting listeners through clever dramatization of serious topics. 'Cavalcade of America', a radio series produced and sponsored by the Du Pont Company, featured professionally written dramas about the lives of historical figures and aimed to instill confidence in the corporation. Its first episode in 1935 declared that Du Pont's research chemists worked "in the same spirit" as national patriots and pioneers.[44] By 1938, the series was extolling the importance of invention and ingenuity, and occasionally engaging in fanciful history of science to enliven its message. One episode created a chance meeting between nineteenth-century scientists Robert Hare and Benjamin Silliman, in which Silliman asserted that "The progress of science is like an endless chain, Mr. Hare, each link joining what is behind and what goes before."[45] Similar inspirational rhetoric infused the Smithsonian Institution's 'The World is Yours' series on NBC. Beginning in 1936, its half-hour dramas, co-produced with the U.S. Office of Education, starred a

---

[43] Script for radio talk ('The Romance of Tung Oil') located in SIA RU7091, Box 194, Folder 6.

[44] 'Cavalcade of America', Episode number 1 (1935), p. 1; Cavalcade of America Collection, Hagley Library.

[45] 'Cavalcade of America', Episode number 117 (1938), p. 11; Cavalcade of America Collection, Hagley Library.

cheerful character called 'The Old-Timer', who explored topics from art to archeology, engineering to entomology. When the new CBS version of 'Adventures in Science' looked at Antoine Lavoisier, therefore, its writers imitated a familiar radio drama pattern, focusing more on that chemist's sensational death than his ideas.[46]

Within a month, CBS had dropped the dramatizations and shifted to an abbreviated interview format. On September 16, 1938, the CBS announcer introduced chemist Harold C. Urey by saying: "We're off today on the trail of a drop of water that spread itself into a thunderstorm and washed up on the tables of research scientists a thousand new problems to face and fathom. It's the story of Heavy Water, a magic potion as fascinating as any witch's brew and the key, perhaps, to the next door of human progress."[47] By the end of September, listeners had tired of such trivializations and tuned in elsewhere; the series was cancelled.

In late 1938, CBS asked Watson Davis to resume production with his previous news-and-interview format, but Davis was now keenly aware of who controlled the microphone and how easily he could lose access to the airwaves.[48] He and the trustees had consistently rejected commercial sponsorship. As long as the series remained a 'sustaining' (*i.e.*, non-commercial) program, with production partially underwritten by Science Service but the air time provided by the network (and therefore at the network's discretion), Davis had to attend to the CBS suggestions. As a consequence, the revived 'Adventures in Science' series blended attention to academic science with occasional promotion of research-based industries.

In February 1939, for example, CBS executive Sterling Fisher wrote to Davis that the network planned to cooperate with the Associated Grocery Manufacturers in their April 'Parade of Progress' campaign, and he asked Davis to arrange interviews with scientists "from the research laboratories of large food product companies."[49] Handwritten notes in the

---

[46] 'Adventures in Science' script for August 12, 1938; SIA RU7091, Box 386, Folder 1.
[47] 'Adventures in Science' script for September 16, 1938; SIA RU7091, Box 386, Folder 1.
[48] The series ran until 1958, with occasional interruptions for world events and Saturday afternoon football games.
[49] Sterling Fisher to W. Davis, February 7, 1939; SIA RU7091, Box 385, Folder 15.

margins of the Fisher letter indicate that Davis immediately asked various grocers associations for suggestions of potential guests. Fisher continued the pressure with a telegram: "WOULD APPRECIATE ANY INFORMATION RE ADVENTURES IN SCIENCE APRIL 8 DEALING WITH EARLIER SUGGESTION MADE TO YOU RE INTERVIEWING SCIENTISTS IN LABORATORIES OF GROCERY FIRMS."[50] Davis, who was on the road, wired that Science Service staff should locate a guest with an acceptable industry connection: "PROBABLY SAFEST GROCERY PROGRAM WOULD BE SOME REPUTABLE SCIENTISTS CONNECTED GENERAL FOODS ... KINDLY EXPLORE BUT KEEP IT NONCOMMERCIAL." On his return to Washington, Davis wired Fisher: "WE ARE WORKING ON A FOOD PROGRAM FOR THE APRIL 8 ADVENTURES IN SCIENCE TO TIE IN WITH THE GROCERS' PARADE OF PROGRESS, IN ACCORDANCE WITH YOUR SUGGESTION."[51] They eventually scheduled Lewis W. Waters, Vice-President of General Foods, who spoke about "Better Meals Tomorrow" and assured listeners that "Food scientists and the food industry are helping to build a bigger and better America of tomorrow".[52]

The most unusual broadcast that year involved a chemist who did not appear. That program exemplifies the attempts to sensationalize science while also emphasizing its role in national preparedness. It also offers an example of how scientists' attitudes to popularization had evolved since Science Service had been founded. On Saturday afternoon, November 13, 1939, after his usual four-minute news segment (*e.g.*, world's highest and lowest-recorded temperatures, new building insulation materials, and discovery of a new undersea mountain off the Alaska coast), Davis declared "now let's turn to the war." One question "most often asked in connection with the war," he said, is about "the delay in using gas warfare": "The failure to use gas is puzzling to those of us who read about every man, woman, and child in warring countries of Europe fitted out

---

[50] Sterling Fisher telegram to W. Davis, March 8, 1939; SIA RU7091, Box 385, Folder 15.

[51] W. Davis to Sterling Davis, March 11, 1939; SIA RU7091, Box 385, Folder 15.

[52] Draft outline of talk by Lewis W. Waters; SIA RU7091, Box 385, Folder 15.

with gas masks."[53] The program then focused on what had been advertised as a live interview of Winford Lee Lewis, inventor of lewisite.

Lewis had developed a powerful respiratory irritant, chloro-vinyl-dichloro-arsine ('lewisite'), while working for the U.S. Chemical Warfare Service during World War I. Formerly chairman of the Northwestern University chemistry department, he was now director of scientific research for a Chicago firm. Davis had interviewed Lewis years before, in a September 1933 program on 'Friendly Germs', and so the chemist agreed to appear again but explained that he had been having trouble with his voice: "I will be glad to undertake the broadcast providing Mrs. Lewis [his wife, Myrtiela Mae Lewis] might give my talk in the event I am out of voice."[54] He assured Davis that she had a "most unusual speaking voice [...] with exceptional enunciation" and that she had been "one of my chemistry students" so would be conversant with the topic. Mrs. Lewis did appear, in fact, reading her part from a prepared script that celebrated the "usefulness" of chemical weapons:

> Interviewer: The development of a country's chemical industry has a very real bearing on its disposition to use or not use chemical weapons.
>
> Mrs. Lewis: Yes, it has been frequently pointed out that a country with a strong chemical industry has a tremendous advantage in a conflict involving chemical weapons. Chemists, chemical knowledge, chemicals and chemical plants are needed to produce chemical weapons. These resources cannot be developed overnight.[55]

At the end of the broadcast, the announcer asked, "Would you like to have more information on war gases?" Listeners received a free bulletin ('War Gases') that described the chemical characteristics and physio-

---

[53] Script for 'Adventures in Science', November 13, 1939; SIA RU7091, Box 386, Folder 2.

[54] See W. Davis to W. Lee Lewis, September 26, 1939; W. Davis telegram to W. Lee Lewis, October 16, 1939; W. Lee Lewis to W. Davis, October 16, 1939; and W. Lee Lewis to W. Davis, October 25, 1939; SIA RU7091, Box 386, Folder 2. The interview section of the broadcast actually took place in the studios of station WBBM in Chicago, where a local announcer read questions to Mrs. Lewis from the prepared script. See annotated scripts for November 13, 1939, in SIA RU7091, Box 386, Folder 2.

[55] Script for November 13, 1939, broadcast; SIA RU7091, Box 386, Folder 2.

logical effects of substances like mustard gas, chlorine gas, lewisite, and toxic smokes.[56]

That episode demonstrates how much the scientific establishment's acceptance of popularization had changed. Many historians, myself among them, have long pointed to chemists' outrage at the news coverage of poison gas after World War I and have assumed that such outrage not only fueled their postwar campaigns to improve chemistry's public image but also left many scientific leaders leery of certain types of popularization. By 1939, however, an organization praised and supported by scientists, including the most prominent chemists of the time, was discussing poison gas research on its Saturday afternoon radio program and doing so without any apparent defensiveness. This circumstance suggests that the scientific establishment had embraced a more pragmatic acceptance of media attention, perhaps seeing participation in such communication as potentially useful in attracting economic and political support, as a necessary evil rather than an enemy of science's cause.

Several other late 1939 broadcasts sounded celebratory notes about chemistry and its contribution to national self-sufficiency and defense. Sidney D. Kirkpatrick, editor of *Chemical and Metallurgical Engineering*, assured listeners on December 4 that "America now has a chemical industry second to none [...] we are more nearly self-sufficient from a chemical standpoint".[57] And on December 25, Davis opened his annual 'Review of the Year' program by wishing listeners "A Merry and Scientific Christmas" and giving a "scientific balance sheet, to judge what has been important and significant".[58] "Long after the war of 1939 is forgotten," he explained, "the splitting of the uranium atom with release of energy, hinting practical production of power from within the atom, may be listed as the year's outstanding achievement." Davis then listed science's ten major contributions to American health and households, including "Number 6 [...] The success of the chemical sulfapyradine in treatment

---

[56] Bulletin for 'Adventures in Science' broadcast of November 13, 1939; SIA RU7091, Box 386, Folder 2.

[57] 'Adventures in Science' script for December 4, 1939, p. 3; SIA RU7091, Box 386, Folder 6.

[58] 'Adventures in Science' script for December 25, 1939; SIA RU7091, Box 386, Folder 10.

of pneumonia and the continued promising treatment of many other disease with sulfanilamide and related chemicals" and "Number 9 [...] Development of synthetic fibers for clothing, including nylon, vinyon, synthetic wool from milk". This last achievement was the subject of another Science Service project which combined department store mercantilism with adult education.

6. Chemistry in Department Store Windows

Early in 1939, after a meeting of the Science Service executive committee, some members went to inspect a new exhibit about synthetic fibers, set up a few blocks from the National Academy of Sciences building.[59] It must have been a remarkable sight as a dignified trio – chemist W.H. Howell, Edwin G. Conklin of the American Philosophical Society, and C.G. Abbot, head of the Smithsonian Institution – stared at a display of women's clothing in the central window of the Woodward & Lothrop department store (Figure 2). The window, in which garments made of new synthetic textiles were surrounded by jars of the fabrics' constituent chemicals, represented Science Service's latest innovation: a traveling exhibit displayed in department store windows and sponsored by local newspapers which published a coordinated series of articles about the chemistry of 'Fabrics of the Future'.

On one side of the Woodward & Lothrop window (Figure 2) can be seen bottles of new chemicals and samples of metal and glass; on the other side, nylon stockings and lengths of rayon cloth. The mannequin's dress is made of lanital (synthetic wool). Over the front of the window is a 'spider web' design representing the 'spinning' of artificial fabrics. This project – both the middle-class context in which the exhibit was displayed and its central themes – exemplified the organization's attempts to diffuse science beyond traditional outlets and to infuse social and economic relevance into its news. What could be more accessible to Americans than a downtown department store? Or more appealing than the latest fashions?

---

[59] See 'Minutes of the Executive Committee of Science Service... February 11, 1939'; SIA RU7091, Box 4, Folder 7.

Public reaction to the 'Fabrics of the Future' installation in Washington, D.C., sponsored by the *Washington Daily News*, proved to be enthusiastic. The store's advertising manager called it "one of the most instructive and interesting displays of a merchandise nature that we have been able to make in a long while [...] spectators crowded the window throughout the day for the duration of the display."[60] Washingtonians' interest was so great that a competing newspaper, the *Washington Times-Herald*, even reproduced photographs of the window with a half-page of explanatory text. Similar praise came from newspaper sponsors and department store managers as the exhibit was shown in dozens of U.S. cities over the next two years.[61]

The series of six articles, written by Robert D. Potter, wove themes of national self-sufficiency, economy, creativity, efficiency, wizardry, and progress into a tapestry sprinkled with technical terms and domestic metaphors. The text offered substantial promises for chemistry as science's "wonder worker" and contributor to national defense. "The fibers and fabrics of tomorrow stagger the imagination and leave the mind speculating in fantasy that has a good chance of some day becoming true, regardless of how crazy it may seem," Potter wrote.[62] A promotional advertisement for the series read:

CHEMISTS SYNTHESIZE TOMORROW'S FABRICS. 'Wool' out of milk [...] 'silk' out of coal, air and water [...] fibers of glass and metal [...] here are the wonders of modern science [...] bringing new discoveries to the home [...] influencing the nation [...] swaying international trade [...] even swinging the balance that may decide future wars. See what the future holds in store for Americans through modern research now molding the future.[63]

---

[60] James W. Hardey, quoted in 'Information Memorandum on Progress of Science Service, June 10, 1939', p. 5; SIA RU7091, Box 4, Folder 8.

[61] See other descriptions of crowds and compliments from newspaper editors in: W. Davis to Max B. Cook, April 21, 1939, and Austin Winant to Max B. Cook, July 19, 1939, and July 28, 1939; SIA RU7091, Box 427, Folder 77.

[62] Quotations throughout this section are taken not from the various published versions but from a mimeograph copy of the 'Fabrics of the Future' text, version of August 12, 1939, located in SIA RU7091, Box 408, Folder 23.

[63] Promotion box text suggested by Science Service for use with the 'Fabrics of the Future' Series, August 12, 1939, mailing; SIA RU7091, Box 385, Folder 39.

The articles outlined the significance of this work: how countries "under the spur of national defense" needed to develop synthetic fibers so that they might be "liberated from foreign imports that might fail in time of war" yet not "exhaust" their own natural resources.

Figure 2. Installation of the Science Service 'Fabrics for the Future' display in the window of the Woodward & Lothrop department store, Washington, D.C., February 1939 (SIA RU7091, Box 457). Courtesy of Smithsonian Institution Archives.

Chemists were described in the same glowing, positive terms found elsewhere in popular science in 1939: persistent, ingenious, creative, and able to identify the simplicity hidden in nature's complexity (LaFollette 1990). The articles emphasized traits like economy, frugality, and inventiveness. These "man-made wool fibers" were "economical" and cheap to produce because they used either less expensive raw materials or dairy by-products like dried casein powder. Potter praised chemists' "ingenuity" and creativity; in part six, he described how "two advertising men turned inventors" had developed a new rayon fabric they called "Perval", that "could be made so cheaply it would be thrown away instead of being sent to the laundry".

Both the articles and photograph captions frequently referenced wizardry and alchemy: chemists were spinning cloth out of coal, and wool out of "mechanized sheep" or buckets of milk; they were "turning wood chips into the finest of fibers and fabrics" and making nylon "from coal, air and water". Figures 3, 4, and 5 show three of twenty-four photographs sold with the articles, some of them taken by the Science Service photographer but others (as was standard practice) obtained from industry sources and supplied with new captions.

Figure 3. Steps in making rayon, a photograph by Fremont Davis which was supplied with the Science Service 'Fabrics for the Future' newspaper series, 1939. The suggested caption read "Eight different chemical steps go into the making of acetate rayon in turning raw wood chips into the finest of fibers and fabrics." (SIA RU7091, Box 408, Folder 23). Courtesy of Smithsonian Institution Archives.

As with so much of popular science of the 1930s, the articles assured readers a future of endless progress; they promised more science to come, with little attention to the consequences (LaFollette 1990, ch. 10). Potter suggested that the "great advances of the past" were "only a small part of what will appear in the future." "Still stronger" or "potent" products are "in store for the future" and this was just a "foretaste". As science continued to widen "its circle of achievement and usefulness", it would weave fabrics with longevity – "rot-proof", "moisture-proof", and "fire-proof". Even rayon's "future as a fiber" was not "exhausted" because chemists were devising new uses for it.

Although the series did not refrain from anthropomorphizing science (see the photograph of 'Lanital Lady', a 'doll' made of synthetic material, in Figure 4), its approach was more pragmatic than romantic. It promoted a spiritual duality. Nature remained the best fabric producer; scientists could only copy or improve on nature, not replace it. Science, however, provided an advantage in that its processes, unlike nature, could be controlled.

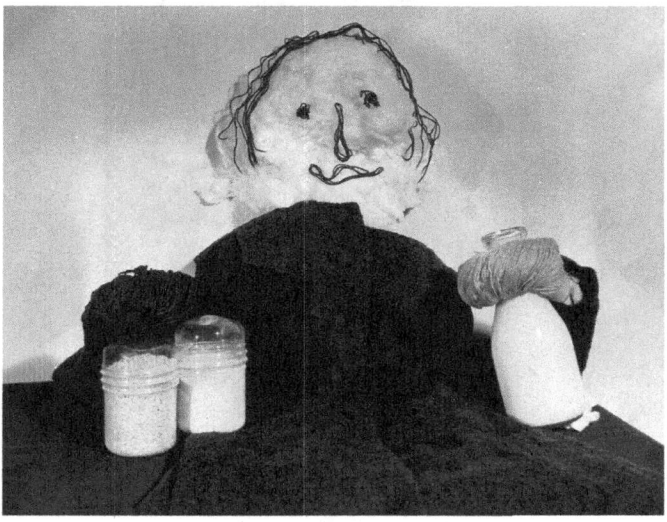

Figure 4. 'Lanital Lady', a photograph by Fremont Davis which was supplied with Science Service 'Fabrics for the Future' newspaper series, 1939. The caption explained that "various steps in the production of lanital – the synthetic 'wool' – have been used to create the lady.' The doll's head was 'wool' made from cow's milk; the hands held bottles of raw casein and milk (SIA RU7091, Box 408, Folder 23). Courtesy of Smithsonian Institution Archives.

These articles also included a substantial number of domestic analogies and examples, as if the editors had made a conscious effort to appeal to women readers (although no explicit evidence of this approach survives in correspondence or is mentioned in the associated promotional material). The text as well as the photograph captions include many references to such products as flour, face powder, bread baking, aprons, upholstery, curtains, laundry, and frying pans. Four of the photos sent with the series explicitly depicted women's clothing – a blouse made of synthetic wool, nylon stockings modeled by female college students, and a three-piece suit made of synthetic wool (Figure 5) – and the store window display centered on the female mannequins.

Figure 5. Synthetic wool suit, a photograph supplied by the Hamilton M. Wright advertising firm, which represented the Italian textile industry, for use with Science Service 'Fabrics for the Future' newspaper series, 1939. The suggested caption read "Synthetic wool, made out of the casein in cow's milk, was the basic raw material for this beautiful woman's three-piece suit. The casein cost 50 cents and was obtained from 63 quarts of milk." (SIA RU7091, Box 408, Folder 23). Courtesy of Smithsonian Institution Archives.

These domestic and gender-linked references appeared in articles that were sprinkled liberally with technical details and terms, including detailed descriptions of the spinneret process and other aspects of synthetics production. Article two compared the chemical analyses of synthetic and natural wool, breaking them down into percentages of carbon, hydrogen, oxygen, nitrogen, and sulfur. Words like 'protein', 'coagulate', 'formaldehyde', 'bacterial enzyme', 'nitrocellulose', 'chemical bonds', and 'polyamides' were used throughout the text, usually without further definition, as if assuming that readers would find them as familiar as the associated references to milk production and sheep farming.

By April, with the exhibit almost fully booked, Science Service was turning down requests. "We appreciate your interest in the Science Service exhibit on 'Fabrics of the Future'. I regret that there has been such a great demand for this throughout the country by the newspapers [...] that it is not possible at the present time to arrange for its use by colleges," Potter wrote to a chemistry student in New York who had read about the exhibit in *Industrial and Engineering Chemistry*.[64] That spring, the exhibit traveled to major cities in Indiana, Ohio, and New York. During May, it was in the windows of the Joseph Horne Company in Pittsburgh, Pennsylvania, sponsored by the *Pittsburgh Press*. In June and July, the *San Francisco News*, *San Diego Sun*, and *Berkeley Gazette* sponsored California appearances, and other newspapers and stores in New Mexico, Texas, Alabama, North Carolina, New Jersey, and Michigan scheduled the project. Public reaction remained enthusiastic. In Buffalo, New York, "It didn't matter whether it was day or night, there were people examining the exhibit and all expressed amazement at it."[65]

Sponsored by the *Boston Transcript*, the exhibit went on display at the Jordan Marsh department store during the week of September 11, 1939, coordinated with the annual American Chemical Society conference. Davis asked chemist H.E. Howe to appear on the 'Adventures in Science' broadcast directly from the Boston meeting. In his introduction, Davis extolled the wonders of synthetic fibers, emphasizing (in the context of world events) that such fibers could step "into jobs previously performed by silk" from Japan, make use of products like milk casein that might otherwise go to waste, and help create new production jobs.

---

[64] R.D. Potter to Sherman Finneran, April 1, 1939; SIA RU7091, Box 208, Folder 6.
[65] 'Information Memorandum on Progress of Science Service', June 10, 1939; SIA RU7091, Box 4, Folder 8, p. 6.

Howe explained that chemists had "learned how to make synthetic substances that are better than rubber" because of research "initiated in pure or fundamental science without thought of immediate commercial application and without seeking the answer to any pressing industrial problem", a theme further reinforced in a November broadcast when Davis interviewed U.S. Department of Agriculture chemist E.O. Whittier about 'Wool from Milk'.[66] After each of these programs, listeners could obtain a free bulletin summarizing the newspaper series or a sample of 'synthetic wool'.

The 'Fabrics for the Future' exhibit continued on tour throughout 1940, shipped to the Princeton University chemistry department that summer, and on to Maine for a New England Association of Chemistry Teachers meeting, but the war interrupted any further plans for such multi-media approaches.[67] Starting in the 1940s, Science Service's efforts began to focus increasingly on science education projects and away from its news syndication activities, other than through radio.

7. Conclusion

What can the history of Science Service reveal about public images of chemistry and other parts of science and about how or why scientists engaged in the popularization process? Was the organization merely a promotional agent for scientists, or did it play a more complex, subtle role? Because Science Service, Inc., continued beyond those first decades, and focuses today on science education and the publication of the small weekly magazine *Science News*, there has been a tendency to see the past mirrored in the present, to regard its mission today as reflective of its initial purposes and approaches.

My research suggests a different interpretation, one that views the history of Science Service – like that of nations, corporations, scientific

---

[66] Script for 'Adventures in Science', September 11, 1939, p. 5; SIA RU7091, Box 385, Folder 39. Also see script for 'Adventures in Science', November 20, 1939; SIA RU7091, Box 386, Folder 4.

[67] Science Service attempted to work with *Modern Plastics* magazine on a similar "plastics exhibit for newspapers and cooperating department stores", but that project never went beyond the planning stages. See correspondence in SIA RU7091, Box 220, Folder 2.

disciplines, or families – as having distinct phases. The first decades of its existence represented a phase that stretched until World War II. After that time, not just Science Service but also its contextual partners (the scientific community and mass media) changed. Watson Davis continued to deliver speeches declaring that accuracy and timeliness comprised the 'essence' of science news but his organization no longer needed to convince publishers or the public of science's relevance to every aspect of modern life, nor did it need to persuade scientists that public opinion mattered to the health of science. Consolidation of newspapers, market expansion, television, and internationalization – each altered the media marketplace in which Science Service had been functioning. Davis became preoccupied with promoting science education and the organization became a marginal (although still respected) player in the hardnosed world of news journalism.

During the 1920s and 1930s, though, Science Service had facilitated communication between scientists and the public and been at the hub of a network of people creating what we now call 'science journalism'. In that initial phase, it negotiated standards for a new public-private space in which complex and potentially empowering information could be explained precisely to people with little or no education in science. It also cultivated relationships with corporate sources, especially in the chemical industry, and promoted popularization through dramatization, scientists as celebrities, and, as in the department store project on chemistry, the marketing of science through connection to consumer goods. Like nations, families, and other organizations, the history of Science Service is a complex mix of positive and negative outcomes.

Americans, Thone had argued, wanted information that was comprehensible and accessible, that could be rolled up, stuck in a pocket, and consumed on demand.[68] Scientists may have found such informality unsettling but Science Service's marketing success helped enable it. The popularization of science was strutting resolutely toward today's familiar landscape of multiple, diverse, and commercialized outlets. By the end of

---

[68] Frank Thone, 'The Press as an Agency for the Diffusion of Science', text of a speech to the American Association for Adult Education, May 21, 1936, p. 2; SIA RU7091, Box 4, Folder 2.

the 1930s, no one had to persuade newspapers to attend to science. From the *New York Times* to *Saturday Evening Post*, Hollywood movies to network radio, *Arrowsmith* to World's Fair exhibitions, science and scientists were accepted as suitable subjects for news, entertainment, promotion, merchandizing, and even satire. Understanding the development of Science Service during its formative years, and the motivations of the people associated with it, will assist historians in unpacking further the array of forces that shaped (and continue to shape) popular science content.

Acknowledgments

The author gratefully acknowledges the role played by Dr. Audrey Davis, a historian whose foresight enabled the original transfer of the Science Service editorial records to the Smithsonian Institution. The author also thanks the staff of the Smithsonian Institution Archives and Hagley Library for assistance with this research, and participants in the April 2005 conference 'Science for Sale? The Public Communication of Science in a Corporate World' at Cornell University, and especially Professor Trevor Pinch, for comments on presentation of this history.

References

Burnham, J.C.: 1987, *How Superstition Won and Science Lost: Popularizing Science and Health in the United States*, Rutgers University Press, New Brunswick.

Douglas, S.J.: 1999, *Listening In: Radio and the American Imagination*, Times Books, New York.

Hilmes, M.: 1997, *Radio Voices: American Broadcasting, 1922-1952*, University of Minnesota Press, Minneapolis.

Kevles, D.J.: 1978, *The Physicists: The History of a Scientific Community*, Alfred A. Knopf, New York.

Kirchhofer, A.H.: 1932, 'Science Service Conference', *Science*, **76** (August 19), 154-5.

LaFollette, M.C.: 1990, *Making Science Our Own: Public Images of Science, 1910-1955*, University of Chicago Press, Chicago.

LaFollette, M.C.: 2002, 'A Survey of Science Content in U.S. Radio Broadcasting, 1920s through 1940s: Scientists Speak in Their Own Voices', *Science Communication*, **24**, 4-33.

Rhees, D.J.: 1979, *A New Voice for Science: Science Service under Edwin E. Slosson, 1921-1929*, M.A. thesis, University of North Carolina.

Scripps, R.P.: 1932, 'Science Service Conference', *Science*, **76** (August 19), 156.

Slosson, E.E.: 1922, 'Popular Science', *Science*, **60** (May 5), 480-482.

Smulyan, S.: 1994, *Selling Radio: The Commercialization of American Broadcasting, 1920-1934*, Smithsonian Institution Press, Washington.

Tobey, R.C.: 1971, *The American Ideology of National Science, 1919-1930*, University of Pittsburgh Press, Pittsburgh.

Thone, F.E.A. & Bailey, E.W.: 1927, 'William Emerson Ritter: Builder', *The Scientific Monthly*, **24** (March), 256-262.

CHAPTER 11

THE IMAGE OF CHEMISTRY PRESENTED BY THE SCIENCE MUSEUM, LONDON IN THE TWENTIETH CENTURY: AN INTERNATIONAL PERSPECTIVE

Peter J. T. Morris

The Science Museum, Exhibition Road, London SW7 2DD, U.K.;
peter.morris@nmsi.ac.uk

How has chemistry been presented at the Science Museum, London, during the twentieth century? After an overview of the history of the Science Museum and its chemistry galleries, four galleries are considered in depth (1906, 1926, 1977, and 1999). The importance of the curators' external constituency of chemists and chemical educators is emphasized. The image of chemistry at the Science Museum has concentrated on the general utility of chemistry and chemistry as a skilful craft. The presentation has been low-key rather than boosterist. A comparison is made with the chemistry galleries at the Deutsches Museum. Chemistry in the Deutsches Museum has put more emphasis on hands-on exhibits and the chemical industry. Science and technology museums have promoted chemistry in a quiet but successful way for many years, but their influence may have waned along with chemistry kits.

1. Introduction

Before we examine the image of chemistry that has been presented by the Science Museum during the twentieth century, it is worth asking if science and technology museums have any influence on the public's perception of chemistry. While the impact of museums is inevitably less than, say, the mass media, they do attract large audiences: the Science Museum had 1.2 million visitors in the 1930s, a peak of 4.2 million visitors in 1980 and 2.6 million visitors in 2004. It is also clear that such museums have a strong and lasting emotional effect on some visitors. The impact of museums is also important insofar as they appeal to young people whose image of chemistry may not be completely formed. If we accept that the way museums portray chemistry can have an impact on its public image, has the presentation of chemistry in museums changed over the years and in what way has their portrayal of chemistry changed? How do museums develop their chemistry displays? Are they created purely by the curators, by an external group of leading chemists and chemical educationalists, or are they shaped by the visitors themselves?

As a curator in a leading science museum who has both looked after and developed chemistry galleries, I am able to show how chemistry is displayed in museum from the curatorial point of view. On one hand this means that I am able to see influences and connections which might be missed by an external observer. I also have access to printed materials and documents that an external author might not be aware of. I have been able to discuss developments in the Science Museum with colleagues whose experience goes back to the 1970s. On the other hand, my analysis will be limited by being a curator, my view although deeper will inevitably be narrower than that of an acute external observer. However, I believe this exercise is worthwhile. This is a good time to take stock as museums have changing radically over the last few years and will continue to change. We are not likely to see entire galleries devoted to academic chemistry in the future. My main aim is to present an insider's view of gallery development and to show the importance of external influences. I do not seek to place these developments within the latest historiography, nor am I able within the limits of this chapter to place these galleries within their broader museological and educational contexts. Nonetheless, I hope this chapter will provide the material for future research on these aspects of the topic.

The term 'chemical gallery' can mean many things and can cover many different areas of chemistry, broadly defined. For example, chemistry galleries often cover the chemical industry and its products including plastics and metals. It might be argued that any study of the development of chemistry galleries should cover these outlying fields. In practice, however, I have found that the image presented by the chemical industry displays of chemistry galleries is very different from that by academic chemistry exhibits. Therefore, the image of industrial chemistry will be the subject of a subsequent paper.

2. History of Chemistry at the Science Museum

The Science Museum has its origins in the South Kensington Museum which was founded in 1857 following the great popularity of the Great Exhibition of 1851 which garnered a considerable financial surplus (Hobhouse 2002). The mission of the South Kensington Museum was the promotion of art and science, art in this context being what we would now call crafts and design, and it came under the control of the Department of Science and Art (Follett 1978). The relatively few chemistry exhibits were in the wall cases of the Education Museum, which was part of the South Kensington Museum. The science and engineering collections were expanded after the Royal Commission on Scientific Instruction and the Advancement of Science ('Devonshire') Commission reported on the South Kensington collections in its fourth report of 1874. As a consequence, the Royal Commission for the Exhibition of 1851 offered to build a science museum if the government provided the site, but this offer was not taken up. For their part, the Lords of Committee of the [Privy] Council on Education, led by Viscount Sandon, set up a committee chaired by the Lord Chancellor (Baron Cairns) to organize a temporary international exhibition of scientific instruments (Special Loan Catalogue 1876). This Special Loan Exhibition held in 1876 was supported *inter alia*, by Frederick Abel, Edward Frankland, Jean Baptiste Dumas, and Wilhelm Hofmann. It was displayed in the Western Galleries of the Royal Horticultural Society's exhibition halls, which had originally been erected for the International Exhibition of 1862. The Special Loan Exhibition was an important watershed in the development of the Science Museum as many of the objects on loan for this exhibition were left at the museum, although only a few in the case of chemistry, including demonstration apparatus developed by Hofmann.

After the control of the Patent Museum moved from the Commissioners of Patents to the Department of Science and Art in 1883, that museum was amalgamated with the Science Museum. This collection had hitherto been completely distinct in institutional terms, but displayed alongside the South Kensington Museum in the so-called 'Brompton boilers' (from the appearance of the buildings and their location on the Brompton Road). The non-art collections of the South Kensington Museum had been known as the Science Collections, presumably to reflect the dichotomy in the title of the Department of Science and Art, and following the amalgamation with the Patent Museum, the Department changed the name of the collections to the Science Museum. As Sir Phillip Cunliffe-Owen was still in post as Director of the South Kensington Museum, a separate director for the Science Museum was not appointed until he retired in 1893. The first director was Major-General Edward R. Festing FRS, who had joined the South Kensington Museum in 1864, and had explored the potential of infrared spectroscopy as an analytical tool with Sir William Abney in the 1880s.

The Science Museum's collections were transferred in 1888 from the South Kensington Museum to the Western and Southern Galleries occupied up to that date by the Royal Horticultural Society. Science was in the Western Galleries, which were to the west of the current Imperial College Library building. They were smaller in area than the Southern Galleries and away from the main entrance on Exhibition Road. The Western Galleries did not attract many visitors, only 86,216 in 1908 compared with 384,889 for the technological collections in the Southern Galleries (Board of Education 1909). In fact the name 'Science Museum' has always been a complete misnomer. Technology not science has always been the dominant aspect of the Science Museum and until the directorship of the chemist and historian of chemistry Frank Sherwood Taylor in the early 1950s, chemistry was a relatively minor part of the Science Museum's displays. The modest chemistry galleries were on the first (top) floor of the Western Galleries at the north end just to the south of Prince Consort Road, near the present-day Blackett Laboratory of Imperial College.

The South Kensington Museum was renamed the Victoria and Albert Museum in 1899, when Queen Victoria laid the foundation stone of the new building for the art collections. By what seems to have been a bureaucratic oversight, the Science Museum was considered a division of the Victoria and Albert Museum. In 1909, the famous chemist and politician Sir Henry Enfield Roscoe led a delegation of scientists and engineers to the new Board of Education to demand that greater attention be given to the development and accommodation of the Science Museum's collections. The Science Museum was at long last separated from the Victoria and Albert Museum in the same year, when the latter's building was formally opened by King Edward VII. A Departmental Committee was set up in March 1910 to advise on the future direction of the Science Museum and to recommend what new buildings were required. It was chaired by Sir Hugh Bell, a director of the steel firm Dorman Long and a former Mayor of Middlesbrough. He was the son of the leading ironmaster Sir Isaac Lowthian Bell and the father of the explorer and orientalist Gertrude Bell. In a landmark report in 1911, the Bell Committee laid out the future of the museum, proposing the construction of three wings (or blocks) in turn, beginning with the East Block on Exhibition Road. Construction began in 1913, but World War I intervened and the half-finished building was taken over by the Civil Service for war use. The East Block was finally opened by King George V in 1928, but the Central Block was not finished until 1961. The West Block (now called the Wellcome Wing) only saw the light of day in 2000, almost nine decades since the publication of the Bell Report which had envisaged the completion of the central block in 1923 and the West Block as and when required a few years later!

The period between 1916 and 1925 was a dismal period for chemistry in the Science Museum largely because of World War I. The museum was closed to the general public in March 1916 and the chemistry gallery was occupied by clerks from the War Office between 1917 and 1921. The space vacated by the War Office was then taken over by the new Imperial War Museum Library just over a year later (Board of Education 1924a/b). There was still some chemistry (and industrial chemistry) on display, but space was very limited. Matters improved when the East Block was fitted out in 1925 and 1926. Chemistry and industrial chemistry, which had been brought together in 1912, were on the third floor of the new East Block, and the new gallery was opened to the public in April 1926 (Board of Education 1926). This gallery – Gallery 66 in the museum's internal numbering scheme – is now a mixture of offices and simulators. In this period, the chemistry collections were curated by Alexander Barclay, an Imperial College (Royal College of Science) educated chemist who had joined the museum in 1921 when he was taken on to help with the preparations for the new gallery and who became an Assistant Keeper in 1930. Eight years later, he became the Keeper of Department IV (chemistry, photography, optics, astronomy, and mathematics, which became chemistry and photography in 1949 [Who Was Who 1991]). The museum was closed to the public between September 1939 and February 1946, except for a brief period in the spring (February-June) 1940.

Chemistry increased in importance following the appointment of Frank Sherwood Taylor as director in 1950. Taylor died in office after serving for only six years. He was in conflict with his Keepers who opposed his publications on science and religion, but he promoted the career of Frank Greenaway, an Oxford-trained chemist who had joined the museum as an Assistant Keeper in 1949. Greenaway, as the first chemistry curator to be an active historian of chemistry, was to have a decisive influence on the presentation and development of chemistry at the Science Museum in the 1960s and 1970s. The Chemistry and Industrial Collections had mostly been moved into store during World War II. The task of putting the collections back on display occupied the Chemistry Department for ten years. Chemistry returned to Gallery 66 on the third floor in 1952. The redisplay of Industrial Chemistry in Gallery 46 on the second floor took place very slowly with considerable input and some financial support from industry. The Industrial Chemistry gallery was still only partly completed in 1957 (Science Museum Guides 1952, 1953, 1957). Barclay was succeeded as Keeper of Chemistry and Photography in 1959 by Stanley Janson, a Cambridge-trained chemist who worked on the industrial chemistry collections and especially glass technology (Science Museum 1970).

After building the new chemistry and industrial chemistry galleries on the second floor of the East Block in 1963-4, Greenaway became Keeper of Chemistry in 1967 while Janson, who retired two years later, became Keeper of Astronomy and Geophysics. Greenaway built up a team of young enthusiastic and knowledgeable curators – including Robert Anderson, Derek Robinson, and Ann Newmark – who were responsible for the revamping of the chemistry and industrial chemistry galleries in 1977. Greenaway was succeeded in 1980 by Robert Anderson, who left the museum in 1984 to become Director of the Royal Scottish Museum (subsequently the National Museums of Scotland). The chemistry department was then amalgamated with the physics department and the new Keeper was the former Keeper of Physics, David Thomas (who had been an Assistant Keeper of Chemistry between 1961 and 1973). During this period Robert Bud curated a new chemical industry gallery sponsored by ICI in 1986. On Thomas's retirement in 1987 he was succeeded by Derek Robinson who had become Keeper of Museum Services in 1978. He was given the new title of Head of Physical Sciences when the keeperships were abolished soon afterwards. Robinson took personal charge of Industrial Chemistry and Ann Newmark was Senior Curator of Experimental Chemistry. When Newmark became Head of Documentation in 1991, she was succeeded by Peter Morris who also took over Industrial Chemistry on the retirement of Derek Robinson in 1999 (by then Head of Physical Sciences & Engineering). The chemistry galleries on the second floor were cleared in the same year and replaced by a much smaller gallery entitled 'The Chemistry of Everyday Life'. The industrial chemistry gallery was cleared a few years later in 2004.

3. Gallery Development at the Science Museum

From my own experience as a curator and drawing on the experiences of my colleagues and former colleagues at the Science Museum, I believe that it is possible to show how the development of a new gallery is shaped by external factors; for a very different view of gallery development by an external observer, see Macdonald 2002. Up to now, all the chemistry galleries at the Science Museum have been put together, if not explicitly designed, by curators. In order to understand the development of these galleries we need to understand the environment in which these curators operate. We have to begin with the curators themselves. Nearly all the curators who have had a major influence on the chemistry galleries have been chemists, at least four of them were even Fellows of the Royal Society of Chemistry or its predecessor, the Royal Institute of Chemistry. To a lesser or greater extent they have also been interested in the history of chemistry and in more recent times, they have been professionally trained historians of chemistry. In passing it should also be noted that they have also been predominantly white and male, and have gone to leading English universities, especially Oxford and Manchester.

As employees of the Science Museum, the work of curators is overseen by the Director, once a hands-on manager of new galleries, but now somebody who has to concentrate on the strategic management of three museums, and by an advisory council (the Board of Trustees since 1983) made up of leading scientists, engineers, and other members of the establishment. Also the government has had some influence, initially through the Department of Education and Science (and its predecessors) and more recently via the Department of Culture, Media, and Sport. The government's influence on gallery development deserves closer examination, but it would be fair to say that it was – until recently – minimal as far as specific galleries were concerned. As long as the galleries promoted science education in a broad sense and did not generate politically embarrassing controversy, the Department was happy to leave the content of the museum's displays to the Director and his staff. Nonetheless, since the 1960s the government has increasingly pushed museums to seek external funding for new galleries and, since the late 1980s, to cater for increasingly diverse audiences.

As civil servants until 1983, and as government employees even now, curators operated within a specific institutional ethos. Their personal political and religious views were not supposed to impinge on the content of displays, and I have not found any case where this has in fact occurred. The civil service ethos has also ensured that curators have worked with external bodies and companies in an even-handed manner, not favoring one firm's products over a rival's, or one institution's research over another. There are some exceptions to this general rule of neutrality. There has been a tendency to highlight the work done by other government bodies, such as the Laboratory of the Government Chemist. The museum has also been supportive of the aims of professional societies and official industry-wide organizations – such as the Royal Society of Chemistry and the Association of British Chemical Manufacturers – and it has worked closely with these organizations over the years. Finally for geographical and personal reasons, the chemistry curators at the museum have tended to work closely with leading London colleges (Imperial, UCL, and King's) and to a lesser extent with Oxford and Cambridge. For the same reasons, they also frequented the showrooms of the leading London-based scientific instrument suppliers and manufacturers, which were a leading force in the industry up to the 1960s. Although there is no evidence that the curators favored one firm's products over another, some companies were better than others at donating objects, as I know well from personal experience. Up to the mid-1960s, firms often lent objects on the assumption they could be 'silently' replaced by more up-to-date models over the years, although in practice the museum often retained the initial object. It has to be emphasized however, that 'branded' instruments always formed a minority of the museum's chemistry collections, at least until recently.

In theory a new gallery could have a client, an external person or body, who has funded or at least has provided moral support for its construction. Certainly this would almost invariably be the case nowadays, but most of the galleries considered here were developed without external funding and the only client-funder was the government. But when there has been an external sponsor, we have taken the client's aspirations for the gallery into account, but have also taken great care not to give a client any undue influence on a gallery's content. At the same time, industrial and institutional sponsors (notably ICI and the Royal Institute/Society of Chemistry) have shaped the content of galleries over the years by offering advice, making donations of objects, making exhibits (for instance, the model of an ammonia plant in the 1977 Industrial Chemistry Gallery) and by generally stimulating the development of the content. For example, the Royal Society of Chemistry set up working parties to produce interactives for the 1999 Chemistry Gallery.

There is, however, one key aspect of the development of galleries which has not been widely understood and that is the importance of the curators' 'constituency'. Curators have historically had a dual role similar to that of Members of Parliament. On one hand they represent the museum to their external constituency and on the other they are the representatives of that constituency within the museum. The chemistry galleries have largely been a product of this curatorial interaction with their constituency. But what is a 'constituency' in this context? It can be defined as a group of educated people that a curator enjoys strong links with and wishes to gratify and impress. Although it is often said that curators create galleries for other curators, this has never been the case for the chemistry galleries, partly for the lack of any similar curators to impress. The chemistry curator's constituency is first and foremost other chemists, including biochemists and industrial chemists, particularly leading chemists and chemical educators. Chemical societies and industrial chemical organizations also play an important role, but less than might be imagined. Their influence has greatly varied from gallery to gallery and thus over time. Historians of chemistry and other historians of science have become increasingly important members of the constituency, especially since the formation of the Society for the History of Alchemy and Chemistry in 1937, but their influence has never been as great as that of the chemists. This constituency can easily be distinguished from the Advisory Council as the board always included only a small number of chemists. There were no chemists on the Advisory Council in the 1920s, and Trevor Williams, the historian of chemistry and editor of *Endeavour*, was one of the few chemists in the 1970s. Professor Arthur Smithells, who advised the museum on the chemistry display in the early 1920s, was never on the Advisory Council; and Professor Edward T. Hall, a key advisor to the curators during the 1977 redisplay of the chemistry galleries, only joined the Advisory Council two years later in 1979. While this lack of chemists on the council gives this constituency a heightened importance, I would argue it would always have been more important as it was a larger group and furthermore a group close to the curators' own intellectual and social milieu, for instance, through meetings of the Chemical Society at Burlington House, Annual Chemical Congresses, and social events at the Royal Institution. It has to be emphasized that this constituency has never been the target audience for the gallery, the actual audience for the gallery, or even an influential group of visitors. Paradoxically many members of this group rarely visited the museum. They influenced the gallery at the planning stage not as commentators on an existing gallery. Their direct experience of the museum would have taken place when they were schoolchildren or students. In more recent times, they would have only seen the chemistry galleries on special occasions, such as gallery openings, or when taking their children or grandchildren to the museum.

Despite the current emphasis on meeting the needs of a 'target audience', the putative audience for the chemistry galleries did not play a major role in shaping the content or design of these galleries until the last chemistry gallery in 1999. The collections were taken as a given and the displays were constructed to house them. To be sure, the curators have always had an idea of the kind of people they were addressing, but in the absence of detailed knowledge of the needs or interests of general visitors, how did the curators gauge the needs of their audiences? Senior members of staff were encouraged to mingle with visitors on the galleries and ask them for their impression of the displays. To some extent they must have also been influenced by the views of their family and friends. Successive Directors, especially Sir Henry Lyons, ensured that any new displays met the needs of the ordinary visitor as laid down by the Bell Report. Here too, nonetheless, the constituency played an important role. If the displays met with the approval of the constituency it was assumed to be suitable for the public at large, not least because many of its members were educators or public lecturers.

4.   The Image of Chemistry Presented by Science Museum Galleries

As we are looking specifically at the image of chemistry, I have deliberately chosen not to examine industrial chemistry, plastics, and metallurgy, all of which have been displayed with chemistry over the years, although these subject areas have had their own galleries in more recent times. However, precisely because they were displayed alongside chemistry and developed by the same curators, excluding these related subjects will not make any significant difference to my analysis with the marked exception of the 1986 chemical industry gallery, which introduced a striking and original 'mythopoetic' approach into the Science Museum. I have built up a picture of the different galleries by examining the printed catalogues and photographs. The archival records are sparse, but there are valuable comments in the annual reports for the earlier galleries and for the more recent ones I have been able to obtain recollections from the relevant curators. I would argue that the objects displayed on the galleries are central to understanding the image of chemistry the curators sought to communicate to visitors and their constituency.

This is fortunate, for it is relatively easy to find out what objects were specifically acquired for a new gallery and which ones were considered to be of particular significance by the curators. The new objects illustrate changes in chemical practice but also in the curators' changing aims for the gallery. Of course, the objects are only part of the story, and the medium – the display – is a vital part of the image production. Although there are fewer photographs than one would like, especially for the earliest galleries, it is possible from these photographs to make an intelligent analysis of the display techniques which were used.

4.1 The Western Galleries, 1890-1916

The chemistry galleries in the Western Galleries existed from 1890 to 1916. They were lofty and generously illuminated by natural light, in many respects similar to the Smithsonian's Arts and Industries building which opened in 1881. The cases were traditional mahogany cases with elegant piano-style legs. They were fairly tall and judging by the photograph of the Time Gallery from this period tended to dwarf the smaller objects in them. In the late nineteenth century the museum was very much under the thumb of the Department of Science and Art (Board of Education from 1900) of which it was a part. The emphasis was on current scientific practice and on education of young people, almost entirely men, embarking on a technical or scientific career. Part of the purpose of the museum was to show teachers, including college lecturers, the latest scientific apparatus and achievements. The constituency was a combination of scientific civil servants (*e.g.* William Abney, Frederick Abel), leading chemists (*e.g.* Henry E. Roscoe), the staff at Imperial College (who could borrow the apparatus), educationalists, and the scientific instrument trade which was very active in London until the 1960s.

The chemistry collections were very small in the early 1880s and they did not benefit from the amalgamation with the Patent Museum, so that there was a need to acquire a large number of objects. Most of these new acquisitions were new scientific apparatus lent or (more rarely) donated by scientific instrument makers and suppliers (Catalogue 1906). Various set-ups for gas analysis were particularly well represented, perhaps reflecting the importance of the gas industry and the steel industry in the late Victorian period. There were a few historical pieces but they were greatly outnumbered by chemical specimens. The emphasis was on copies or replicas rather than the 'original'. There was a copy of Cailletet's oxygen liquefaction apparatus, a replica of Moissan's apparatus for the isolation fluorine, and a Bunsen thermostat (for keeping gas samples at a constant temperature) purchased from the firm established by Bunsen's technician Peter Desaga. The tenor of the display was thus a mixture of the trade show or international exhibition and the 'chemical museum' which was often found in larger chemistry departments (such as in Manchester, Leeds, Columbia in New York, and Berlin) which consisted almost entirely of chemical samples. By 1906, the key objects on display also included the collection of the elements bequeathed by Prince Louis Lucien Bonaparte in 1891, the diffusion apparatus used by Thomas Graham, a balance constructed by John Fidler around 1800, the Tintometer developed by Joseph Lovibond, and a model of a school laboratory in Leiden which had been on display at the Special Loan Exhibition. The method of display was what would now be called 'visible storage': cases filled with a large number of objects and packed close together in rows. The captions appear to have been often long descriptions of the objects and the techniques they represent. There does not appear to have been any attempt at an overarching narrative or a unifying theme. It is difficult to tell how the gallery was organized in the absence of a gallery plan, but the 1906 catalogue hints at an arrangement by use ("general use", "demonstrations", "special researches", and "technical gas-analyses") rather than by sub-discipline.

In the Western Galleries, chemistry was presented as a comparatively new science which was developing rapidly; there was nothing connected with alchemy and no attempt to give chemistry a distant past. There was an emphasis on the use of intricate apparatus and the use of different methods of achieving the same aim, such as, for instance, fat extraction. The display of samples showed that chemistry was capable of making many different products. The overall effect is one of skill and complexity, neither showing the negative side of chemistry nor aggressively promoting the positive aspects. This display was for the visitor who knew or was learning chemistry and it showed him what the curators perceived as being relevant. The ordinary visitor would have been captivated by the sumptuousness of the brass and fine woods, the elegance of Hofmann's demonstration apparatus, the quirkiness of the Bunsen thermostat, and the mysteriousness of elements. But this would be an almost accidental by-product of the development of the gallery. I say 'almost' because the curators must have been aware of the public's interest in what they could appreciate but not really understand. While they would have accepted this interest, it was not the curators' aim to reach out the general public, but to engage with chemists and their students.

4.2 Chemistry in the East Block, 1925

The Bell Report of 1911 introduced a new line of interpretation which put a greater emphasis on history and the development of science and technology. It called for the "preservation of appliances which hold honoured place in the progress of science" (Follett 1978, p. 21). While the specialist, the technical visitor and the student were still important audiences, the Bell Report and the new Director of the Science Museum from 1920, Henry Lyons, put the ordinary visitor first (Follett 1978, p. 98). There was not enough time to develop this new approach in the Western Galleries before World War I, even if the curators had been keen on it and I suspect they were not. By the time the East Block became available in 1925, there was new blood in the form of Alexander Barclay and the changes in approach were evident in the new chemistry gallery on the third floor. While the approach and the target audience may have changed, the constituency remained much the same as it had been in the 1880s, namely leading chemists and chemical educators together with the scientific instrument trade. For instance, the proposed display scheme was checked by Professor Arthur Smithells (Z Archive, 1924).

The new gallery had a specific aim "to give a general idea of the chief branches of chemistry" (Board of Education 1931) and "the development of chemistry from earliest times" (Science Museum Guide 1937). But it was not typological in the manner of Pitt-Rivers: there was no attempt to show the 'evolution' of chemistry. With a new emphasis on history, it was clearly necessary to acquire more historic objects. However, this demand was not easy to fill and it was met by copies of prints of alchemical laboratories and replicas. Priestley's apparatus, Dalton's atomic diagrams, and De Chancourtois' telluric screw were all reproduced for this new gallery. Models were also popular, including stereochemical models and models of different proposals for the structure of benzene. More modern developments were represented by radioactive minerals and salts, electroanalytical apparatus, and apparatus for the study of explosives. The key objects in the new gallery tended to emphasize chemical achievement and British chemical achievement in particular, with artifacts such as Faraday's benzene, Crookes' thallium samples, and Tilden's synthetic rubber (Barclay 1927, p. 6). Synthetic dyes were also prominent, but curiously there were no artifacts relating to Perkin's synthesis of mauve. Oxygen liquefaction continued to be prominent with Hampson's liquefier joining the earlier Cailletet apparatus. Unusually for the period, there was considerable attention given to biochemistry, and there were exhibits which illustrated the formation of vitamins A and B and the preparation of insulin. For many visitors, especially the younger ones, the centerpiece of the 1926 gallery was the periodic table which was used to display the Bonaparte collection. The cases were the same ones that had been used in the Western Galleries and they were still packed close together, but there was perhaps somewhat greater use of graphics, mainly charts, to explain what was on display. The method of writing the captions had been revised, to make them more comprehensible to the general visitor, with a brief non-technical description in bold, followed by a longer technical explanation. By order of the director, no caption could now be longer than 400 words (Follett 1978, p. 101).

Chemistry was now displayed as a subject with a long history stretching back to the alchemists and Paracelsus and even as far back as the ancient Egyptians – the Science Museum was fascinated by the ancient Egyptians in this period. Notwithstanding this ancient lineage, it was now developing rapidly and chemists were making major discoveries not least in Britain. The 1926 gallery also emphasized the usefulness of chemistry, not only in making new things and helping medicine but also by giving us a better understanding of a wide range of processes. Again, we cannot be certain of the arrangement of the themes in the gallery in the absence of a floor plan, but the 1927 catalogue began with the "Evolution of Chemistry" up to the time of Thomas Graham, then divided the objects by sub-disciplines ("Theoretical and Physical Chemistry", "Inorganic Chemistry", and "Organic Chemistry") followed by "Laboratory Apparatus", all of which were further subdivided into topics such as "Classification of the Elements", "Natural Dyes", and "Filtration Apparatus" which may correspond to specific cases or sets of cases.

Aimed at the general visitor rather than the chemical educator, the gallery did now promote chemistry in a fairly understated manner. There was thus a shift from making the gallery appealing to the curators' constituency directly towards making it appealing to the general public in a manner that would meet the approval of this constituency. Given that academic and academically trained chemists formed the vast majority of this constituency, the gallery emphasized the intellectual respectability and skillfulness of chemistry. This motif was to be continually repeated in later chemistry galleries at the Science Museum up to the end of the twentieth century.

4.3 The 1977 Redisplay

Following the post-war reinstatement of chemistry in the 1950s in Gallery 66 on the third floor, chemistry was moved to Galleries 41-43 on the second floor of the East Block. The space devoted to chemistry increased from 8,300 square feet before 1939 to 11,900 square feet. This new set of galleries was partly funded (£ 30K) by the Association of British Chemical Manufacturers, half the money coming from ICI. Frank Greenaway was the moving force behind this redisplay of chemistry which was opened to the public in 1964 although he did not become Keeper until 1967.

I have chosen here to examine the subsequent redisplay of 1977 rather than the original display of 1964. This version survived for longer – 22 years against 13 years and I was personally familiar with it, being in charge of it for 8 years. I was also able to discuss this redisplay in detail with Robert Anderson whose personal recollections greatly assisted my analysis. The renovation of the galleries in 1977 was overseen by Frank Greenaway, but the then Assistant Keeper Robert Anderson was effectively in charge. In contrast to the 1964 gallery, there was no industrial funding, but the Royal Institute of Chemistry was celebrating the 100th anniversary of its predecessor, the Institute of Chemistry and it did play a role in the development of the gallery. Nonetheless the government through the Department of Environment's Property Services Agency was still the major sponsor of the gallery in terms of direct input into its construction and indirect financial support. The main constituency remained chemists and chemical educators, but the scientific instrument makers had almost entirely disappeared, a major change even since 1964. On the other hand, historians of chemistry had become an important element of the curators' constituency. It is fair to say that any chemistry gallery from this period onwards had to pass muster with the historians of chemistry as a group. The target audience was "The curious but uninformed 16 year old and above" and independent adults (Anderson 2005).

The goal of the redisplay was to show recent changes in chemistry but portray its history as well, with an emphasis on analysis, structure determination, and archaeological chemistry. The curators strove to "broaden out the chronological and thematic coverage beyond that previously attempted" (Anderson 2006). The development of the new displays was strongly influenced by Anderson's close links with the chemistry department at Oxford and the influence of Professor Edward Hall who had set up an archaeological research laboratory at Oxford. Objects acquired from Oxford included a pioneering infrared spectrometer built by Harold Thompson, Leslie Sutton's electron diffraction apparatus, and the large NMR magnet used by Rex Richards. Objects associated with the early development of gas chromatography including Archer Martin's gas density balance, Tony James's gas chromatograph, and an electron capture detector made by James Lovelock were also obtained. Other important acquisitions were associated with X-ray crystallography: the metal plates used in James Watson and Francis Crick's DNA model, Kendrew and Perutz's model of myoglobin (the so-called 'forest of rods') and Kathleen Lonsdale's apparatus and models. By contrast, the more historical sections of the gallery were shaped by Anderson's work on the Playfair Collection at the Royal Scottish Museum and his interest in alembics, as evidenced by his acquisition of a medieval Islamic alembic at an auction. Some of Joseph Black's glassware was borrowed from the Royal Scottish Museum and there was a panel about Edinburgh's 'Mortar Willie', an eighteenth-century grinder called William Wilson.

The cases were modern aluminum showcases with low-level internal illumination. They were less close-packed than in the 1920s. The displays combined objects with illustrations and original documents and the captions were similar to the two-level captions in the 1926 gallery. The technical part was detailed, and with more historical information than the earlier captions which made them sometimes rather long. The three galleries all had a different theme. Gallery 41 which linked the other two galleries was about the "Evolution of Chemistry" to borrow the phrase used in the 1927 catalogue. It began with a small case about alchemy and went via gas chemistry and Thomas Graham to Ramsay on one side, and dealt with great British chemists (Dalton, Davy, Faraday, and Wollaston) on the other side. Gallery 42 was very much about the practical applications of chemistry, with displays of heating apparatus, hydrometers, oil testing apparatus, and, from more recent times, gas chromatography to give some prominent examples. A chronological sequence of chemical balances were displayed – with the scholarly assistance of Peta Buchanan – to illustrate historical continuity. One side of this gallery was dominated by four reproduction laboratories: assaying in the fifteenth century, the Government Chemist's Laboratory from around 1897, a typical laboratory of the 1960s (the former "Modern Laboratory" of the 1964 gallery), and a modern archaeological research laboratory. By contrast Gallery 43 was rather about academic chemistry, with a prevailing theme of the determination of the composition and structure of molecules by various means; for example, combustion analysis, UV spectroscopy, X-ray crystallography, NMR, and electron diffraction. The latest version of the periodic table – extended to cover all the non-radioactive elements with the assistance of William Griffith of Imperial College – stood at the corner between Gallery 41 and Gallery 43 until it was dismantled in 1986.

The 1977 redisplay presented an image of chemistry which had much in common with its predecessors, obviously there was much overlap with the 1964 gallery as it was only a redisplay of those galleries – a redisplay which was furthermore produced under physical and financial constraints – but also with the 1925 displays in Gallery 66. Chemistry was presented as a science with a long history of practical applications, stemming back to the ancient Egyptians, which had developed rapidly during the twentieth century. It showed that British chemists had made a major contribution to its development, especially since the early eighteenth century. The gallery demonstrated the value of chemistry for our growing understanding of life's mechanisms, especially by the determination of increasingly complex chemical and biochemical structures. It used analytical apparatus and chemical balances to illustrate the importance of precise measurement. The overall impression was that the practice of chemistry required intricate skills from early nineteenth-century blowpipes to the latest electron diffraction. It thus promoted chemistry both as an intellectual challenge and a highly skilled craft rather than concentrating on the benefits of chemistry to the public at large – this task was undertaken, insofar as it was addressed, by the neighboring industrial chemistry gallery.

4.4 'Chemistry of Everyday Life', 1999

In 1999, the three Chemistry Galleries (Galleries 41-43) were cleared and replaced by a new Chemistry Gallery on the eastern side of Gallery 41. This was a much smaller gallery, with only 13% of the original space. The gallery was developed by Senior Curator Peter Morris. There was no direct sponsorship for this gallery but it was indirectly sponsored by the Analytical Division of the Royal Society of Chemistry (RSC) as it provided a setting for three interactives which had been developed by the RSC in collaboration with the museum. The space was also the home for two large molecular models, including the famous 'forest of rods' model of myoglobin, that had come from the Laboratory of Molecular Biology in Cambridge which was another indirect influence on the gallery. The constituency, as before, was mainly leading chemists and biochemists, and historians of chemistry. Part of the new gallery had been a temporary exhibition ('New for Old') a year earlier based on a close collaboration with scientific instrument suppliers. The collaboration continued while the gallery was under development, so this sector was again part of the constituency. In addition, however, the needs of the gallery's audience were taken into account using the results of visitor surveys carried out by the museum's audience research unit.

The title of the gallery was 'The Chemistry of Everyday Life' and its goal was to show the contribution of chemistry to everyday life, specifically through quality control, and to our understanding the biochemistry of life. It also aimed to illustrate how chemistry, especially analysis and organic chemistry, had developed since 1800. The display was designed to be a series of contrasts, between pure and applied chemistry, between the chemical apparatus of the late nineteenth century and modern digital chemical equipment, and between the scientific and the personal life of chemists, for instance, Charles Friedel's sword and Marcelin Berthelot's fez. The target audience was family groups with children over 14, independent adults, university and college students, not very different from the audience for the 1977 redisplay.

The new acquisitions for the gallery were mainly modern examples of chemical equipment, such as a pencil-sized pH meter, a digital polarimeter, and a FTIR spectrometer. Some artifacts were very similar to Victorian predecessors in their basic operation, but the modern versions looked different, for example, the Tintometer or the Pensky-Marten flashpoint apparatus. Another key acquisition was the donation of an early NMR magnet by Jack Powles which had the virtue of being small enough to go into the display case. The key objects in the gallery were a combination of molecular models – ranging from Dalton's wooden atoms and an early glyptic model kit to Hodgkin's model of insulin and the 'forest of rods' – and classic scientific instruments including the Beckman Model G pH meter, the Beckman DU ultraviolet spectrometer, and the Perkin-Elmer Model 21 infrared spectrophotometer. I also made a point of displaying a number of historic chemicals including alkaloids isolated by Pelletier and Caventou, fatty acids prepared by Chevreul, and chemicals synthesized by Wurtz, Friedel, and Grignard. The gallery had one long wall case and for a while it had a large freestanding case which housed the large molecular models. Originally it also had three freestanding interactives, which were the first interactives in a pure chemistry gallery at the Science Museum, although there had been interactives in the earlier Industrial Chemistry Galleries. Subsequently, they were moved to make way for a temporary exhibition and were not replaced, partly because they had started to become faulty even after only a year. Information panels replaced the traditional captions and the objects had only very brief identifying labels. It was originally intended to supply additional information about the artifacts and the displayed chemists on computer screens outside the cases, but in the end the necessary funds were not available.

The image of chemistry presented in this gallery is a science which contributes to everyday life in unexpected ways, through quality control and analysis rather than wonderful new products. It also shows the ability of chemists to decode the structure of huge molecules such as myoglobin and the enduring significance and usefulness of molecular models. The gallery illustrates the enormous changes in chemistry over the last two centuries but also reveals that many techniques have remained the same, but in a new casing and with the addition of electronics and then computers, either alongside the instrument or within it as a microchip. This gallery, probably the last of its kind at the Science Museum, thus stands in a long tradition of showing the importance of chemistry in understated terms of its basic utility rather than through spectacular achievements or amazing products. In historical terms, the 1999 gallery reverts to the late Victorian presentation of chemistry as a comparatively recent science rather than one with an ancient lineage. This was partly a result of a severe lack of space but also stems from recent historiography which portrays chemistry as a largely nineteenth-century creation which sought legitimacy by claiming an ancestry from alchemy, metallurgy, and natural philosophy.

5. Chemistry in the Deutsches Museum

It would be desirable, and indeed logical, to compare the image of chemistry presented by the Science Museum with leading science and technology museums in other countries. In practice, however, it is only possible to make a proper comparison with the Deutsches Museum in Munich. This is partly a matter of available sources, I only have access to an adequate number of guides for the period from 1930 to the present in the case of the Deutsches Museum, but also a reflection of the amount of space devoted to chemistry in other major museums. The Smithsonian only gave over a small amount of its exhibition space to chemistry, as opposed to materials, until the opening of 'Science in American Life' in April 1994. The Conservatoire national des arts et métiers in Paris has the famous reconstruction of Lavoisier's laboratory and its associated artifacts, but little else connected with chemistry.

According to Elisabeth Vaupel, the format of the pure chemistry galleries on the first floor of the Deutsches Museum was developed for the opening of the museum in 1906 by three leading chemists, Hans Bunte, Walther Nernst, and, above all, Wilhelm Ostwald, who had a strong interest in the history (and philosophy) of chemistry (Vaupel 2003). As well as drawing on their own experience as teachers of chemistry, the three professors drew on the World Fairs for inspiration. Certainly their schema was very different from the Science Museum's Western Galleries. The chemistry galleries were divided into three roughly equal parts: the history and development of chemistry, the contemporary science, and finally what we would now call an interactive section where visitors could carry out their own experiments. While the Science Museum did adopt a mixture of history and contemporary chemistry in the 1920s, there was certainly no interactive elements at all until 1999, and even then only briefly. Underpinning this approach, with its expensive use of chemicals and other materials in the interactives, was massive financial support from the German chemical industry, which was at its peak in the early years of the twentieth century. The scale and the continuity of this support are in stark contrast to the Science Museum where only one set of pure chemistry galleries (1964) has received any significant financial support from industry. With the obvious exception of the content of the contemporary chemistry section, the basic plan drawn up by Bunte, Nernst, and Ostwald has remained largely unchanged up to the present day (Deutsches Museum Guides 1930, 1957, 1968, 1988, and 2000). Industrial chemistry was originally an integral part of the chemistry gallery, as it was at the Science Museum between 1912 and 1939, but a chemical technology gallery was opened on the second floor in 1965, which displayed the chemistry of everyday life as well as process engineering and industrial processes (Rehn 2006). This gallery was replaced in 1979 by a gallery on the first floor which dealt with industrial chemistry with an emphasis on chemical products, rather than processes, and the use of chemistry in medicine (Deutsches Museum Guide 1988, pp. 173-179). This in turn was closed in 1998 and replaced by a gallery on pharmacy in 2000.

Three reconstructed laboratories have always been the mainstay of the historical section of the chemistry gallery at the Deutsches Museum. The alchemical laboratory (based largely on Agricola) is linked to the development of distillation, herbs, and iatrochemistry. The Science Museum introduced a similar laboratory based on Agricola in 1964, but was careful to describe it as an assaying laboratory (not alchemical, a distinction lost on nearly all the visitors) and placed it within the context of metallurgical analysis by blowpipes and balances. This is followed by a "laboratory of the eighteenth century" which according to the 1930 guide contained a range of apparatus from Boyle's period through Priestley and Cavendish to Lavoisier. It is interesting that no attempt was made to place this laboratory within the context of German chemistry in this period, for instance, by Stahl, Wiegleb, and Gren. All of this leads up to the central exhibit, Liebig's laboratory. But this is the Liebig of the Munich period rather than Giessen, which is not surprising given the museum's location. There never has been a parallel at the Science Museum to Liebig's laboratory or to Lavoisier's laboratory in the Conservatoire. The equivalent period in the 1964 gallery, the first gallery to have reconstructed laboratories (previously the museum had used small dioramas to show laboratories), was the Government's Chemist's laboratory which puts the emphasis on public service and utility rather than greatness. The space devoted to contemporary chemistry is simply a series of exhibits relating to the structure of matter, including the periodic table, and modern chemical apparatus for analysis and synthesis as there were "so many subsections in modern chemistry, it was impossible to show a typical modern laboratory in one room" (Deutsches Museum Guidebook 1930, p. 48). After World War II, this section was described in the guidebook as a "modern laboratory", but I suspect this was more a shift of presentation in the guidebook than any change on the museum floor (Deutsches Museum Guide, 1957, p. 32). The numerous interactives are embedded within the display of modern chemistry. They are a striking feature of the Deutsches Museum's presentation of chemistry and are only possible because of the chemical industry's financial support. It is difficult to assess how they affect the visitors' image of chemistry. From personal observation, some visitors find them interesting but others are alienated by the technical complexities. My own view is that in trying to make chemistry more accessible many of the interactives actually make chemistry appear incomprehensible 'magic in a box'.

What is the image of chemistry portrayed by the Deutsches Museum's galleries? It has always emphasized the long history of chemistry, although not as far back as the Science Museum's ancient Egyptians. The development of chemistry is largely seen through its intellectual development and fundamental principles. In contrast to the Science Museum, there appears to be less emphasis on specific discoveries, but this is perhaps a matter of emphasis rather than a significant difference. In the Deutsches Museum's presentation, chemistry has developed rapidly but mainly in the twentieth century. There is a curious gap in the late nineteenth century, which is very evident in the 1930 guide. The Deutsches Museum emphasizes the numerous sub-divisions of modern chemistry instead of its many ways of doing things, perhaps a Germanic concern with structure rather than action. While the Science Museum, at least in the pure chemistry galleries, has presented chemistry as the useful science across a broad front, the Deutsches Museum has focused on its role within the chemical industry, perhaps inevitably so given its main source of funding. The 1930 gallery had a 'hall of honor', a parallel to the museum's main *Ehrensaal* (now translated as the 'Hall of Fame'), but this was dedicated to "famous founders of the German chemical industry" not famous academic chemists. Both the Science Museum and the Deutsches Museum have consistently highlighted the contribution of chemistry to medicine and physiology, although the Germans in the 1930s seemed curiously interested in the relationship between the energy content and the cost of food, perhaps a reflection of the cost of food in Germany at the time.

Given the strength of German chemistry in 1906, and for some time afterwards, the chemistry galleries at the Deutsches Museum were surprisingly international even in the (early) 1930s. The detailed description of the chemistry galleries in the 1930 guidebook mentions six German chemists and alchemists (Agricola, Ercker, Liebig, Mitscherlich, Bunsen, Wöhler), three British chemists (Boyle, Priestley, Cavendish), two Swedish chemists (Scheele, Berzelius) and a French chemist (Lavoisier). It is difficult to make a direct comparison with the Science Museum, but there was definitely a strong bias towards British chemists until the 1999 gallery gave over some of its limited space to French chemists. In the 1977 redisplay, there were 19 cases in the historical display in Gallery 41 devoted to British chemists and only the equivalent of 2 cases to foreign chemists (Lavoisier, van Helmont, Kipp, and Döbereiner).

6. Conclusions

The most striking feature of this study of chemistry in museums has been the persistence of a particular style of presenting chemistry in a given museum during the twentieth century. The Science Museum did shift ground, especially in its presentation of historical chemistry, in the 1920s but has remained faithful to the model adopted in 1923 for the last eighty years. The basic format of the chemistry displays at the Deutsches Museum has been unchanged since it opened in 1906. The Conservatoire has always concentrated on Lavoisier. The Smithsonian (in its current guise as the National Museum of American History) is the exception. Its 'Science in American Life' gallery is very different from earlier presentation of chemistry – even the focus of the reconstructed laboratory switched from Priestley to Remsen – and this is currently the only chemistry gallery which draws extensively on the modern historiography of science and technology. It has been criticized for presenting too negative a view of science but it also stands in a broad tradition of being fairly neutral in its support of chemistry and science. It may be more quizzical about the benefits of science than its counterparts elsewhere, but none of the leading chemistry galleries have promoted chemistry in the extravagant manner of many popular books on chemistry, the archetype of the latter of course being A. Cressy Morrison's *Man in a Chemical World* (1937). But if all the chemistry galleries have been quietly understated in their support of chemistry, there are differences between them. The Science Museum (along with the Conservatoire and the Smithsonian) has always been immensely dependent on state funding and thus it has always highlighted on the public value of chemistry (medicine and quality control) and the use of chemistry by the state (notably the Laboratory of the Government Chemist). The Deutsches Museum on the other hand, although formally administered by the State of Bavaria, has always been associated, as far as chemistry is concerned, with the German chemical industry. Its galleries have thus concentrated on the products of the industry, including scents in the pre-World War II period, rather than the use of chemistry as a service science.

While these institutional contexts are important, I would argue that the chemistry galleries at the Science Museum, and probably elsewhere, have hitherto been shaped not so much by curators (although they decide the exact form of the displays), the overseers of the museum (the Director, Advisory Council, Board of Trustees) or less still, by visitors, but by an external constituency that curators have sought to please. The composition of this group remained fairly constant during the twentieth century. They comprised leading academic chemists, if not usually Nobel Laureates like Nernst and Ostwald, chemical educationalists, and state-employed chemists. Chemical industrialists have generally not had much influence on the pure chemistry galleries and popularizers of science have had even less impact. As they have grown in number and professional status, historians of chemistry have become members of constituency but generally have had less influence than chemists. This is partly because the curators have become historians of chemistry themselves and partly because the history of instruments has been very much a minority interest in the history of chemistry. To some extent the historians have hitherto had a veto rather than a direct influence. Up to now a new gallery had to be acceptable to them, *i.e.* avoid any major errors or excessive Whiggism, rather than positively appeal to them or incorporate the latest historiography.

The galleries at the Science Museum, and as far as I can tell at the Deutsches Museum, have portrayed chemistry as a science which has a long history, with particular reference to the breadth and variety of chemistry. This image has been presented in a carefully crafted and exquisitely balanced – almost low-key – manner emphasizing skilful practice rather than controversy. The image of chemistry presented in this way has been positive – largely chemistry as useful – without making any extravagant claims for chemistry or chemists. On the other hand, criticism has also been muted, indeed almost invisible. In keeping with the neutral stance of the civil service, emotion and all matters touching on politics or religion have hitherto been strenuously avoided.

Has the Science Museum changed or at least influenced people's perception of chemistry? Has the low-key approach been successful where boosterism has failed? The focus of this chapter has been on the image of chemistry presented by museums from within. A paper on the impact of museum galleries on the public perception of chemistry would require a completely different methodology and additional sources of information, such as visitor surveys, public opinion polls, and the like. Furthermore this information would be mostly lacking for the interwar period when museums may have had their greatest impact. Nonetheless it is possible to make a few generalizations. Although millions of people visit science museums, this activity is still a minority activity. According to a Eurobarometer survey in 2002-3, only 11% of respondents in the old EU of 15 countries had visited science and technology museums in the previous year and the figure for the new members of the EU was even lower (Gallup 2003). Furthermore, the media is in a far stronger position to shape people's perception of chemistry than museums. People are constantly bombarded by the media through newspapers, radio, television, and increasingly via the Internet, whereas a museum visit will last only a few hours at most. On the basis of the experience of Oliver Sacks and the late John Stock, I infer – and in the absence of hard evidence, it can only be a surmise – that traditional chemistry galleries were inspirational in the 'chemistry-set era' from 1920s to early 1960s when suitably enthused visitors could go home and develop their new-found interest by producing exciting bangs and smells in the garden shed (Sacks 2001, Stock 2004). I also strongly suspect that the galleries appealed mainly to boys rather than girls, and to children aged 10-14 rather than older teenagers. It is impossible to even guess how many young visitors were stimulated to take an interest in chemistry in this way and how long their enthusiasm survived on average. Given that we know the profound effect it had on some visitors, the results for chemistry – in terms of an improved image and recruitment to the profession – must have been generally positive if inevitably limited in terms of the number of people thus influenced.

Science and technology museums are going through a period of great change. Interactivity is now central to the museum visit and this works against chemistry which is not easy to turn into attractive interactives de-

spite the Deutsches Museum's best efforts. As the practice of science becomes increasingly interdisciplinary and the teaching of science becomes
largely the teaching of general science at least in Britain, the single-
discipline gallery has become outmoded. The first gallery in a major science museum to completely integrate different scientific disciplines was
the 'Science in American Life' gallery at the National Museum of
American History which opened in 1994. This is not wholly surprisingly
as the galleries at the Washington museum were always multi-disciplinary if not interdisciplinary (Smithsonian Guide 1976). The Science
Museum's multidisciplinary science gallery is projected to open in 2009,
the museum's centenary year. This gallery will be built around the
themes of belief, power, and trust, and will cover astronomy, mathematics, physics, geophysics, and biomedicine as well as chemistry. A particular feature of this gallery will be its coverage of non-western science.
The goal of this gallery is to promote scientific citizenship by illustrating
the relationships which have existed and currently exist between science
and its publics and within science. The target audience will have a significantly lower age limit than the chemistry galleries considered here, as
the new gallery is aimed at school groups aged 10 and above, parents
with children aged 10 and above, and independent adults. Chemistry will
be well represented in the science gallery but inevitably its footprint in
the Science Museum will be much smaller than in the period when there
were three chemistry galleries (1964-1999). The Deutsches Museum is
also transforming the way it presents chemistry with the aim of opening a
new chemistry gallery in 2008. One way or another, museum curators
will continue to present chemistry in new multi-disciplinary and histo-
riographically sophisticated contexts which will draw on the best museological traditions while also developing new ways of encouraging visitors to take science seriously.

Acknowledgements

I wish to acknowledge the enormous debt I owe to John Liffen, the
curator of telecommunications at the Science Museum, who is a fount of
knowledge about all aspects of the museum's history. I am also very
grateful to my predecessors at the Science Museum, Dr. Robert

Anderson and Dr. Derek Robinson for their recollections and comments, and to my colleagues Dr. Robert Bud and Dr. Tim Boon for their feedback. I would also like to thank Dr. Susanne Rehn for her remarks on the section about the Deutsches Museum. Of course, all mistakes that remain are wholly my own.

References

All the non-archival sources cited here, except the private communications and the online document, are available at the Science Museum Library. The unpublished Annual Reports of the Science Museum and much of the published Science Museum material are kept in the semi-rare book room. In addition to these sources, I also had access to the chemistry curator's collection of gallery photographs and a set of labels with floor plans for the 1977 Gallery.

Anderson, R.G.W.: 2005, private communication, 11 August.

Anderson, R.G.W.: 2006, private communication, 2 February.

Barclay, A.: 1927, *Catalogue of the Collections in The Science Museum, South Kensington, with Descriptive Notes and Illustrations. Chemistry*, His Majesty's Stationery Office, London.

Board of Education: 1909, *Reports for the Year 1908 on The Geological Survey, The Geological Museum in Jermyn Street, The Science Museum at South Kensington and the Work of The Solar Physics Committee*, His Majesty's Stationery Office, London, pp. 26 and 29.

Board of Education: 1924a, *Report for the Years 1921 and 1922 on The Science Museum*, His Majesty's Stationery Office, London, p. 15.

Board of Education: 1924b, *Report for the Year 1923 on The Science Museum*, His Majesty's Stationery Office, London, pp. 6, 15.

Board of Education: 1926, *Report for the Year 1925 on The Science Museum*, His Majesty's Stationery Office, London, p. 21.

Board of Education: 1931, *Report of the Advisory Council of The Science Museum for the Year 1930*, His Majesty's Stationery Office, London, p. 31.

Catalogue: 1906: *Catalogue of the Science Collections for Teaching and Research in the Victoria and Albert Museum. Part III. Chemistry*, His Majesty's Stationery Office, London.

Deutsches Museum Guide: 1930, *Deutsches Museum von Meisterwerken der Naturwissenschaft und Technik, Munich, Brief Guide Official Edition*, Deutsches Museum, Munich, pp. 47-50.

Deutsches Museum Guide: 1957, *Deutsches Museum of Masterpieces of Natural Science and Technology, Munich, Short Guide Through the Collections,* 1st edn., Deutsches Museum, Munich, pp. 31-33.

Deutsches Museum Guide: 1968, *Deutsches Museum of Masterpieces of Natural Science and Technology, Munich, Illustrated Guide Through the Collections,* 5th edn., Deutsches Museum, Munich, pp. 59-61.

Deutsches Museum Guide: 1988, *Deutsches Museum Guide through the Collections,* Deutsches Museum, Munich, pp. 164-172.

Deutsches Museum Guide: 2000, *Guide to the Museum,* 2nd rev. edn., Deutsches Museum, Munich, pp. 72-75.

Follett, D.: 1978, *The Rise of the Science Museum under Henry Lyons,* Science Museum, London.

Gallup: 2003: *Candidate Countries: Eurobarometer: Public Opinion in the Countries Applying for European Union Membership. CC-EB 2002.3 on Science & Technology.* The Gallup Organisation, Hungary. [http://europa.eu.int/comm/public_opinion/archives/cceb/2002/2002.3_science_technology.pdf, accessed on 24 January 2005].

Hobhouse, H.: 2002, *The Crystal Palace and the Great Exhibition: Science, Art and Productive Industry: a History of the Royal Commission for the Exhibition of 1851,* Athlone, London.

Macdonald, S.: 2002, *Behind the Scenes at the Science Museum,* Berg, Oxford.

Morrison, A.C.: 1937, *Man in a Chemical World: The Service of Chemical Industry,* Scribner's Sons, New York.

Rehn, S.: 2006, private communication, 25 January (citing the Deutsches Museum's *Jahresberichte).*

Sacks, O.: 2001, *Uncle Tungsten: Memories of a Chemical Childhood,* Picador, London.

Science Museum: 1968, "Report of the Science Museum for the Year 1967" (mimeographed).

Science Museum: 1970, "Report of the Science Museum for the Year 1969" (mimeographed).

Science Museum Guide: 1937, *Science Museum. Outline Guide to the Exhibits,* His Majesty's Stationery Office, London, p. 30.

Science Museum Guide: 1952, *Science Museum. Outline Guide to the Exhibits,* His Majesty's Stationery Office, London.

Science Museum Guide: 1953, *Science Museum. Outline Guide to the Exhibits,* His Majesty's Stationery Office, London.

Science Museum Guide: 1957, *Science Museum. Outline Guide to the Exhibits,* His Majesty's Stationery Office, London.

Smithsonian Guide: 1976, *Official Guide to the Smithsonian,* CBS Publications, pp. 29-31.

Special Loan Catalogue: 1876, *Catalogue of the Special Loan Collection of Scientific Apparatus at the South Kensington Museum, MDCCCLXXVI,* 3rd edn., Her Majesty's Stationery Office, London.

Stock, J.: 2004, 'Pilgrim's Progress: The London Science Museum: A Chemical Reminiscence', *Chemical Heritage,* 22 (3), 10-11, 38-9.

Vaupel, E.: 2003, 'Scientific chemistry', in: W.P. Fehlhammer (ed.) *Deutsches Museum: Ingenious Inventions and Masterpieces of Science and Technology*, Prestel, Munich, p. 132.

Who Was Who: 1991, *Who Was Who*, vol. VIII, Black, London, p. 39.

Z Archive: 1924, Notes by the Director [H. J. Lyons] and by Alexander Barclay, both dated 11 March in Scheme for development file ED 79/141 "Pure chemistry, 1923-1955".

CHAPTER 12

ON THE SELF-IMAGE OF CHEMISTS, 1950-2000

Pierre Laszlo

15 Juniper Lane, Pinehurst NC 28374, USA (October 15-March 15);
"Cloud's Rest", Prades, F-12320 Sénergues, France (March 15-October 15);
pierre@pierrelaszlo.net

The field of chemistry is highly diverse. Yet, the aggregate picture of chemists, according to this study, shows them to constitute a highly homogeneous and even gregarious group, in terms of their self-image. They see themselves as creative, as benefactors of humankind, and as craftsmen upholding a tradition of intelligent hands and preserving, even in the time of Big Science, a relatively low-tech profile. The stereotypical public image as the sorcerer's apprentices who befoul the environment and who manufacture chemical weapons is way off target. Chemists find it a caricature, it only reinforces the good conscience within the chemical community. Other conservative forces are the common language of structural formulas, a widespread phobia about mathematics, and the very length of the apprenticeship to be served. Conversely, between the mid-twentieth century and the advent of the twenty-first century, chemists displayed an impressive adaptability in the face of swift changes, regarding the tools of the trade – which the NMR Revolution had contributed to upgrade –, the funding of their activity at a much higher level, the oil crises, and the Biological Turn that affected them during that period.

1. Introduction

Why should one attempt to characterize the self-image of a group of scientists, during a relatively recent period? And how to go about it? A tough assignment.

The answer to the former surely has to involve the relationship between the group's production of new knowledge (in the form of publications, patents, and textbooks for students) and the prevailing culture: I cannot do better to define this otherwise vague and catch-all entity than to refer to anthropological practice. I adopt a by now classic characterization:

> (The ethnographer figures out what the devil natives are up to) by searching out and analysing the symbolic forms – words, images, institutions, behaviors – in terms of which, in each place, people actually represented themselves to themselves and to one another. [Geertz 1983]

As to the second question, given the difficulty of the task, my methodology will be eclectic. My first tool for gaining a glimpse at the self-image of chemists takes advantage of the strong iconic dimension of chemical language. Modes of representation may somehow provide insight into their self-representations too. My second tool is to focus on landmark achievements, those which the chemical community regards as highly significant, as another step towards this elusive goal, the definition of a collective self-image. The third, obviously related tool is the consideration of eminent chemists. These women and men, selected for admiration by their peers, stand for something. A fourth tool is topographic: what is, at a given time, the territory of the chemist? What does it include? Even more important, what does it exclude? Blind spots, delayed recognition of achievements can thus be highly significant. The fifth and last tool, all too obvious, is a look at the vogues and fads: when a large number of chemists rush towards the same goals, this involves individual self-interest, which in turn reflects the image individuals hold of themselves, an image both furthered and reinforced by the group.

I shall resort to periodization, to subdivisions into decades.[1] It has the advantage of simplicity, and the further merit of being neither too coarse nor too fine-grained.

---

[1] The periodization I suggest is of course debatable. For instance, it has been proposed to decompose the activity in chemical science during the last 25 years along the categories of determination of protein structures; genetic engineering's debut; molecular mass production (combinatorial chemistry); microscopes, polymers, and lasers; light, sound, and atmosphere (sonochemistry & atmospheric chemistry); buckyballs and beyond (Gwynne 2001).

The 1950s saw the birth of the research university in the USA, together with that country seizing the lead in world chemistry, both academic and industrial. This was the time of birth and of explosive development of the nuclear magnetic resonance tool (Becker 1996). This was also the period when chemistry opened itself to molecular biology. Also in the 50s, the chemical science restructured itself, focusing on bonding and structure rather than on mere description and cataloguing of chemicals and their characteristic properties and reactions, as had prevailed since Lavoisier's time.

The rethinking of the science went on during the 1960s. This was a time for questioning previously held dogmas, such as the rules governing valence, rudely pushed aside with the discovery of noble gas compounds. But there were other upsets too, to such an extent that one may wish to call the 60s the 'Age of Hubris':[2] biological chimeras, spontaneous generation, high-temperature superconductivity, and the dissolution of potassium permanganate in benzene are some of the examples of such a mental attitude, calling for disrespect for tradition. The 60s were noteworthy also for a major breakthrough, the Woodward-Hoffmann rules governing electrocyclic reactions (Woodward & Hoffmann 1971). And a social phenomenon, actually the converse of a mass movement, should not be forgotten: when in 1968 the university came under attack, worldwide, from students, from the media and from the local communities, and even from its faculties, chemists as a whole camped within their ivory tower, oblivious of outside disruptions.[3]

The 1970s were the time of the first oil crisis. The petrochemical industry suffered from the consequences. As a profession, chemists worked on developing alternative energy sources. Photochemistry, with goals such as catalyzed photocleavage of water providing fuel for a hydrogen economy, came to the fore. There were many other projects, such as gasification of coal, or attempts at direct functionalization of

---

[2] The culmination of which came about later with the synthesis of palytoxin in 1989 by Y. Kishi's team at Harvard, a monument to the Promethean ability of chemists.

[3] Only negative evidence can be adduced in support of this assertion. For instance, the series of autobiographies that Jeffrey Seeman edited for the American Chemical Society does not include, to my recollection, evidence of such concern on the part of the academic leaders of the profession who were authors.

natural gas, which were pushed forward at an impressive pace. The search for substitutes of oil went hand in hand with a significant rise in environmental consciousness among chemists – given especially some of the industrial spills during that period, which the media exploited relentlessly against the chemical profession as a whole, not only against the chemical industry.

During the 1980s, chemists as a group were willing participants in a *fuite en avant*, converts to a mystique of growth, even of exponential growth. This was a time for proliferation of newly made compounds, as if their preparation were synonymous with innovation. This was the time of the rise of combinatorial chemistry (Breslow 1997, Borman 1998), whose products in the tens and hundreds of thousands were screened for lead molecules by laboratories in pharmacology and in materials science. This was also the time of the preparation of organometallics in large numbers, vastly encouraged by the thrust from multinuclear NMR.[4]

The 1990s saw the spawning of nanoscience and nanotechnology, building on some major advances, such as the discovery of carbon nanotubes, following up on the serendipitous finding of buckminsterfullerenes (Baggott 1994). While chemists redirected themselves into these novel areas, they also had to come to grips with chemophobia on the part of the public.

2. Academic and Industrial Chemistry

Now that I have sketched in these few bold strokes what may have characterized those five successive decades, what exactly is the task at hand?

There is considerable evidence for the strong group identity of chemists. Chemistry has the distinguishing feature of being both a science and an industry. It is important to understand their solidarity. Even at the time of strong media presence by industrial accidents (Seveso in 1976), episodes of criminal negligence (Love Canal, pollution of the Rhine), or catastrophes (Bhopal), academic chemists, even though they felt victimized

---

[4] The field started being populated substantially only after the discovery of ferrocene (Laszlo & Hoffmann 2000, Rich 2004).

by the finger-pointing of public opinion, would not turn against their industrial colleagues.

Academic chemistry and industry share an umbilical cord. Universities train chemists for an industrial career. In return, the chemical industry funds some academic training (fellowships) and research (grants). Many professors of chemistry serve as occasional industrial consultants, receiving a handsome fee for their expert advice. Moreover, it is not infrequent for chemical careers to be hybrids, with scientists moving from an academic institution to an industrial environment, or vice versa.

Examples which come to mind are those of Philip E. Eaton, who owed his interest in cage molecules to industrial work on chlorinated pesticides, which led him to the epochal synthesis of cubane in 1964 (Traynham 1997); of Fred McLafferty and George Olah, who both worked for a time in a laboratory of Dow Chemical; of Richard E. Smalley, an industrial chemist before he enrolled as a graduate student at Princeton (Smalley 1996); of Earl Muetterties, who left the Experimental Station at DuPont in Wilmington for a professorship at the University of California; of Howard E. Simmons who, when heading central research also at DuPont, turned down the offer of a professorship at Harvard (Bohning 1993, Roberts & Collette 1999); and so on.

A strong group spirit extends across the chemical board, even at the cost of seemingly exonerating managers of industrial plants from grievous oversights or mistakes – in spite of their belonging to a social group distinct from that of laboratory chemists, whether academic or industrial. Put in another way: do chemists suffer from collective guilt? From none, is the answer.

However, granted that chemists share a strong group identity, what does it consist of, and how did it evolve during the second half of the twentieth century? I shall now proceed to build answers to those queries.

3.   The 1950s: Rise of the Research University and Chemistry

The 1950s saw the rise of the research university. The U.S. was its breeding ground: *Science, the Endless Frontier*, the report to the President by Vannevar Bush (1945) had urged such support by the federal government, to which chemist James B. Conant, then president of Harvard

University and a close friend of V. Bush, was no stranger. The main feature was funding the advancement of science with public money, on a much-expanded basis (Weaver 1961).[5] Chemistry benefited from it, in like manner as the other hard sciences.

In disciplinary terms, physics was the leader in this novel way of conducting scientific research, which reflected the predominant part physicists had played during World War II (Kevles 1987).[6] Moreover, the close association of physicists with the military during the war translated into mission-oriented research, a concept which trickled down from physics to chemistry. As a rule, physicists were funded more handsomely than chemists. The latter became envious and compared themselves often to physicists (Lind 1952, Anon 1958).

After Sputnik, one saw a massive increase in the popularity of science (Weinberg 1955) and in the numbers of young scientists. Research became paradigmatic and entered the undergraduate curriculum, even in liberal arts colleges (Kraus 1950, College of Wooster 1959). The way in which chemists did their work also changed. Electronic instrumentation came into the laboratory. Benches which in previous times, for centuries indeed, had been furnished almost exclusively with glassware, started receiving spectrometers (UV-visible, infrared) and chromatographs. Another influence from both physics and the military was the standardization of parts, making for easier replacement. To mention but two examples, Heathkit electronic components started being assembled, by chemists (Roberts 1990) or electronic technicians, in both academic and industrial departments; likewise Bantamware provided chemists with easily assembled glassware, for running reactions reliably on a much smaller scale than had been the norm.

Thus, physics had a deep-seated influence on chemistry. It triggered a mutation from a *craft*, with manual skills learned during an apprenticeship, to a manifold of standardized *procedures*, each of which made of steps, recorded in written instructions, which could then be followed similar to a pilot using a flying manual and a checklist. Chemistry, as a

---

[5] A development of which a few lone voices warned (Warner 1957).
[6] Whereas World War I had been termed 'The Chemists' War' (Kevles 1972), World War II was 'The Physicists' War', witness atom bombs, radar, sonar, *etc.* (Kevles 1987).

discipline, lost a measure of autonomy; it became more of a physical science, owing many of its tools ('physical methods') to physics too. Moreover, it became solidly fixed in the classification of sciences in-between physics and biology.

The birth of molecular biology saw to such an anchoring between physics and biology. The discovery of the DNA double helix (Watson & Crick 1953) was a turning point in the affirmation of chemistry and biology as sister sciences. Correspondingly, the notion of the interdependency of disciplines came to the fore, chemistry getting its tools from physics and biology, in turn, getting hers from chemistry. The influence from biology was not restricted to molecular biology. To give another instance, prebiotic chemistry came of age in the 1950s with the discovery of interstellar molecules (Ewen & Purcell 1951) and with the classic experiment in prebiotic chemistry (Miller 1953, Asimov 1960).

A chemist, Linus Pauling, embodied such a physics-chemistry-biology alloy. A crystallographer by training, he had taught himself the new quantum physics at its inception in the early 1930s and imported it into chemistry. Later on, during the 30s and 40s, he was one of the pioneers in molecular biology, elucidating key features of protein structure (Nye 2001). Pauling was much admired, an emblematic figure to chemists worldwide (Lipscomb 1993, Hager 1995, Kauffman *et al.* 2001).

However, in spite of and perhaps also because of the tendency to the blurring of disciplinary lines between chemistry and her sister sciences biology and physics, inner lines within chemistry endured and may even have become stronger. F. H. Westheimer tells a revealing anecdote in this respect:

> it is hard to understand the tightly compartmentalized minds of the chemists of that day. (An extreme example of compartmentalization: at the chemistry library at Cambridge University, an imaginary line divided the room into two parts, one for physical chemists and one for organic. The library had two sets of the *Journal of the Chemical Society*, since an organic chemist was not supposed to cross that imaginary line to use the volumes on the physical chemistry side of the library, and vice versa.) [Westheimer 2003]

A traditional aspect of chemistry also became stronger, its iconic language of formulas that the structural theory of the 1860s had established and which G. N. Lewis had bolstered with the notion of the electron pair in the 1910s. Pauling and his concept of mesomery (valence-bond theory) were responsible for this 'formulaic turn', which became a *lingua franca* among chemists. While physicists may have been virtuosi in estimating orders of magnitude for their data or in setting up differential equations, chemists could find shelter in their different language and, instead of back-of-the-envelope calculations, jot a few Lewis structures and make qualitative or semi-quantitative predictions, based on mesomery (Nye 2001).

I have emphasized so far the bonds between chemistry and physics and between chemistry and biology. An overarching notion for chemistry was to be of service to society. During World War II, the penicillin project, second in importance only to the Manhattan Project, had involved synthetic organic chemists and microbiologists (Harris 1999, Raber 2001, Shama & Reinarz 2002). The search for new antibiotics was a major thrust of pharmaceutical R&D during the 1950s. This turned out to be an epochal period in the alliance of pharmacology and synthetic organic chemistry, with the syntheses of morphine (Gates & Tschudi 1952), cholesterol and cortisone (Woodward *et al.* 1951a/b), cantharidin (Stork *et al.* 1953, Bohning & Fine 1991), strychnine (Woodward *et al.* 1954), penicillin (Sheehan & Henery-Logan 1957), colchicine (Schreiber *et al.* 1961), chlorophyll (Woodward *et al.* 1960); with the elucidation of the biosynthesis of steroids (Eschenmoser *et al.* 1955); and with applications of profound social impact, such as the discovery of neuroleptics by Henri Laborit, Jean Delay, and Pierre Deniker in 1950 (Healy 2002), that of the first benzodiazepine tranquilizers librium and valium by Leo Sternbach and Lowell Randall in 1957 (Bello 1957, Baenninger *et al.* 2004) and the devising of oral contraceptives by Carl Djerassi and Gregory Pincus in 1955 (Asbell 1995, Djerassi 1970, 2001). Chemists could see and indeed saw themselves as agents of social change, even more so as they provided society with entire crops of new materials, often made of polymers (textile fibers, plastics).[7] This was also the time for the rise of great industrial laboratories, such as at DuPont (Roussel 1959a/b, Hounshell & Smith 1988), IBM, Bell Telephone, or Xerox from the success of the

---

[7]   Stereoregular polymerization was invented by Karl Ziegler and Giulio Natta in 1953.

newly devised (1950) xerography, which all thrived from applying discoveries in pure science (Stokes 1997, National Research Council 1998).[8]

To sum-up this section: chemists may have cultivated an individual self-image of entrepreneur and a collective self-image of social benefactors. This ploy preserved the age-long, traditional image of craftsmen while adapting it to the flow of easy money. Note, in passing, that entrepreneurship was not a new notion for chemists. There had been quite a few examples in the past, such as Perkin's, Baekeland's, or Mond's. Furthermore, Justus von Liebig's laboratory at Giessen had pioneered a two-tiered organization of chemical laboratories, egalitarian among group leaders and feudal within each research group.

The 1950s, if dominated by university expansion and the attendant demographic increase among chemists, also portended things to come. I shall only mention here a few: the interdiction of fishing in Minimata Bay, which the poisoning by methyl mercury had brought to a stop; the first rumblings of opposition to the widespread use of pesticides (Anon. 1959); the devising of a ground-breaking solid-state peptide synthesis (Merrifield 1963); and the discovery of the NMR chemical shift (Dickinson 1950, Proctor & Yu 1950), which went a long way towards explaining the major influence of NMR on chemistry that we shall consider now.

4.　The 1960s: The NMR Revolution

The impact of NMR (nuclear magnetic resonance) was three-fold, intellectual, social, and psychological. As NMR superseded both earlier spectroscopic tools (such as IR and UV-visible) and contemporary ones (MS), it enforced among chemists a new kind of visual literacy. Chemists learned the skill of reading a spectrum, translating its features into words belonging to the language of chemistry, words such as 'carbonyl', 'phenyl', or 'methyl'. Earlier on, structural analysis had been a field in itself. Henceforth, the NMR tool gave every chemist such expertise (Becker 1993).

---

[8]　A lesson the pharmaceutical industry had implemented early on (Bohmfalk 1953b).

The impact of NMR was revolutionary (Zandvoort 1985, Anet 1996, Diehl 1996, Feeney 1996) also in bringing a host of new questions to the fore. These concerned, to mention only a few, nonequivalent groups of atoms and distinctions among stereoisomers, fluxionality, nonbonded atomic contacts. NMR gave a boost to the study of stereochemical relationships in molecules, which the contemporary conformational analysis had brought to the fore in the 1950s and 1960s (Barton 1972, Eliel 1990).

The A-60 was the instrument of change. Built in Palo Alto, California, by Varian Associates, it was a hands-on, routine instrument that graduate students in chemistry could operate. Precalibrated charts, together with an internal lock on a water sample tube, allowed for a single sweep to record a spectrum (Anon. 1961). The A-60 brought NMR to the masses. Chemists took to it like fish to water (Jackman 1996).

The NMR tube replaced the test tube. This assertion echoes that by Victor Hugo when he claimed so perceptively, in *Notre Dame de Paris*, in the superb 'ceci tuera cela' digression, that when Gutenberg invented movable types, the book killed the cathedral and its imagery, which had been so important earlier in educating Christians.

For centuries, chemists were associated with test tubes, not only in the popular imagination. The test tube was used primarily for qualitative analysis. Adding a few drops of a reagent would trigger a response, maybe a color change, a turbidity, or a precipitation, from which the chemist would infer the likely presence of a component in the liquid mixture, be it a ketone or sulfate anions.

With the NMR tube, chemists were offered a lighter and subtler perturbation. The reagent now consisted only of radiofrequencies (RF). Their resonant absorption by the sample in the NMR tube yielded a comprehensive inventory of the groups of atoms present. The NMR tube did not alone replace the test tube, because it came at the heels of other spectroscopic cells, such as for electronic absorption (UV-visible) or in vibrational (IR and Raman) spectroscopy.

Moreover, NMR was revolutionary in provoking a *Gestalt* switch (to borrow Kuhn's phraseology) in the chemists' perceptions. Earlier, molecules were identified by their functional groups, carbonyls, hydroxyls, and the like, which were like beacons (as reflected in chemical nomenclature, in its affixes and priorities). Now, especially at the beginning of the NMR era (50s and 60s) when ^{1}H NMR thrived by itself, not yet complemented by ^{13}C NMR, the hydrocarbon skeleton was primarily revealed by the spectrum.

Matter, when in a magnetic field and tickled by RF waves, gained in meaningfulness. NMR was a micro-scope of a different order. It displayed inter-relationships between atoms in a molecule (Barton 1972). Couplings among nuclei, whether scalar or dipolar couplings, were the silk threads in the spider web that the NMR spectrum revealed. NMR was truly the Ariadne's thread guiding chemists to their Holy Grail of structure elucidation.

The web of interactions thus revealed in turn mapped molecular structure. Spectral analysis (the NMR tube) had replaced chemical analysis (the test tube). Analyzing a spectrum, furthermore, was an exact science, not an interpretation fraught with uncertainty, open to skepticism and dispute.

How did chemists greet the new tool made suddenly available to them towards the mid-1950s? Their obvious alacrity was tinged with ambivalence. Chemists of the old school did not always embrace the new situation that they were dependent on young upstarts, called 'NMR specialists'. They retrained themselves. They had to. In addition, they had to contend with the shadow cast by physics, which obscured the cherished notion of the autonomy of chemistry, of its non-reducibility to physics. The mixed feeling expressed itself in a catch phrase of those times, 'physical methods'.

With the advent of NMR, new values – in the strongest sense of moral, ethical, and axiological values – came to dominate chemistry, while more traditional values were made redundant and obsolete (Campbell 1960). Take the example of elemental analyses. Before NMR came on the scene, they were the equivalent of a moral obligation. They linked laboratory notebooks to the final publication of the results. Now, elemental analyses became dispensable by the information from the new spectroscopies, high-resolution mass spectrometry (Laidler 2004) even more so than NMR. In spite of this new aspect of laboratory life, journals insisted for a long time (measured not in years but in decades) on the continued insertion of elemental analytical data in the experimental part of manuscripts submitted for publication.

Such rearguard action denotes lingering distrust of the powerful new tools. It points to a kind of umbilical cord linking chemists with their distant past. One can date the rise of the elemental analysis, as the first step in establishing the structure of an unknown, to Justus von Liebig's devising of the *Kaliapparat* in April 1830 (Usselman & Rocke 2005). For one-and-a-half century, the elemental analysis had remained central to the activity of the chemist. Quite suddenly, it was taken off its pedestal, to be discarded on the junk heap of history.

NMR caused some unease in the profession for other reasons too. Early on, a chemist, whether inorganic, organic, or physical, had to become self-taught in the rudiments and intricacies of NMR. Given the pace of change in NMR methodologies, that made for some insecurity. Add to this the uncertainty about the true nature of the profession. Was being a chemist simply a matter of isolating a compound, putting it in an NMR tube, and publishing the results? Somehow, this seemed like cheating. Something was lacking. The NMR revolution brought a challenge to one's self-image as a chemist. The profession was visibly changing. It was taking a turn, but was it for the better?

There were many aspects of the interactions between chemistry and NMR. I have commented so far on the impact of this new instrumentation upon the laboratory in its daily activity. One should add that there were chemists who also contributed to the development of NMR methodologies. Names which come to mind most forcefully are those of Frank A. L. Anet, Axel A. Bothner-By (Bothner-By 1996), H. S. Gutowsky (Gutowsky 1996), William D. Phillips, and John D. Roberts (Roberts 1996).[9]

In its spectral patterns NMR embodied a spectacular proof of the underlying quantum physics, and of the uncanny accuracy of its predictions of line frequencies and intensities. Thus, it brought with it, if not an understanding, at least an acceptance of quantum physics. Rank-and-file chemists thus became somewhat informed about the key developments of physics in the 1930s. They became inadvertent converts to quantum ideas.

---

[9]   Roberts was made a convert in part by a scientist at DuPont (Ferguson 1996).

Any revolution, political or scientific, affects the language. It comes with its own lexicon. NMR was no exception. It gave chemists a *lingua franca*, an idiom that not only extended the vocabulary, but also deepened their understanding of molecules, of their electronic distribution for instance (Anon. 1962). Almost as an aftereffect, such an improved understanding of the structure of molecules vastly improved communication among the tribe. Chemists became more conversant with one another, from being given a language with improved performance.

Equally interesting is the profound effect that NMR had on chemical thinking. An outstanding case is that of Jean-Marie Lehn. In the 1960s, Lehn oversaw NMR in his mentor's, Guy Ourisson's, laboratory at the University of Strasbourg. Lehn thus started his career as an NMR specialist. It gave him a lifelong attention to even minute details in NMR spectra. Their deep chemical meaning for sure would have escaped another chemist's eye. Many of Lehn's experiments were designed either starting from such observations or with NMR in mind as the main tool of study.[10]

Was NMR a mere tool for chemists? It fulfilled several other roles in the tribal culture. It was a prestige item. Status accrued to scientists who, somehow, had access to the latest, most expensive, and state-of-the-art instrumentation. When a visitor came to a laboratory, the tour did not fail to include a proud display of one's NMR spectrometer(s) – usually in the basement of the building, given the weight of electromagnets, until superconducting magnets came into general use during the 1970s and 1980s.

Showing off one's NMR equipment (Huisgen 1994)[11] was also done in scientific journals. Inclusion of an NMR spectrum or several gave allure to one's publications. A cursory look at chemistry journals shows the start of such practice in the early 1960s, with a steep rise to a maximum in the 1970s – 1D spectra making room for their 2D siblings (Ernst 1992) – followed by a slow, gradual wane. The cost of the printed page

---

[10] A representative example is one of his numerous studies in supramolecular catalysis (Hosseini *et al.* 1987).

[11] The evolution was lightning-swift, with superconducting magnets superseding electromagnets (McLauchlan 1996) and with the advent of Fourier transform NMR, which ushered in multidimensional NMR.

saw to it. The picture shown was worth, literally, a thousand words. Of course, as the Golden Sixties gave way to the Stagnant Seventies (Smith & Karlesky 1977, Graham & Diamond 1997), expensive laboratory equipment became more difficult to procure; but by that time it had become a vital necessity.

Besides a 'keeping-up with the Joneses' element, publication of NMR spectra conformed to another, more of a long-term trend (in the sense of braudélian *longue durée*): displaying one's evidence, as if scientific journals had turned into courtrooms. NMR spectra, in that respect, were showcase data. They brought forward prime evidence.

In addition to those two roles, showing-off and confounding critics, published spectra were also iconic of the excellence of the laboratory work behind the paper. They underlined how neat and careful it had been. One would see at a glance not only the quality of the spectrum with sharp, well-resolved, tell-tale lines, one could also not help noticing the absence of impurities, or that statements made in the text about the coexistence of different reaction products were borne out by the data, and so forth.

Last but not least, NMR weighed hard on the budget of chemical laboratories. It gave chemistry, starting in the 1960s, a new need for money, for big money. The small science, that of a lone craftsman, was being displaced by another form of small science, no longer that of the single investigator but that of the small research group, a considerably more expensive endeavor.[12] The NMR spectrometer had to be replaced every three to five years with a new instrument (Roberts 1990). In order to stay competitive, one had to somehow secure grant money for such hefty investments.

---

[12]   The simple running costs for daily operation of a chemical laboratory also escalated. This is easily seen on the example of fluids. Prior to the 1950s, water and gas for Bunsen burners were the only ones routinely provided. After the 1960s, supplies that became standard included: compressed air; tanks of helium, argon, nitrogen; liquid nitrogen; special oils for thermostatic baths or vacuum pumps; *etc*.

5. The 1960s: Chromatographic Takeover and Other Laboratory Changes

The chemistry laboratory changed more between 1950 and 2000 than from 1600 until 1950 (Prelog 1991, Streitwieser 1996). So much is undeniable. Even though chromatography dates back to the turn of the twentieth century (Twsett 1906) – equally significantly it was rediscovered in the 1930s by Richard Kuhn and Edgar Lederer – it underwent a blossoming during the second half of the twentieth century. A.J.P. Martin and R.L.M. Synge devised paper chromatography (1943), due to penury during World War II. Together with other chromatographic methods, such as thin-layer, gas phase, and high-pressure liquid phase chromatography, paper chromatography rose to the ascendancy in laboratories during the 1950s and 1960s. These chromatographic methods superseded earlier separation techniques, such as fractional distillation, crystallization, sublimation, *etc.*, because they were considerably more powerful, could be automated, and required only miniscule amounts of material for analytical purposes; in addition, they could be redirected to preparative purposes.

Many of these chromatographic techniques became implemented in simple-to-operate instruments. In the 50s, they benefited, just like NMR, from the huge progress in electronics brought about by World War II; and later on, from the invention of the transistor. These methods achieved a revolution in the separation and isolation of chemicals from mixtures. The time required for this truly preliminary stage in chemical research was rather suddenly cut-down from weeks to hours. But, again just like NMR, such progress was costly. It weighed on the budget of chemical laboratories.

The chemical laboratory was radically transformed by the mid-1960s.[13] In addition to NMR and chromatography, other molecular spectroscopies, which were then implemented in commercial instruments, first and foremost mass spectrometry, also invaded the chemical laboratory (Morris 2002). The combination of chromatographic isolation and

---

[13] A development that swept through the whole of chemistry like wildfire. It was not confined to, say, organic chemistry. There is a contemporary testimony of the impact on inorganic chemistry (Lewis & Nyholm 1961).

structural determination using predominantly mass spectrometry, NMR, and, to a smaller extent, infrared spectrometry, allowed chemists to go, typically in a week and sometimes in a single day, from an unknown chemical in a mixture to a structure on paper. During the same period of the 1960s, routine use of X-ray diffractometry[14] for molecular structure determination – the timescale was also the week –, at the hands of a few pioneers such as R.B. Woodward started to rival the joint use of mass spectrometry and NMR for the same purpose.

The 1960s were noteworthy too for the arrival of computation at the service of the chemical laboratory, whether industrial or academic. At that time, mainframe computers, housed in a computer center, were still the norm. It was only later, in the 1970s and 1980s that personal computers started to displace them. The introduction of the Macintosh by the Apple company was the analog for computation of what the A-60 spectrometer had been for NMR: it enabled hands-on operation by the individual graduate student. Developments of software were even more important than the steady, Moore-Law abiding, progress in hardware. Roald Hoffmann introduced his Extended Hückel theory in 1963, implemented in a molecular orbital program parametrized for many elements in the Periodic Table. It allowed chemists to calculate properties such as energies and geometries for many chemical structures. Two years later, John Pople came out with another semi-empirical tool for molecular orbital calculations (Mulliken 1972, Ransil 1989), known by the acronym of CNDO. At the same time, the Quantum Chemistry Program Exchange (QCPE) was set-up in 1963 at the University of Indiana as a clearinghouse for software; many of the programs could be acquired by chemists for a nominal fee. QCPE did much for the dissemination of molecular orbital calculations as a new tool. Another highly significant development, based on the computer too, was retrosynthetic analysis, by which synthetic pathways to a target molecule could be identified and compared (Corey 1992).

It would be an oversimplification to subsume under the heading of 'Big Science' (Weinberg 1967) the equipment of the chemical laboratory

---

[14] By tackling large biological molecules, pioneers from the British School initiated by J.D. Bernal paved the way for such ultimately routine use (Hodgkin 1972).

during the 1950s and 1960s just because it included relatively expensive instruments such as chromatographs and spectrometers. One could make a case for the resilience of the notion of 'chemistry as craft'; supporting evidence would be, for instance, the recourse to thin-layer, paper, or column chromatography in complement with gas or high-pressure liquid chromatographies. The former, low-tech tools required a measure of dexterity and care in their use and turned out to be as important to the daily laboratory life as the latter, high-tech methods. Accordingly, before the Golden Sixties[15] came to an end, chemists to some extent could see themselves with a foot in each of the two worlds, that of traditional chemistry, basically unchanged for two or three centuries, and that of modern chemistry, with a plethora of new and powerful physical methods at their fingertips.[16]

The tension between tradition and modernity expressed itself not only in laboratory practice, but also in the conceptualization of chemical entities, such as key intermediates in chemical reactions. The 1960s saw the flare-up of the 'classical-nonclassical ion' controversy within physical organic chemistry (Bartlett 1965, Weininger 2000). Its acme came in 1967 when H.C. Brown published an article in *Chemical and Engineering News*, presenting his orthodox views and criticizing the unorthodox, non-classical proposal, first formulated by S. Winstein, using the language of molecular-orbital theory.

The controversy failed to be resolved decisively by the end of the 1960s. However, it led to the demise of physical organic chemistry,[17] previously at the top of the totem pole in prestige (and in funding). Synthetic organic chemists took advantage of the very public and extremely acrimonious discussions to grab the lead in the pecking order among sub-

---

[15] A representative example is that of the University of North Carolina, in Chapel Hill (Bursey & Crockford 1982).

[16] Physical organic chemistry, as a sub-discipline, embodied such a duality. In the hands of leaders such as J.D. Roberts or J.A. Berson, it synthesized the molecules it needed for physical measurements. A contemporary survey of the mechanistic role of the physical organic philosophy is available (Hine 1960).

[17] The recollections of J.A. Berson, a leader of the field, make very interesting reading for his historical consciousness (Gortler 2001).

disciplines of organic chemistry, and, arguably, of chemistry proper.[18] Further factors were involved in synthetic organic chemistry's rise to the top: the exceptional personality and achievements of R.B. Woodward; his influence in getting his students appointed to coveted faculty positions; the economic pull of the pharmaceutical industry, its need for well-trained preparative chemists to staff its laboratories; the enduring notion of chemistry as a craft, which, in a defensible description, was a silent protest against physics turning into factory mode (Latour 1987, Galison 1997). Furthermore, with the narrowing of the job market, synthetic organic chemistry reasserted itself forcefully, at the expense of both physical and physical organic chemistries.

Accordingly, to go back to the self-image of chemists, one might say that the 'classical-nonclassical ion' controversy helped to firm up a dividing line between, roughly speaking, two groups A and B. Group A was that of the traditionalists and conservatives, led by synthetic organic chemists who draw their power from the labor market, trained people for employment by the pharmaceutical industry, and gave primacy to observation and experiment opposed to theory and calculations (Boyd 1958). Group B was that of the modernists, led by physical and quantum chemists to whom the Schrödinger equation was the Rosetta Stone, who gave primacy to deducing conclusions from first principles and to numerical calculations, and who saw themselves as pioneers.

In the 1950s and 1960s, the chemical community was bound together by a set of assumptions held so deeply that chemists themselves were largely unconscious of them. The first of these shared assumptions was linguistic: everyone spoke English. Turning to organic and biological chemistry, as distinct from physical chemistry, another assumption was a collective distaste for mathematics and any part of chemical theory that called for a mathematical input. Yet another assumption from the same

---

[18] Many people thought the non-classical ion controversy was the modern equivalent of the medieval argument about how many angels could stand on the head of a pin. In addition, physical organic chemistry was to some degree a victim of its own success. By the late 1960s mechanistic thinking was everywhere, and physical organic chemists who wanted to be on the cutting edge (and get funding) went into bioorganic chemistry, enzymatic biochemistry, and even molecular biology. So hordes of people were using and even contributing to physical organic chemistry but not calling themselves physical organic chemists (Weininger 2005).

rather reactionary quarters, in industry especially, was the superiority of trial-and-error, Edisonian research to any other approach. This cluster of assumptions affected the behavior in many ways.

In spite of the split between organic and physical chemists, a group identity asserted itself that featured the same ambivalent aspects of the culture as a whole. The combined strengths of organic and physical chemists would enable them to explore, appropriate, rule over, and (in some cases) settle vast territories beyond the horizon.

The victory of the As over the Bs, at the end of the 1960s, was consolidated by the polywater debacle, a story to be alluded to later, in conjunction with some other episodes of lemmings-like collective behavior.

6. The 1970s: Acquiring Environmental Consciousness

I have referred to the Minimata mercury intoxication already. Other accidents, due to chemical spills from industrial production, struck closer to the homes of European and American chemists (Taube 1983). A book published right at the beginning of the decade heralded the new environmental concerns (Benarde 1970). Chronic pollution of the Rhine led countries responsible for the effluents (France and Germany) and countries suffering from the toxic wastes (The Netherlands) to sign a treaty in 1976. In principle, it guaranteed a return to a healthier state of the water. But that did not prevent industrial plants close to the Rhine from continuing, or resuming to use, the river as a sewer. A disaster occurred during the following decade, in 1986: a major dump in the Basel area of 30 tons of fungicide and mercury wastes killed 500,000 fish. The U.S. saw a number of similar episodes. For instance, Union Carbide was sentenced in 1981 for having dumped nearly 100 cubic meters of carcinogenic chemicals in a river in Virginia, the Kanhawa.

In 1974, Sherwood Rowland and Mario Molina published their conclusion of an extremely careful study of atmospheric chemistry: chlorofluorocarbons, chemicals used in a number of applications (*e.g.*, as refrigeration fluids and propellants in spray cans), when bombarded by solar UV-rays in the upper atmosphere, released chlorine atoms, which in turn destroyed ozone molecules to the tune of 10,000 per chlorine atom.[19] These authors drew attention to the threat to life on the planet from the destruction of the protective ozone layer (Rowland 1995, 1997).

At first, and for more than a decade, the response from the chemical industry was belligerent and obscurantist. They tried to impugn the credibility of those scientists. There seems to be a deplorable pattern in the attempts from the chemical industry to smother criticism with personal attacks and the setting of artificial controversies, with its salaried scientists toeing the party line. Similarly disgraceful treatments were meted out to F. Sherwood Rowland as had been to Rachel Carson many years before.[20]

James Farman's report of the ozone hole over Antarctica in 1981 was the turning point. The major producers of CFCs (companies such as Dow and DuPont de Nemours), a $9 billion business with annual growth rates of 10% (Thomas 2000) then espoused the worldwide concern. That would finally result in the Montreal Protocol in 1987, banning CFCs, stopping their production, and promoting substitution by HCFCs.

In 1976, the Seveso accident appeared on the front pages of newspapers worldwide: 2 kg of 2,3,7,8-tetrachlorodibenzoparadioxin had been dispersed by a Givaudan plant in the neighborhood. This industrial spill, which did not cause any human casualties (cattle grazing on nearby meadows were killed in large numbers as a safety precaution) nor had any long-term effects on human health, nevertheless raised the level of consciousness about dioxins and their release by papermaking mills and municipal waste incinerators, among other sources. As a consequence, careful controls were instituted in industrial countries, leading within a couple of decades to at least halving the amount of dioxins discharged in the environment in France, for instance.

The chemical community was the butt of unrelenting criticism from the public and the media,[21] who regarded it the chief culprit of environ-

---

[19] The devising of highly sensitive detection of CFCs by Lovelock was an important part of the story (Dronsfield & Morris 2002).

[20] To be fair, the position from industry was sometimes stated in a temperate manner (Anon. 1962).

[21] Such hostility to chemistry from the public can be dated back to the publication of Rachel Carson's masterpiece, *Silent Spring*, in 1964. This book drew the public attention to the inconsiderate use of pesticides such as DDT by farmers, with dramatic ef-

mental pollution, in the form of acid rain (Cowling 1982, Mohnen 1988, Baedecker & Reddy 1993) and harmful chemicals in surface water (Baker *et al*. 1991) such as the Great Lakes (Hilleman 1988), in tainting supplies of drinking water (Ross & Amter 2002), and in irresponsibly and illegally dumping toxic wastes (Love Canal near Niagara Falls, NY;[22] the Hudson River was continuously polluted by PCBs).[23]

The chemical community responded, as a rule, rather promptly – over less than two decades – and responsibly. The chemical industry cleaned up its operation, as a rule allowing only innocuous effluents from its plants. Environmental research was funded handsomely, and drew significant numbers of chemists. Chemical education also followed suit, for instance the American Chemical Society sponsored textbooks of general chemistry for non-chemistry undergraduate majors, focused on environmental issues.[24]

A yet more interesting trend developed. I contend that the new environmental consciousness among chemists, with lasting value (Mossman *et al*. 1990) led them to move in the direction of biology (Bensaude-Vincent 2002), rather than continue with traditional mainstream chemical science.[25] This 'Biological Turn' was marked by the vitamin B12 synthesis (Woodward 1973), the much admired biomimetic steroid syntheses (Johnson 1977, 1998), the synthesis of natural products (Woodward 1972, Nakanishi 1991) such as giberellic acid (Corey 1978) or multifidene (Boland & Jaenicke 1979), the considerable research effort by E.J. Corey in the field of prostaglandins, the pioneering studies by Martin

---

fects on the ecology and on animal species accumulating the toxic chemical in their tissues (Baker & Wilkinson 1990).

[22] Hooker Chemical and Plastics Corporation dumped an estimated 350 million lbs of hazardous chemical wastes in this trench between 1942 and 1953. After it was filled and covered, it was sold to the Niagara Falls Board of Education. The scandal broke in 1977, after the New York Department of Environmental Conservation reported the extent of soil and groundwater contamination (Levine 1982).

[23] Unsurprisingly, public support of chemical research went down. In the US, federal funding decreased by 14 percent in constant 1972 dollars between 1971 and 1975 (Smith & Karlesky 1977, pp. 86-101).

[24] Chemistry departments lowered their standards during that period. The average student quality dropped. Faced with declining applications for admission, departments wanted to avoid losses in undergraduates (Smith & Karlesky 1977, pp. 114,156).

[25] Synthetic organic chemists were thus updating their concerns, turning away from their more traditional pursuit.

Karplus on protein molecular dynamics (1977), and so on (Todd 1983, Williams 1990). Quite a few small start-up companies banked on the public taste for natural products, for instance, in the form of herbal over-the-counter drugs (Anon. 1999).

The 1970s had opened with the first oil crisis. This geopolitical event made political leaders seek alternative energy sources. The chemical profession followed the money. Since grants were awarded for work on alternative energy sources and environmental issues, chemists started work in such areas. They became environmentally conscious (Baird 1995) and started cleaning-up their operation, whether in industrial plants or in academic laboratories. Everybody became safety-conscious, and pollution of the environment became drastically curtailed (Ember 1991, Rodrick 1992, McGinn 2000).

7. The 1980s: Mystique of Growth

I will now, in some detail, document my assertion of the intoxication by growth for its own sake, basing myself on the Pimentel Report (PR), first published in 1985 by the American Chemical Society (Pimentel & Coonrod 1987).

An illustration in PR shows, as a small icon of spectroscopic progress, the improvement in sensitivity of nuclear magnetic resonance spectrometry. In only 15 years, the solid-state ^{13}C spectrum of adamantane, with only two types of carbons, CH and CH_2, had turned from inaccessibility to an easy routine. Such solid-state ^{13}C spectra became important diagnostic tools for the chemical industry in the areas of polymers, whether as elastomers, textile fibers, or plastics such as polypropylene.

However, if NMR spectrometers improved considerably in performance, their cost increased likewise. A graph in the Pimentel Report depicts these twin trends: the increase of NMR spectrometers in magnetic field strength, thereby in resolution, in sensitivity, and in cost. Chemists in the 1980s were clamoring for increased public support from granting agencies, such as the National Science Foundation and the National Institutes of Health, and battling with one another for grants from those agencies. Instrumentation was costly across the board, a cost-quality diagram in PR made the same point for mass spectrometry. Half-a-million dollars was the price of a state-of-the-art mass spectrometer in the mid-80s. The implicit message was 'give us the funding necessary to study biopolymers such as proteins, we are willing, we only need the money'.

Both academic and industrial chemists became increasingly dependent on computers. The PR includes another exponential plot, showing that American industry had equipped itself with large mainframe computers during the post-World War II period. A complementary graph conveys the steadily increasing cost of computation.

In the 1980s, chemists set up materials science as an offshoot of their discipline. They strove for polymers to replace wood, glass, and metals in many of their uses, and to open-up brand new applications. Plastics underwent an exponential growth during the post-World War II period, which the PR depicted graphically. And chemists took pride in the petrochemical industry rivaling metallurgy in output. One of the illustrations in the PR aimed at informing the public that sales of chemicals were comparable in volume with those of motor vehicles or machinery. The curve goes through a maximum, reflecting the downturn caused by the second global oil crisis of 1979-1980 with the attendant worldwide recession.

The PR prided itself, not only on the production of man-made fibers and plastics, but also on the sheer number of new chemical compounds. It showed their growth, as registered by *Chemical Abstracts* during the second half of the twentieth century, in a picture of self-satisfaction and hubris. Chemists prided themselves on the proliferation of chemicals and the increased density of the chemosphere.[26]

This was the time also of the uncontrolled proliferation of organometallics. In countries with powerful chemical organizations, but lacking a share in the leadership then exercised by American chemists in concepts and methods, primarily in the United Kingdom, Italy, and France, the field of organometallics became the province of unimaginative scientists who would prepare compounds, based on analogies from the Periodic Table, only because such compounds were heretofore unknown. They assimilated newness and innovation.

---

[26] A valuable chemometric study on the proliferation of new chemicals is available (Schummer 1997).

Chemists in the 1980s enjoyed their self-image as, not only good citizens who had cleaned-up their operation during the previous decade, but as human benefactors (Woodburn 1976) through their crucial contribution to pharmaceutical research. The message of the PR is loud and clear: since chemists are helping humankind by devising new, efficient drugs against disease, if they are to continue doing so successfully, they need more money for equipment.

That brought up the battle for funding with the rival discipline, physics. Physicists in the 80s were better than chemists at grantsmanship and public relations and were henceforth more successful in getting mammoth collective projects financed. Chemists, conversely and as illustrated in the PR, prided themselves on demographics, on beating physicists in sheer number of jobs – or better yet in the production of Ph.D. scientists.[27]

Chemical science was moving at such a furious pace in the 80s that the scientists were unable to keep up with the information they were generating. Fullerenes are an outstanding example of such an information overload. Richard Smalley made a point in his Nobel Lecture by referring to pioneering work by a number of scientists in several countries of which he, Kroto, and Curl were unaware at the time of their discovery of C_{60} (Smalley 2003).

8.   The 1990s: Attempts at Rebranding

The 1990s were the period of rather massive retirement of the post World War II baby boomers from their positions in academia and industry. How would this generation change impact chemistry? Would there be a takeover by Generation X? Would it bring in an entirely new set of human and professional values? The perhaps surprising answer is that continuity stifled mutation.

I base this assessment on a study I made of young faculty members in American chemistry departments, and of their stated research goals, us-

---

[27] The statement has to be balanced with the disaffection of undergraduate students with the sciences, for chemistry in particular, starting in the 70s (Neckers 1979).

ing the standard source for such information (ACS 1995). I picked at random the letter G. These then were my findings.

Faculty members born after 1955 – my arbitrarily chosen cutoff date – numbered 44; only five were women. By far, the dominant research area was biochemistry and molecular biology – even though the names were selected from the chemistry section of the directory that excluded departments of biochemistry. Ten of the junior faculty members were engaged in such bio-work. Half-a-dozen other areas, more or less equally populated, accounted for most of the remainder of this sample: organometallics (6), organic synthesis (5), surfaces (5), NMR (4), spectroscopy other than NMR (4), and catalysis (3). To my surprise, traditional topics going back to the 1960s continued to be popular with some of these budding academics. Stereochemistry and conformational analysis was one of them.

Indeed these young faculty members, the vast majority of which were still assistant professors, were playing a safe game. They obviously picked areas of work that were both funded more easily and promised to provide publishable results in short time. I failed to identify highly adventuresome profiles. To the contrary, quite a few among those individuals posted a number of different research orientations: 'something will have to work out', seemed to be the guiding motive. One of these young investigators for instance – he was quite representative in such an across-the-board sweep – announced he was working on "organic and polymer self-assembly; electronically conductive polymers; liquid crystals; self-assembled monolayers; host-guest interactions; organic electrochemistry."

The background for such a behavior – and the US were representative of an almost worldwide trend – was an erosion in public support of chemical science. To give a simple figure, between the 1960s and 1990s, there was a ca. 60% drop in funded research proposals submitted to the National Science Foundation and the National Institutes of Health. From 1983 to 2002, funding of chemistry and physics by the US Departments of Energy and Defense, had plummeted. Correspondingly, there were 9% fewer graduate students in chemistry in the US in 2000 than in 1993 (Eiseman *et al.* 2002).

In response to the wane of public support for chemistry, some chemists became more vocal. They praised not only the field and their individual contributions with a more emphatic tone. Hyperbole as a rhetorical tool was resorted to more often. It marked scientific publications especially, research proposals even more. Advertising hype displaced the more modest, objective, and neutral style of reporting. Results became routinely 'divulged' or 'revealed'. Facts were praised by the authors as 'unprecedented', 'novel', and 'remarkable', to quote some of the routine adjectives.

Such advertising belonged to a relatively new trend. Science, in addition to being conducted according to the norms, had to be marketed adequately. Science results were sometimes publicized as if they were a commercial commodity. Hence, one witnessed attempts at renaming and rebranding chemistry, in part or as a whole.

Renaming as a whole? The Department of Chemistry at Harvard took the lead. It added to its name the complement 'Chemical Biology'. Other universities (Cornell) followed suit. They had a good excuse in improving their name and their image, so they thought: their new name was more accurate. As mentioned above, the younger faculty members were moving towards more biological topics.

Against the profit background (Hounshell 1998) and in the face of decreasing public support of science, the research university sought to reinvent itself (Kumar & Patel 1995). With academic and industrial sciences continuing to be structured in different ways (Ziman 1994), both the chemical industry and the pharmaceutical industry supported two of the vogues[28] which were foremost in the conceptual landscape of the 1990s, those of biotechnologies – both within small start-up companies

---

[28] Industrial research is not immune to fashions that, as a rule, hit at the academic-industrial interface. The pharmaceutical industry, in its search for blockbuster drugs, has tried a whole litany of means, among which one may recall Hantzsch partition coefficients, linear free energy relationships, MO calculations of electronic distribution in molecules, docking into receptor sites using computer modeling, *etc*. The chemical industry proper has had its own vogues, which influenced also some academic research. For instance, shape-selective catalysis, as performed by zeolites, led to a major undertaking in the area of pillared clays, whose results little matched the expectations.

and within large corporations such as Novartis in Basel[29]– and of nano-science and technology (Welch Foundation 1996, National Science Board 2002, Schummer 2004, 2005).

Even within academia, chemists were shifting their focus (Ivory Tower, intellectual distinction, remoteness from public concerns) to the marketing of their productions. Those products continued to take the form of publications and patents. The novelty was the hype, often com-bined with the perceived need to disassociate oneself from the negative image carried by the discipline.

A solution was to rename the subdiscipline one belonged to. The new name would avoid the 'chemical' adjective. Surface science thus thrived during the 90s. Another renaming occurred with the nanoscience and nanotechnology bandwagon.[30]

That brings up the twin issues of branding and rebranding (Rivkin & Sutherland 2004). Were you living off your heritage as a traditional chemist, without paying attention to negative public opinion, without thinking about the future at all? Such a stance was risky at a time when, to mention just one country, the government was closing down chemistry departments in British universities.[31] It was much more advisable either to brand yourself as trading on your heritage, but with the future in mind – which accounted for combinatorial chemistry.[32] Better yet, you could

---

[29]   Other pharmaceutical companies, in Germany in particular (Boehringer, BASF, Hoechst, *etc.*) chose another option, subcontracting to specialized companies, in the U.S. predominantly. By and large, this choice was an economic failure.

[30]   The move was protracted, as so often in history. The incentive came from the discov-ery of the DNA double-helix by Watson and Crick, and from the ensuing lecture by Richard P. Feynman in 1959, calling for the devising of small mechanical engines and devices operating at the nanometer scale.

[31]   18 British universities closed their departments of chemistry between 1992 and 2001, an overall 27% reduction. The trend did not stop with the decade though. By 2004, 28 departments of chemistry had been closed since 1996. Some pessimists predicted that only six departments of chemistry might survive in the UK.

[32]   A name with an obvious redundancy, most of chemistry being combinatorial by na-ture. This vogue was long overdue, Merrifield had pioneered his peptide synthesis on small beads of polymers in the 1960s (Merrifield 1963), meeting collective indiffer-ence from the profession. When such a technique was rediscovered towards the end of the century, it came back with a big splash with, behind it, big financial support from both materials science and the pharmaceutical industry. The latter was intent, as it always is, upon finding shortcuts to promising lead molecules, in terms of drugs both patentable and profitable.

establish your business as a brand-new endeavor, with the future predominant on your horizon (Schultz 2000).

Green Chemistry was such a ploy. It was a renaming and rebranding of industrial chemistry, terming research in environmentally-friendly processes: under mild conditions of pressure and temperature, dispensing with organic solvents, releasing innocuous wastes only, if at all.[33,34]

The Internet was influential in such attempts at rebranding parts of chemistry, to the benefit of individual scientists. Those were able to build an allegiance with their constituency through the Web, to set-up networks too, in a much shorter time than within the traditional pre-existing brands – analytical or physical chemistry, say – and became more relevant to perceived needs in doing so (Schultz 2000).

The Internet made networking easier (Bachrach 1996), so much is incontrovertible. However, would it facilitate regrouping the chemical community, its various segments each into its mainstream? Or conversely, would it make it easier to splinter into finer and finer subdisciplines, as a symptom of disciplinary maturity? Both of these trends, the centripetal and the centrifugal, can be discerned.[35]

The former, the rush into conformity,[36] explains the continued pull of various fads, the appearance of ephemeral vogues that would enlist sup-

---

[33] James Clark at the University of York was one of its leading advocates. Professor Clark is Head of the York Green Chemistry Group, Scientific Editor of the *Green Chemistry Journal*, Director of the Green Chemistry Network, Joint Co-ordinator of the Green Chemistry Research Network, and Series Editor of the RSC *Clean Technology Monographs*.

[34] *The New Yorker* published on July 5, 2004, p. 84, a cartoon by artist Mick Stevens. It depicts the headquarters of a chemical company. While the chimneystacks are spewing-out dark, presumably noxious smoke, the corporation advertises its efforts at controlling its own image. The cartoon illustrates how comically self-defeating such an attempt appears to the lay public. As illustrated in this cartoon, the efforts by the chemical industry to redeem itself in the public eye were doomed. There was a backlash in public opinion against the new image promoted by the chemical industry. The very fact that, at the same time, high-profit pharmaceutical branches divorced from their low-profit, cyclical chemical siblings, made even more unbelievable the claims by the chemical industry that it was safe and clean – even though such claims were the truth. To eradicate a prejudice ain't easy!

[35] It was the Age of Globalization too, which greatly affected, in particular, recruitment of graduate students and postdocs in American universities (Tobias *et al.* 1995, COSEPUP 2000, Walker *et al.* 2004).

[36] Michael J. S. Dewar has been not only lucid, delightfully sarcastic too, about this unfortunate tendency (Dewar 1992).

port from chemists. This was neither new nor original to chemistry. Chemists had earlier on been swept into brief stampedes, such as the polywater 1972 episode (Franks 1981) or the cold fusion 1989 foray into pathological science (Langmuir & Hall 1989), Gold Rushes and inflationary bubbles both ending with a quick crash.

That the 1990s were not immune from such collective and highly cooperative phenomena was a sign of the maturing of the discipline. This permeated the collective consciousness of chemists. The perceived needs for renaming and rebranding came against such a background of a mature, well-established science.

Some topics for scientific research at times become very popular, to such an extent that a chemometric description as an epidemic may become relevant (Franks 1981). During the 90s, within synthetic organic chemistry, the devising of pathways to target molecules such as taxol or brevicomin was highly fashionable (Lowe 2004). Petrochemistry had its own vogues too. One of those was triggered in the 1990s by the devising of efficient catalysts for the olefin metathesis reaction: "a few years ago, it seemed that everyone with two alkenes in their lab was finding a way to get them in the same flask with some Grubbs catalyst" (Lowe 2004). The Nobel Prize in chemistry occasionally puts the ultimate seal of approval on such popularity polls. The metathesis reaction was thus distinguished in 2005.

9. Conclusions

Chemists have to face chemophobia. Such public hostility is rooted in a multiplicity of factors. Some are mythical, such as the Biblical account of the destruction of Sodom and Gomorrah from the befouling of air for breathing and of water for drinking, or the twin medieval anguishes over the cognate poisoning of wells or polluting of the air. Some are very real, such as chemical warfare or Bhopal.

Hence, a significant segment of the population sees the chemists as if in a ghetto. Such scapegoating of the chemical community – a scapegoating indeed, chemists bear the brunt of complaints against environmental pollution, of which other industries and the public itself (automobiles) are largely responsible – was met with stoical equanimity[37] during the 1950-2000 period. It made for a remarkably close-knit, worldwide community, united through its use of a common language, that of structural formulas (Cram 1990).

Outer pressure from criticism did not only make chemists close ranks, it also sharpened their self-image as providers of material benefits to society. For the whole period (1939-1980s) during which DuPont advertised its motto "Better Things for Better Living ... Through Chemistry", chemists identified readily with this slogan and regretted its passing. They saw themselves as a social group, honest (Roussel 1959a) and well-meaning, doing essential work, and unjustly attacked, not recognized properly.

The worldwide chemical community has countered otherwise potentially disruptive tensions in embracing rapid change (in laboratory tools, in the attendant training of young chemists [National Research Council 2003, 2004] in topics of interest, *etc.*), while upholding traditional values of craftsmanship and small science. The truly remarkable adaptability, in the face of enormous changes (Havinga 1991),[38,39] arguably stems from chemistry being the science of material transformations, and from chemists thus being trained in both monitoring and controlling change.

Moreover, chemists see themselves as creative (Pacifico 1958, McGrayne 2001). To quote an eminent member of the profession (Gortler 1999):

---

[37] Which outside observers often mistakenly equate with arrogance.

[38] Consider for instance the manufacture of polymers. Each of the various grades of polyethylene was made using different processes and catalysts during each of the decades under study. Recollections of one of the pioneers make for useful reading (Ziegler 1972).

[39] The visual idiom changed considerably. In the 50s, it was dominated by the octant rule, valence-bond structures, cage molecules, IR and UV-visible spectroscopies. In the 60s, proton NMR, mass spectrometry, linear free energy relationships, and the valence shell electron pair repulsion (Gillespie-Nyholm) came to the fore. The 70s saw the rise of carbon-13 NMR, molecular orbital diagrams, and coordination geometries. In the 80s, zeolite structures, 2D NMR, computer simulations of protein structures with inclusion of molecular dynamics became iconic. The 90s saw new kinds of images with AFM and STM becoming popularized, with entities pictured such as nanotubes.

There's always going to be chemistry, because we are so special, because we create new things. There's almost no other science that creates anything. We create new things, and that creation involves an intellectual creativity in realizing what to do, what to make, and why to make it, and what to do with it when you've got it, that is very special to our field.

This notion of the creativity of chemists not only fits the 'individualism methodology' (Boudon 1979), it also ties in nicely with a metaphor favored by chemists in recent years, that of 'Chemistry, the Central Science' (Breslow 1997, Brown *et al.* 2003).

Acknowledgements

This chapter was first presented (in a highly simplified form, truncated to the section on the 1980s) at the 'Public Images of Chemistry in the Twentieth Century' conference held in Paris, September 17-18, 2004. I gratefully acknowledge material support from the Chemical Heritage Foundation, Philadelphia, and Fondation des Treilles, Tourtour, which gave me the opportunity of two one-week stays in February and in November 2005 to gather documentation in its Othmer Library, and of a two-week stay in May 2005 for the write-up respectively. In addition, I thank Roald Hoffmann for a most enlightening, synthetic, and incisive presentation of the underlying issues, during a discussion we had in Ithaca on February 3, 2005.

References

ACS: 1995, *Directory of Graduate Research*, American Chemical Society, Washington DC.

Anet, F.A.L.: 1996, 'A Lapsed Organic Chemist in the Wonderland of NMR', in: D.M. Grant & R.K. Harris (eds.), *Encyclopedia of nuclear magnetic resonance*, Wiley, Chichester, vol. 1, pp. 187-90.

Anon.: 1958, 'High Dive into the Next Decade', *Chemical and Engineering News*, Sept. 22, 23-5.

Anon.: 1959, 'Normalcy Rules in Pesticides', *Chemical and Engineering News*, Oct. 12, 32-3.

Anon.: 1961, 'Low Cost, Simple Operation Expand NMR Uses', *Chemical and Engineering News*, March 6, 52-3.

Anon.: 1962, 'NMR May Determine Electron Densities', *Chemical and Engineering News*, July 16, 34-35.

Anon.: 1999, 'Herbal Rx: The Promise and Pitfalls', *Consumer Reports*, 44-8.

Asbell, B.: 1995, *The Pill: A Biography of the Drug that Changed the World*, Random House, New York.

Asimov, I.: 1960, *The Wellsprings of Life*, Abelard-Schuman, London.

Bachrach, S.: 1996, *The Internet: A Guide for Chemists*, American Chemical Society, Washington DC.

Baedecker, P.A. & Reddy, M.M.: 1993, 'The Erosion of Carbonate Stone by Acid Rain', *Journal of Chemical Education*, 104-8.

Baenninger, A.; Silva, J.A.C.e.; Hindmarch, I.; Moeller, H.-J. & Rickels, K.: 2004, *Good Chemistry. The Life and Legacy of Valium Inventor Leo Sternbach.*, McGraw-Hill, New York.

Baggott, J.: 1994, *Perfect Symmetry. The Accidental Discovery of Buckminsterfullerene*, Oxford UP, Oxford.

Baird, C.: 1995, *Environmental Chemistry*, W.H. Freeman, Salt Lake City, UT.

Baker, L.A.; Herlihy, A.T.; Kaufmann, P.R. & Eilers, J.M.: 1991, 'Acidic Lakes and Streams in the United States: the Role of Acidic Deposition', *Science*, 1151-4.

Baker, S.R. & Wilkinson, C.F.: 1990, *The Effects of Pesticides on Human Health*, Princeton Scientific, Princeton, NJ.

Bartlett, P.D.: 1965, *Nonclassical Ions. Reprints and Commentary*, W.A. Benjamin, New York.

Barton, D.H.R.: 1972, 'The principles of conformational analysis' (1969), in: Nobel Foundation (eds.), *Nobel Lectures. Chemistry 1963-1970*, Elsevier, Amsterdam, 298-311.

Becker, E.D.: 1993, 'A brief history of nuclear magnetic resonance', *Analytical Chemistry*, **65**, 295A-302A.

Becker, E.D.: 1996, 'NMR at the NIH: Inception and Growth Over Four Decades', in: D.M. Grant & R.K. Harris (eds.), *Encyclopedia of nuclear magnetic resonance*, Wiley, Chichester, pp. 207ff.

Bello, F.: 1957, 'The tranquilizer question', *Fortune*, 162-188.

Benarde, M.A.: 1970, 'The Politics of Pollution', in: *Our Precarious Habitat*, Norton, New York.

Bensaude-Vincent, B.: 2002, 'Changing Images of Chemistry', in: I.H. Stamhuis, T. Koetsier, C.d. Pater & A.v. Helden (eds.), *The changing images of the sciences*, Kluwer, Dordrecht, pp. 29-42.

Bochvar, D.A. & Galpern, E.G.: 1973, *Proceedings of the Academy of Science, USSR*, **209**, 610-2.

Bohmfalk, J.F.Jr.: 1953a, 'Research – Blend of Efforts', *Chemical and Engineering News*, 5186-91.

Bohmfalk, J.F.Jr.: 1953b, 'Markets for Pharmaceuticals', *Chemical and Engineering News*, 5006-12.

Bohning, J.J. & Fine, L.W.: 1991, 'Gilbert J. Stork', Chemical Heritage Foundation, oral interview no. 0100, August 6, transcript (108 pp.).

Bohning, J.J.: 1993, 'Howard E. Simmons Jr.', Chemical Heritage Foundation, oral interview no. 0111, April 27, transcript (70 pp.).

Boland, W. & Jaenicke, L.: 1979, 'Synthesis of multifidene', *Journal of Organic Chemistry*, **44**, 4819-24.

Borman, S.: 1998, 'Combinatorial Chemistry', *Chemical and Engineering News*, April 6, 47-67.

Bothner-By, A.A.: 1996, 'Computer Analysis of High-Resolution NMR Spectra', in: D.M. Grant & R.K. Harris (eds.), *Encyclopedia of nuclear magnetic resonance*, Wiley, Chichester, pp. 233-7.

Boudon, R.: 1979 (1973), 'Hypothèses, individualisme méthodologique et éducation', in: R. Boudon (ed.), *L'inégalité des chances*, Hachette/Pluriel, Paris, pp. 106-13.

Boyd, T.A.: 1958, 'Theorizing – No Substitute for *Trying*', *Chemical and Engineering News*, Feb. 3, 70-2.

Breslow, R.: 1997, *Chemistry today and tomorrow: the central, useful, and creative science*, American Chemical Society, Washington DC.

Brown, T.L.Jr.; LeMay, H.E.; Bursten, B.E. & Burdge, J.R.: 2003, *Chemistry: The Central Science*, 9th ed., Prentice Hall, Englewood Cliffs, NJ.

Bursey, M.M. & Crockford, H.D.: 1982, *Carolina chemists: sketches from Chapel Hill*, Department of Chemistry, University of North Carolina at Chapel Hill, NC.

Bush, V.: 1945, *Science – The Endless Frontier. A Report to the President on a Program for Postwar Scientific Research*, National Science Foundation, Washington, DC (reprint 1990).

Campbell, J.A.: 1960, 'Changes in College Chemistry', *Chemical and Engineering News*, Aug. 22, 88-92.

College of Wooster: 1959, Research and Teaching in the Liberal Arts College. A Report of the Wooster Conference, June 22-July 2, Wooster, OH, USA.

Corey, E.J. *et al.*: 1978, 'Stereospecific synthesis of giberellic acid', *Journal of the American* Chemical Society, **100**, 8034-6.

Corey, E.J.: 1992, 'The Logic of Chemical Synthesis: Multistep Synthesis of Complex Carbogenic Molecules', in: B.G. Malmström (ed.), *Nobel Lectures, Chemistry 1981-1990*, World Scientific Publishing, Singapore, pp. 686-708.

COSEPUP: 2000, *Enhancing the Postdoctoral Experience for Scientists and Engineers. A Guide for Postdoctoral Scholars, Advisers, Institutions, Funding Organizations, and Disciplinary Societies*, National Academy Press, Washington, DC.

Cowling, E.B.: 1982, 'Acid Precipitation in Historical Perspective', *Environmental Science and Technology*, 110A-123A.

Cram, D.J.: 1990, *From design to discovery*, American Chemical Society, Washington, DC.

Dewar, M.J.S.: 1992, *A semiempirical life*, American Chemical Society, Washington, DC.

Dickinson, W.C.: 1950, 'Dependence of the F^{19} Nuclear Resonance Position on Chemical Compund', *Physical Review*, **77**, 736.

Diehl, P.: 1996, 'NMR at the Physics Department of the University of Basel, Switzerland (1949-96)', in: D.M. Grant & R.K. Harris (eds.), *Encyclopedia of nuclear magnetic resonance*, Wiley, Chichester, pp. 277-9.

Djerassi, C.: 1970, 'Birth Control after 1984', *Science*, **169**, 941-51.

Djerassi, C.: 2001, *This Man's Pill. Reflections on the 50th Birthday of the Pill*, Oxford UP, Oxford.

362 *Pierre Laszlo*

Dronsfield, A.T. & Morris, P.J.T.: 2002, 'Finding a molecule in a billion', *Education in Chemistry*, **39**, 157-159.

Eiseman, E.; Koizumi, K. & Fossum, D.: 2002, *Federal Investment in R&D*, Rand Science and Technology Policy Institute, Washington, DC.

Eliel, E.L.: 1990, *From Cologne to Chapel Hill*, American Chemical Society, Washington, DC.

Ember, L.R.: 1991, 'Strategies for Reducing Pollution at the Source are Gaining Ground', *Chemical and Engineering News*, July 8, 7-16.

Ernst, R.R.: 1992, 'Nuclear magnetic resonance Fourier transform spectroscopy', *Bioscience reports*, **12**, 143-187.

Eschenmoser, A. *et al.*: 1951, 'Synthesis of colchicine', *Helvetica Chimica Acta*, **44**, 540-97.

Eschenmoser, A.; Ruzicka, L.; Jeger, O. & Arigoni, D.: 1955, 'Zur Kenntis der Triterpene. 190. Mitteilung. Eine stereochemische Interpretation der biogenetischen Isoprenregel bei der Triterpenen', *Helvetica Chimica Acta*, **38**, 1890-1904.

Ewen, H. & Purcell, E.M.: 1951, 'Radiation from Galactic Hydrogen at 1420 Mc./sec', *Nature*, **168**, 356.

Feeney, J.: 1996, 'Personal Reminiscences on NMR', in: D.M. Grant & R.K. Harris (eds.), *Encyclopedia of nuclear magnetic resonance*, Wiley, Chichester, pp. 308-9.

Ferguson, R.C.: 1996, 'William D. Phillips and Nuclear Magnetic Resonance Spectroscopy at DuPont', in: D.M.Grant & R.K. Harris (eds.), *Encyclopedia of nuclear magnetic resonance*, Wiley, Chichester, pp. 309-13.

Franks, F.: 1981, *Polywater*, MIT Press, Cambridge, MA.

Galison, P. 1997: *Image and Logic*, University of Chicago Press, Chicago.

Gates, M.D.J. & Tschudi, G.: 1952, 'Total synthesis of morphine', *Journal of the American Chemical Society*, **74**, 1109.

Geertz, C.: 1983, '"From the Native's Point of View": On the Nature of Anthropological Understanding', in: *Local Knowledge: Further Essays in Interpretative Anthropology*, Basic Books, New York.

Geiger, R. *et al.*: 2004, 'Responses to Changing Needs in U.S. Doctoral Education', *Journal of Chemical Education*, **81**, 1698-1704.

Gortler, L.B.: 1999, 'Ronald C. Breslow', Chemical Heritage Foundation, oral interview no. 0181, 19 March and 9 April, transcript (90 pp.).

Gortler, L.B.: 2001, 'Jerome A. Berson', Chemical Heritage Foundation, oral interview no. 0196, March 21, transcript (102 pp.).

Graham, H.D. & Diamond, N.: 1997, *The Rise of American Research Universities. Elites and Challengers in the Postwar Era*, Johns Hopkins UP, Baltimore, MD.

Gray, H. *et al.*: 2004, 'Responses to Changing Needs in U.S. Doctoral Education', *Journal of Chemical Education*, **81**, 1698-1704.

Gutowsky, H.S.: 1996, 'The Coupling of Chemical and Nuclear Magnetic Phenomena', in: D.M. Grant & R.K. Harris (eds.), *Encyclopedia of nuclear magnetic resonance*, Wiley, Chichester, pp. 360-8.

Gwynne, P.: 2001, '25 Years of Hot Fields in Chemistry', *Chemistry*, anniversary issue, 50-7.

Hager, T.: 1995, *Force of nature: the life of Linus Pauling*, Simon & Schuster, New York.

Harris, H.: 1999, 'Howard Florey and the development of penicillin', *Notes and Records of the Royal Society of London*, **53**(2), 243-52.

Havinga, E.: 1991, *Enjoying organic chemistry, 1927-1987*, American Chemical Society, Washington, DC.

Healy, D.: 2002, *The creation of psychopharmacology*, Harvard UP, Cambridge, MA.

Hilleman, B.: 1988, 'The Great Lakes Cleanup Effort', *Chemical and Engineering News*, Feb. 8, 22-39.

Hine, J.: 1960, 'Physical Organic Chemistry', *Chemical and Engineering News*, May 9, 101-6.

Hodgkin, D.C.: 1972, 'X-ray analysis of complicated molecules', in: Nobel Foundation (eds.), *Nobel Lectures. Chemistry 1963-1970*, Elsevier, Amsterdam, pp. 71-94.

Hoffmann, R.: 1997, 'Tapeworm quadrilles', in: L. Wolpert & A. Richards (eds.), *Passionate minds: the inner world of scientists*, Oxford UP, Oxford, pp. 18-25.

Hosseini, M.W.; Lehn, J.-M.; Maggiora, L.; Mertes, K.B. & Mertes, M.P.: 1987, 'Supramolecular Catalysis in the Hydrolysis of ARP Facilitated by Macrocyclic Polyamines: Mechanistic Studies', *Journal of the American Chemical Society*, **109**, 537-44.

Hounshell, D.A. & Smith, J.K.J.: 1988, *Science and Corporate Strategy. Du Pont R&D, 1902-1980*, Cambridge UP, Cambridge, UK.

Hounshell, D.A.: 1998, 'Measuring the Return on Investment in R&D: Voices from the Past, Visions of the Future', in: National Research Council (eds.), *Assessing the Value of Research in the Chemical Sciences*, National Academy Press, Washington, DC, pp. 6-17.

Huisgen, R.: 1994, *The adventure playground of mechanisms and novel reactions*, American Chemical Society, Washington, DC.

Jackman, L.M.: 1996, 'NMR in Organic Chemistry – the Fabulous Fifties', in: D.M. Grant & R.K. Harris (eds.), *Encyclopedia of nuclear magnetic resonance*, Wiley, Chichester, pp. 397-98.

Johnson, W.S. *et al.*: 1977, 'Asymmetric total synthesis of 11a-hydroxyprogesterone via a biomimetic polyene cyclization', *Journal of the American Chemical Society*, **99**, 8341-3.

Johnson, W.S.: 1998, *A fifty-year love affair with organic chemistry*, American Chemical Society, Washington, DC.

Kauffman, G.B. & Kauffman, L.B.: 2001, 'Linus Pauling, scientist of the century', *Chemistry & Industry*, February 19, 106-9.

Kevles, D.J.: 1972, 'On the moral dilemmas of the American chemist', in: J.W. Beranek (ed.), *Science Scientists and Society*, Bogdden & Quigley, Tarrytown-on-Hudson, NY, pp. 2-17.

Kevles, D.J.: 1987, *The Physicists. The History of a Scientific Community in Modern America.*, Harvard UP, Cambridge, MA.

Kraus, C.A.: 1950, 'The Present State of Academic Research', *Chemical and Engineering News*, Sept. 18, 3203-4.

Kumar, C. & Patel, N. (eds.): 1995, *Reinventing the Research University. Proceedings of a Symposium Held at UCLA, June 22-23, 1994*, Office of the Vice Chancellor for Research, UCLA, Los Angeles.

Laidler, K.J.: 2004, 'Essay Review. From Classical to Modern Chemistry: The Instrumental Revolution', *Annals of Science*, **61**, 219-25.

Langmuir, I. & Hall, R.N.: 1989, 'Pathological Science', *Physics Today*, Oct., 36-48.

Laszlo, P. & Hoffmann, R.: 2000, 'Ferrocene: Ironclad History or Rashomon Tale?', *Angewandte Chemie*, **39**, 123-124.

Latour, B.: 1987, *Science in Action*, Harvard UP, Cambridge, MA.

Levine, A.G.: 1982, *Love Canal: Science, Politics, and People*, D.C. Heath, Toronto.

Lewis, J. & Nyholm, R.S.: 1961, 'Modern Inorganic Chemistry', *Chemical and Engineering News*, **49**, 102-8.

Lind, S.C.: 1952, 'Chemistry at Mid-Century', *Chemical and Engineering News*, 4144-8.

Lipscomb, W.N.: 1993, 'The boranes and their relatives', in: S. Forsén (ed.), *Nobel Lectures, Chemistry 1971-1980*, World Scientific, Singapore, pp. 224-45.

Lowe, D.: 2004, 'Le Dernier Cri', *The Pipeline blog* (http://www.corante.com/pipeline/archives/2004/06/21/le_dernier_cri.php).

McGinn, A.P.: 2000, 'Phasing Out Persistent Organic Pollutants', in: L.R. Brown, C. Flavin & H. French (eds.), *State of the World 2000*, Norton, New York.

McGrayne, S.B.: 2001, *Prometheans in the lab: chemistry and the making of the modern world*, McGraw-Hill, New York.

McLauchlan, K.A.: 1996, 'NMR Memories', in: D.M. Grant & R.K. Harris (eds.), *Encyclopedia of nuclear magnetic resonance*, Wiley, Chichester, pp. 494-5.

Merrifield, R.B.: 1963, 'Solid phase peptide synthesis. Synthesis of a tetrapeptide', *Journal of the American Chemical Society*, **85**, 2149.

Miller, S.L.: 1953, 'A production of amino acids under possible primitive earth conditions', *Science*, **117**, 528-529.

Mohnen, V.A.: 1988, 'The Challenge of Acid Rain', *Scientific American*, August, 30-8.

Morris, P.J.T. (ed.): 2002, *From Classical to Modern Chemistry: The Instrumental Revolution*, The Royal Society of Chemistry, London.

Mossman, B.T.; Bignon, J.; Corn, M.; Seaton, A. & Gee, J.B.L.: 1990, 'Asbestos: Scientific Developments and Implications for Public Policy', *Science*, Jan. 19, 294-301.

Mulliken, R.S.: 1972, 'Spectroscopy, molecular orbitals, and chemical bonding', in: Nobel Foundation (eds.), *Nobel Lectures. Chemistry 1963-1970*, Elsevier, Amsterdam, pp. 131-60.

Nakanishi, K.: 1991, *A Wandering Natural Products Chemist*, American Chemical Society, Washington, DC.

National Research Council: 1998, *Assessing the Value of Research in the Chemical Sciences. Report of a Workshop*, National Academy Press, Washington, DC.

National Research Council: 2003, *Reducing the Time from Basic Research to Innovation in the Chemical Sciences. A Workshop Report to the Chemical Sciences Roundtable*, National Academy Press, Washington, DC.

National Research Council: 2004, *Preparing Chemists and Chemical Engineers for a Globally Oriented Workforce*, National Academy of Sciences, Washington, DC.

National Science Board: 2002, *Science & Engineering Indicators – 2002*, National Science Foundation, Arlington, VA.

Neckers, D.C.: 1979, *On the Quality of Undergraduate Students Choosing Chemistry as a Profession 1961-1979. A Report*, Department of Chemistry, Bowling Green State University, Bowling Green OH.

Nye, M.-J.: 2001, 'Paper Tools and Molecular Architecture in the Chemistry of Linus Pauling', in: U. Klein (ed.), *Tools and Modes of Representation in the Laboratory Sciences*, Kluwer, Dordrecht, pp. 117-32.

Pacifico, C.: 1958, 'For Creativity – Ignorance Helps', *Chemical and Engineering News*, May 12, 52-5 & 95.

Pimentel, G.C. & Coonrod, J.A.: 1987 (1985), *Opportunities in Chemistry*, National Academy Press, Washington, DC.

Prelog, V.: 1991, *My 132 semesters of chemistry studies: studium chymiae nec nisi cum morte finitur*, American Chemical Society, Washington, DC.

Proctor, W.G. & Yu, F.C.: 1950, 'The Dependence of a Nuclear Magnetic Resonance Frequency Upon Chemical Compound', *Physical Review*, **77**, 717.

Raber, L.R.: 2001, 'Scale-up of a miracle drug', *Chemical and Engineering News*, July 30, 63-4.

Ransil, B.J.: 1989, *Life of a scientist: an autobiographical account of the development of molecular orbital theory with an introductory memoir by Friedrich Hund / Robert S. Mulliken*, Springer, Berlin.

Rich, A.: 2004, 'The Excitement of Discovery', *Annual Review of Biochemistry*, **73**, 1-37.

Rivkin, S. & F. Sutherland: 2004, *The Making of a Name: The Inside Story of the Brands We Buy*, Oxford UP, Oxford.

Roberts, J.D.: 1990, *The right place at the right time*, American Chemical Society, Washington, DC.

Roberts, J.D.: 1996, 'A Personal NMR Odyssey', in: D.M. Grant & R.K. Harris (eds.), *Encyclopedia of nuclear magnetic resonance*, Wiley, Chichester, pp. 590-9.

Roberts, J.D. & Collette, J.W.: 1999, 'Howard Ensign Simmons, Jr.', in: *Biographical Memoirs*, National Academy of Sciences, Washington, DC, pp. 315-38.

Rodricks, J.V.: 1992, *Calculated Risks: Understanding the Toxicity and Human Health Risks of Chemicals in Our Environment*, Cambridge UP, New York.

Ross, B. & Amter, S.: 2002, 'Deregulation, chemical waste, and ground water: a 1949 debate', *Ambix*, **49**, 51-66.

Roussel, P. A.: 1959b, 'Status and the Chemist', *Chemical and Engineering News*, Jan. 5, 84-5.

Roussel, P.A.: 1959a, 'Responsibilities of the Chemist', *Chemical and Engineering News*, Nov. 9, 74-5.

Rowland, F.S.: 1995, 'Autobiography', The Nobel Foundation, Stockholm (http://nobelprize.org/chemistry/laureates/1995/rowland-autobio.html).

Rowland, F.S.: 1997, 'Nobel Lecture in Chemistry', in: B.G. Malmström (ed.), *Nobel Lectures, Chemistry 1991-1995*, World Scientific, Singapore, pp. 273-96.

Schreiber, J.; Leimgruber, W.; Pesaro, M.; Schudel, P.; Threlfall, T. & Eschenmoser, A.: 1961, 'Synthese des Colchicins', *Helvetica Chimica Acta*, **44**, 540-97.

Schultz, T.: 2000, 'Mass media and the concept of interactivity: an exploratory study of online forums and reader email', *Media, Culture and Society*, **22**, 205-21.

Schummer, J.: 1997, 'Scientometric Studies of Chemistry I: The Exponential Growth of Chemical Substances, 1800-1995', *Scientometrics*, **39**, 107-123.

Schummer, J.: 2004, 'Multidisciplinarity, Interdisciplinarity, and Patterns of Research Collaboration in Nanoscience and Nanotechnology', *Scientometrics*, **59**, 425-65.

Schummer, J.: 2005, 'Reading Nano: The Public Interest in Nanotechnology as Reflected in Book Purchase Patterns', *Public Understanding of Science*, **14**, 163-83.

Shama, G. & Reinarz, J.: 2002, 'Allied intelligence reports on wartime German penicillin research and production', *Historical Studies in the Physical and Biological Sciences*, **33** (2), 347-67.

Sheehan, J.C. & Henery-Logan, K.R.: 1957, 'The total synthesis of penicillin V.', *Journal of the American Chemical Society*, **79**, 1262.

Smalley, R.E.: 1996, 'Autobiography', Nobel Foundation, Stockholm.

Smalley, R.E.: 2003, 'Discovering the fullerenes', in: I. Grenthe (eds.), *Nobel Lectures, Chemistry 1996-2000*, World Scientific, Singapore, pp. 89-103.

Smith, B.L.R. & Karlesky, J.J.: 1977, *The State of Academic Science. The Universities in the Nation's Research Effort*, Change Magazine Press, New York.

Stokes, D.E.: 1997, *Pasteur's quadrant: basic science and technological innovation*, Brookings Institution, Washington, DC.

Stork, G.; Tamelen, E.E.v.; Friedman, L.I. & Burgstahler, A.W.: 1953, 'The total synthesis of cantharidin', *Journal of the American Chemical Society*, **75**, 384.

Streitwieser, A.: 1996, *A lifetime of synergy with theory and experiment*, American Chemical Society, Washington, DC.

Taube, H.: 1983, 'Banquet Speech', Nobel Foundation, Stockholm.

Thomas, S.: 2000, 'F. Sherwood Rowland. Nobel Laureate, Bren Professor, Research Professor of Chemistry. A Modern Galileo.', *OCMetro magazine*, May 18.

Tobias, S., Chubin, D.E. & Aylesworth, K.: 1995, 'Rethinking Science as a Career. Perceptions and Realities in the Physical Sciences', Research Corporation, Tucson, AZ.

Todd, A.R.: 1983, *A time to remember: the autobiography of a chemist / Alexander Todd*, Cambridge UP, Cambridge.

Traynham J.G.: 1997, 'Philip Eaton', Chemical Heritage Foundation, Oral History project, oral interview no. 0152, January 22, transcript (47 pp.).

Tswett, M.S.: 1906, 'Physikalische-chemische Studien über das Chlorophyll. Die Adsorptionen', *Berichte der Deutschen Botanischen Gesellschaft*, **24**, 316-28.

Usselman, M. & Rocke, A.J.: 2005, 'Restaging Liebig: A Study in the Replication of Experiments', *Annals of Science*, **61**, 1-55.

Walker, G.E. *et al.*: 2004, 'Responses to Changing Needs in U.S. Doctoral Education', *Journal of Chemical Education*, **81**, 1698-1704.

Warner, J.C.: 1957, 'Education and Research in American Universities – Some Candid Comments', *Chemical and Engineering News*, Dec. 16, 64-5.

Watson, J.D. & Crick, F.H.C.: 1953, 'Molecular structure of Nucleic Acids', *Nature*, **171**, 737-8.

Weaver, W.: 1961, 'Why Is Science Important?', *Chemical and Engineering News*, Feb. 13, 145-8.

Weinberg, A.M.: 1955, 'Future AIMS of Large Scale Research', *Chemical and Engineering News*, 2188-91.

Weinberg, A.M.: 1967, *Reflections on Big Science*, MIT Press, Cambridge, MA.

Weininger, S.J.: 2000, '"What's in a Name?" From Designation to Denunciation – The Nonclassical Cation Controversy', *Bulletin for the History of Chemistry*, **25**, 123-31.

Weininger, S.J.: 2005, private communication to the author (October 2).

Welch Foundation, 1996, *Chemistry on the Nanometer Scale, Proceedings of the 40th chemistry conference*, Houston, TX.

Westheimer, F.H.: 1965, 'Chemistry: Opportunities and Needs (The Westheimer Report)', *Chemical and Engineering News*, Nov. 29, 72-102.

Westheimer, F.H.: 2003, 'Reflections – Musings', *Journal of Biological Chemistry*, **278**, 11729-30.

Williams, T.I.: 1990, *Robert Robinson, chemist extraordinary*, Clarendon Press, Oxford.

Woodburn, J.H.: 1976, *Taking Things Apart & Putting Things Together*, American Chemical Society, Washington, DC.

Woodward, R.B.: 1972, 'Recent Advances in the chemistry of natural products', in: Nobel Foundation (ed.), *Nobel Lectures. Chemistry 1963-1970*, Elsevier, Amsterdam.

Woodward, R.B: 1973, 'The total synthesis of vitamin B12', *Pure and Applied Chemistry*, **33**, 145-77.

Woodward, R.B. & Hoffmann, R.: 1971, *The Conservation of Orbital Symmetry*, Verlag Chemie, Weinheim.

Woodward, R.B. *et al.*: 1960, 'The total synthesis of chlorophyll', *Journal of the American Chemical Society*, **82**, 3800.

Woodward, R.B.; Cava, M.P.; Ollis, W.D.; Hunger, A.; Daniker, H.U. & Schenker, K.: 1954, 'The total synthesis of strychnine', *Journal of the American Chemical Society*, **76**, 4749-51.

Woodward, R.B.; Sondheimer, F. & Taub, D.: 1951a, 'The total synthesis of cholesterol', *Journal of the American Chemical Society*, **73**, 3548.

Woodward, R.B.; Sondheimer, F. & Taub, D.: 1951b, 'The total synthesis of cortisone', *Journal of the American Chemical Society*, **73**, 4057.

Zandvoort, H.: 1985, *Models of Scientific Development and the case of NMR*, Groningen, Doctoral disseration.

Ziegler, K.: 1972, 'Consequences and development of an invention', in: Nobel Foundation (ed.), *Nobel Lectures. Chemistry 1963-1970*, Elsevier, Amsterdam, pp. 804-33.

Ziman, J.: 1994, *Prometheus Bound: Science in a Dynamic Steady State*, Cambridge UP, Cambridge.

BIOGRAPHICAL NOTES ON THE CONTRIBUTORS

Philip Ball is a freelance writer and a consultant editor for *Nature*, where he previously worked as an editor for physical sciences. He writes regularly in the scientific and popular media, and his ten books on scientific subjects include *The Self-Made Tapestry: Pattern Formation in Nature*, *H_2O: A Biography of Water*, *The Devil's Doctor: Paracelsus and the World of Renaissance Magic and Science*, and *Critical Mass: How One Thing Leads To Another*, which won the 2005 Aventis Prize for Science Books. He was awarded the 2006 James T. Grady – James H. Stack award by the American Chemical Society for interpreting chemistry for the public. Philip studied chemistry at Oxford and holds a doctorate in physics from the University of Bristol.

Bernadette Bensaude-Vincent is Professor of History and Philosophy of Science at Université Paris X. Her research interests focus on the history and philosophy of chemistry and on the history of the science and the public issue. Her current research is on ethical and philosophical issues of nanotechnologies. She is a member of the Académie des technologies and of the Comité d'éthique du CNRS. Her book publications include *Lavoisier, mémoires d'une revolution* (1993), *A History of Chemistry* (together with Isabelle Stengers, 1996), *Eloge du mixte Matériaux nouveaux et philosophie ancienne* (1998), *La science et l'opinion. Histoire d'un divorce* (2003), *Se libérer de la matière? Fantasmes autour des nouvelles technologies* (2004), and *Faut-il avoir peur de la chimie?* (2005).

Marika Blondel-Mégrelis graduated in engineering at the Ecole Supérieure de Chimie Industrielle de Lyon and received her PhD in engineering from the Université Nancy. She studied philosophy in Nancy, Lyon, and Paris and received her PhD in philosophy from the Université de Lyon. She was research director of the Centre National de la Recherche Scientifique on Philosophy, Epistemology, and History of Science in Paris. After her retirement in 2006, she continues her research activity in the history of chemistry. Her research interests include the history of organic chemistry during the nineteenth century (Laurent and Gerhardt), organic chemistry applied to agriculture (Liebig and Sprengel), the chemical pioneers of agro-ecology (Boussingault, Liebig, and Winogradski), theoretical chemistry in France (Barriol, Daudel, the Pullmans), French organic chemistry (Grignard), the history of catalysis in France, and the history of the

Société Française de Chimie, which commemorates its 150th anniversary in 2007.

Andrew Ede is an historian of science and technology whose focus is the development of chemistry and chemical industries in North America. He graduated from the Institute for the History and Philosophy of Science and Technology at the University of Toronto. He is the author, along with Lesley Cormack, of *A History of Science in Society*. His current research is on chemists working for the US Chemical Warfare Service during World War I.

Roslynn Haynes is Adjunct Associate-Professor of English at the University of New South Wales, a Fellow of the Australian Academy of the Humanities and recipient of an Australian Bicentenary medal for cultural and communications studies. She is particularly interested in interfaces between disciplines, including science, literature, and art. She has published books on the writings of H.G Wells, on the scientist as a figure in literature and film (*From Faust to Strangelove*, 1994), on the history of Australian astronomy (*Explorers of the Southern Sky*, 1996), and on landscapes as perceived and constructed by writers, artists and photographers (*Seeking the Centre: The Australian Desert in Literature, Art and Film*, 1998; *Tasmanian Visions: Landscapes in Writing, Art and Photography*, 2006). Her current research projects include a cultural history of Antarctica and depiction of science and scientists in art.

Ernst Homburg is Professor of History of Science and Technology at Maastricht University. After writing a dissertation on the rise of the German chemical profession, 1790-1850, he became one of the editors of two book series on the History of Technology in the Netherlands in the nineteenth resp. the twentieth centuries. His research focuses on the history of industrial R&D in relation to academic science. He is book reviews editor of *Ambix*, and chairman of the Working Party on History of Chemistry of EuCheMS. His most recent books are on the history of the fertilizer industry: *Groeien door kunstmest: DSM Agro 1929-2004* (Hilversum: Verloren 2004) and on Dutch chemistry after 1945: E. Homburg and L. Palm (eds.), *De geschiedenis van de scheikunde in Nederland 3: De ontwikkeling van de chemie van 1945 tot het begin van de jaren tachtig* (Delft: Delft University Press 2004).

David Marcus Knight has taught History of Science in Durham University Philosophy Department since 1964: he is now Professor emeritus. He has edited the *British Journal for the History of Science* (1981-8), and been President of the British Society for the History of Science (1994-6). In 2003 he received the Edelstein Award of the American Chemical Society, and in 2007 was Wheeler Lecturer at the Royal Society of Chemistry. His interests have been in the history of chemistry as part of the wider history of science, including natural history; and in the relations of science and religion. He has published *Ideas in Chemistry: a History of the Science* (London: Athlone, 1992), *Humphry Davy: Science and Power* (2nd ed., Cambridge: Cambridge University Press, 1998), *Science and Spirituality: the Volatile Connection* (London: Routledge, 2004), and *Public Understanding of Science: a History of Communicating Scientific Ideas* (London: Routledge, 2006).

Marcel C. LaFollette is an independent historian in Washington, D.C., whose work examines the history of science communication. Her books include *Stealing into Print: Fraud, Plagiarism, and Misconduct in Scientific Publishing* (University of California Press, 1992) and *Making Science Our Own: Public Images of Science, 1910-1955* (University of Chicago Press, 1990). She is the former editor of the journals *Science, Technology, & Human Values* (1977-1987) and *Science Communication* (1991-1998). Dr. LaFollette has also served on the faculties of Harvard University, Massachusetts Institute of Technology, George Washington University, and Johns Hopkins University, but now focuses full-time on research and writing. Her history of science popularization via radio will appear with University of Chicago Press in 2008, and she is currently writing *The Friends of Scopes*, a book about the interactions of a group of journalists and scientists at the 1925 anti-evolution trial.

Pierre Laszlo, a French science writer and Professor of Chemistry emeritus at the University of Liège (Belgium) as well as the École polytechnique (Palaiseau, France) is especially known for his extensive publications in nuclear magnetic resonance methodologies and catalysis of organic reactions by modified clays. As a science writer, he has authored a dozen books to communicate chemical science to the general public, for which he received in 1999 the Maurice Pérouse Prize from the Fondation de France and in 2004 the Paul Doistau-Emile Blutet Prize from the French Academy of Sciences. His latest published books are *Co-pal, et autres gemmes* (Le Pommier, Paris, 2007), *Communicating Science. A Practical Guide* (Springer, Heidelberg, 2006), *Le Phénix et la salamandre* (Le Pommier, Paris, 2004), *NO*, a pedagogic wordplay written jointly with Carl Djerassi (Deutscher Theaterverlag, Weinheim, 2003). The book *Citrus: A History* is ready for publication in the fall of 2007, with the University of Chicago Press.

Peter J. T. Morris, Head of Research for the National Museum of Science Industry, London and Editor of *Ambix*, has written on many aspects of modern chemistry. He has published books on the history of synthetic rubber and polymers, modern chemical instrumentation and the work of Robert Burns Woodward. He has also published popular articles about the history of chemistry in several journals, notably *Chemistry and Industry* and *Education in Chemistry*. Morris curated the "Chemistry of Everyday Life" gallery at the Science Museum in 1999. He was also the consultant editor for the NMSI website ingenious. org.uk which was launched in 2004. He was awarded the Edelstein Award for the history of chemistry in 2006. Morris is currently working on the development of the electron capture detector and a book about the development of synthetic rubber at IG Farben based on his dissertation at Oxford University.

Joachim Schummer is Heisenberg Fellow at the University of Darmstadt. He graduated both in chemistry and philosophy and received his Ph.D. (1994) and Habilitation (2002) in philosophy from the University of Karlsruhe. He has held teaching and research positions at the Universities of Karlsruhe, South Carolina, Darmstadt, Sofia, and the Australian National University. His research interests focus on the history, philosophy, sociology, and ethics of science and technology, with emphasis on chemistry and, since 2002, on nanotechnology. His recent book publications include *Discovering the Nanoscale* (2004, 2005), *Nanotechnology Challenges* (2006), and *Nanotechnologien im Kontext* (2006). He is the founding editor of *Hyle: International Journal for Philosophy of Chemistry* (since 1995) and serves on various international committees, including the UNESCO expert group on Nanotechnology and Ethics.

Tami I. Spector is Professor of Organic Chemistry at the University of San Francisco with a deep interest in aesthetics and chemistry. She has published and presented work on The Molecular Aesthetics of Disease, John Dalton and The Aesthetics of Molecular Representation, and The Visual Image of Chemistry. She has (with Joachim Schummer) co-curated a virtual exhibit, "Chemistry in Art" (www.hyle.org/art/cia/) and co-edited two issues of *HYLE: International Journal for Philosophy of Chemistry* on "Aesthetics and Visualization in Chemistry". She also serves on the board of *Leonardo: International Society for the Arts, Sciences, and Technology* where she chairs the Scientists Working Group. She is currently co-editing (with Tom Rockwell) an on-going special section of the journal *Leonardo* on "Nanotechnology, Nanoscale Science and Art".

Peter Weingart holds a chair in Sociology of Science and Science Policy Studies at the University of Bielefeld and is Director of the Institute for Science and Technology Studies (IWT). His main research interests are currently the analysis of scientific advice to policy making, the relation between science and the media as well as science communication. He has published widely, *e.g.* with S. Maasen: *Metaphors and the Dynamics of Knowledge*, London/New York: Routledge, 2000; with C. Muhl and P. Pansegrau: "Of Power Maniacs and Unethical Geniuses: Science and Scientists in Fiction Film", *Public Understanding of Science*, 12 (2003), 279-87.

ACKNOWLEDGMENTS

The chapters of this volume are reproduced with permission from the journals *Hyle: International Journal for Philosophy of Chemistry* and *Ambix: The Journal of the Society for the History of Alchemy and Chemistry*. They first appeared as:

Ball, P.: 2006, 'Chemistry and Power in Recent American Fiction', *Hyle*, **12** (1), 45-66.

Blondel-Mégrelis, M.: 2007, 'Liebig or How to Popularize Chemistry', *Hyle*, **13** (1), 41-52.

Ede, A.: 2006, 'Abraham Cressy Morrison in the Agora: Bringing Science to the Public', *Hyle*, **12** (2), 193-214.

Haynes, R.: 2006, 'The Alchemists in Fiction: The Master Narrative', *Hyle*, **12** (1), 5-29.

Homburg, E.: 2006, 'From Chemistry for the People to the Wonders of Technology: The Popularization of Chemistry in the Netherlands during the Nineteenth Century', *Hyle*, **12** (2), 163-191.

Knight, D.: 2006, 'Popularizing Chemistry: Hands-on and Hands-off', *Hyle*, **12** (1), 131-140.

LaFollette, M.C.: 2006, 'Taking Science to the Marketplace: Examples of Science Service's Presentation of Chemistry during the 1930s', *Hyle*, **12** (1), 67-97.

Laszlo, P.: 2006, 'On the Self-Image of Chemists, 1950-2000' *Hyle*, **12** (1), 99-130.

Morris, P.J.T.: 2006, 'The Image of Chemistry Presented by the Science Museum, London in the Twentieth Century: An International Perspective', *Hyle*, **12** (2), 215-239.

Schummer, J. & Spector, T.I.: 2007, 'The Visual Image of Chemistry: Perspectives from the History of Art and Science', *Hyle*, **13** (1), 3-39.

Schummer, J.: 2006, 'Historical Roots of the' Mad Scientist': Chemists in Nineteenth-century Literature', *Ambix*, **53**, 99-127

Weingart, P.. 2006, 'Chemists and their Craft in Fiction Film', *Hyle*, **12** (1), 31-44.

INDEX OF NAMES